The Evolution Revolution
Yoga, Ayurveda, and
the Rise of the Soft Power Culture

By
Mas Vidal
(*Maheshananda*)

LOTUS
PRESS
Twin Lakes, WI

Disclaimer

This book is an educational manual and information contained herein is in no way to be considered as a substitute for your inner guidance or consultation with a professional physician or any duly licensed health care professional. The publisher and author are not liable for any injury sustained by the use of the information contained herein.

First Edition, 2021.

Printed in the United States of America

Mas Vidal

The Evolution Revolution–*Yoga, Ayurveda, and the Rise of the Soft Power Culture*

ISBN: 978-1-6086-9274-3

Library of Congress Control Number: 2021946485

Published by:

Lotus Press, P.O. Box 325, Twin Lakes, Wisconsin 53181 USA

Web: www.lotuspress.com

e-mail: lotuspress@lotuspress.com

800-824-6396

TABLE OF CONTENTS

- Three Historical Periods of Yoga (Early Vedic, Classical and Modern)
- Inner and Outer Yoga
- Outer Forms of Yoga for Inner Transformation
- Two Paths of Life
- Sacred Is Secret
- Creating Sacred Spaces
- Sectarianism and Churchianity

- Esoteric Meaning of Listening
- Salutations to the Earth
- Listening with the Mind
- Listening to the Body
- Sleep and Listening
- Subtle Forms of Listening to the Body
- The Three Regions of the Body
- Listening to Nature
- The Language of Listening through Stillness
- The Highest Listening

- The Importance of Dialogue
- Evolution of Language
- Responsibility and Learning
- Knowledge from the Light
- The Importance of Scriptures
- Learning and the Art of Sacred Language
- Mantra Alone is Not Enough
- The Highest Learning

- Life's Driving Force
- Creating Affinity for Divinity
- Personalizing Your Relationship with God
- Converting Emotion into Devotion
- Fear Into Flow
- Anger Into Initiative
- Sadness Into Stability
- The Highest Love

ILLUSTRATIONS

ABOUT THE COVER

Basic Description

The splendor of Goddess Lakshmi is alive in nature. Anytime we recognize the beauty that exists in nature we are seeing Divine Mother radiating through her magnificent forms. She bestows her blessings of love and intuitive feeling when we discover her as the Divine in all living things. This entire planet is Her womb. She feeds humanity, protects us, and encourages us to open our hearts to love and compassion so that we can evolve spiritually. Lakshmi is also known as *Sri*, meaning revered or noble, and ***Bhumi Devi***, the Goddess of the Earth. She symbolizes the beauty of fertility because the terms earth and birth are synonymous. Lakshmi is one part of the trinity, the triple Goddess, along with Parvati and Saraswati. She is the partner of Vishnu, one of the triad of Hindu Gods, who is typically known as the God of, or force of, preservation. Lakshmi is the Goddess of spiritual abundance and wealth in all forms. The dot between her eyebrows signifies the ajna chakra (third-eye), and the attainment of the goal of enlightenment. She is commonly depicted with four arms that represent artha, dharma, kama, and moksha, the four ideals of life.

Symbolism of the Four Hands and Arms

Lakshmi's upper left hand represents Dharma, divine purpose, alignment with our true calling, and the promotion of reciprocity. When we follow the path of dharma, life flows with wealth and energy. The golden vessel symbolizes this. Her lower right hand holds a gesture of bestowing courage, the abhaya mudra, so that we gain the capacity to overcome all fears with respect to Kama, our desires, social attachments, and family life). Her lower left hand is holding healing herbs, linking her to ayurveda and signifies artha, vocation and material abundance. Lakshmi is also known as Padmadevi, Lotus Goddess, and in her upper right hand she holds the colorful blue lotus flower which symbolizes the expansion of heart, the qualities of generosity and forgiveness, and indicates Moksha, spiritual liberation. The lotus also symbolizes evolution. The lotus flower opens as the sun of our consciousness ascends into the sky of awareness. Lakshmi provides the power of sustenance and the capacity to overcome desires, increase cheerfulness, and attain friendships with all.

Nature's Bounty

As Maha-Lakshmi, The Great Goddess, she sits with the Moon above her. This signifies the close relationship the moon shares with the earth. The shakti (power) of the moon is depicted in the fertility of life on earth, her animals, plants, and nature's bounty. Her healing powers are derived from yoga sadhana (practice) and healing through nature as taught in ayurveda. Traditionally, Lakshmi is shown wearing a red sari (Indian dress) that symbolizes radiant energy, rajas, and creative activity. Lakshmi is connected to cows, as they represent the gentle and motherly aspect of nature and are symbols of wealth and abundance. The south Indian sage Ramama Maharshi had a cow companion named Lakshmi who attained liberation during her life at the ashram.

In this illustration, Bhumi Devi is seated inside the lotus flower arising from the earth, symbolizing the enjoyment of living in the world, yet neither influenced nor possessed by it. She sits in the lotus poised in a calm and confident gesture, offering compassion from a place of detachment and observation of the world process. The small owl is a bird with incredible night vision, seeing in the realm of darkness. The owl can see through the negative qualities while focusing on the positive and the abundance that exists in the world. The deer is named Luna and her story is told in the book. She is gazing up at the moon, which symbolizes the soft and graceful nature that exists in both the deer and the moonlight.

The natural and colorful surroundings represent the abundance and radiance that comes when we see Mother Lakshmi's presence in all of creation. The river represents the sacred flow of reciprocity and signifies the importance of abundance and equanimity in all exchanges. The moon's energy promotes wellbeing as it influences the flow of the water in nature and the hormones in any female body.

Art Form

The vibrant cover art is influenced by the classical art forms of ancient India, and has been delicately drawn by Indian artist, Baani Sekhon. The traditional art style of the ancient murals of the Ajanta Caves and temple architecture have been the main source of inspiration; they represent the accurate science of fine arts and crafts that aim to elevate the soul. Indian traditional artform is narrative, based on stories in ancient texts and depict the appearance of deities. The unique details and expressions support the interpretation of meaning. Our observational practice is likened to sadhana, spiritual disciplines, that abolish impurities and distractions from the mind and increase concentration. Traditional artforms include the sacred science of architecture, known as Vaastu. An architect studies how light enters a structure in order to improve the flow of energy (prana). Many geometric factors are considered in terms of how they are related to promoting health, abundance, and spiritual development.

May all embody the beauty, abundance, and courage of Mother Lakshmi by opening our hearts to experience her magnificent living world as love.

Namaste,

Mas Vidal
(Maheshananda)

FOREWORD

A teacher is greatly pleased when his student is able to gracefully place "well-aged wine in new bottles"–to convey ancient truths in fresh and engaging ways that promise to enlighten the hearts and minds of today's and tomorrow's eager aspirants. In his newest book, The Evolution Revolution, Sri Maheshananda (Mas Vidal) has succeeded in doing just that by shining new light on Yoga, Vedanta, Ayurveda, and other ancient–yet revolutionary–religious and philosophical teachings of India and other Eastern and Western traditions.

Pilgrims on the life-transforming path of Integral Yoga–which promotes a harmonious blend of purified action, emotion, will and reason–will be moved by the unique blend of humility and expertise conveyed by the author in his fresh approach to this sublime subject. He has written the text not as an academician, but as a sadhaka, a spiritual aspirant who has been searching to understand the deepest truths about human existence and the supreme purpose of life.

In the course of this journey, while venerating the profound yet practical wisdom of the Vedas and other spiritual teachings, the author has acquired much expertise in ancient and modern arts and techniques. In this excellent book, aided by such skills, he shares insights and experiences that will surely inspire others to aspire for a life filled with greater health, harmony, and happiness–a life that will lead to the ultimate freedom of Enlightenment. May all enjoy the Divine blessings of Shakti (aspiration), Bhakti (love), Mukti (freedom)!

Swami Jyotirmayananda

Yoga Research Foundation

Miami, Florida, USA

ACKNOWLEDGEMENTS

To begin with, I would like to acknowledge Mother India for the sacred land, the unique landscape, the people, and, most of all, the wisdom traditions she has bestowed upon the world. India, as the land of the Vedas, speaks to us through the illumined rishis and guru lineages. The Cosmic Beloved had to leave humanity a key somewhere on earth to unlock the mystery of life that has bewildered humanity for countless ages, and He left it in Mother Earth's womb called India. The aim of this book is to venerate India's great ancient culture for providing the profound yet practical wisdom of the Vedas. This ancient culture is in renaissance today and demonstrates to the world the enduring soft power of spirituality. Soft power has the capacity to transcend all the limitations of time and space. Soft power promotes spiritual evolution in the world for those seeking refuge from the complexities of the human mind, diseases, war, history, and politics.

Before I met Sri Swami Jyotirmayananda, my understanding of Vedanta was merely at the theoretical level. I generally interpreted the term to mean truth, as in the culminating expression of the Vedas. Subsequently, I have discovered a profound deeper meaning of truth as pure consciousness or God. Because of this, the relative world has transformed itself from what I perceived to be a series of dramatic events into a living teacher. Swamiji's teachings of integral yoga, as derived from the highest illumination of the soul, have taught me to listen, to learn, to love the world as it is, and to let it go as part of the process of evolutionary living. Without his humbling and unconditional acceptance, and his tireless dedication to Vedic dharma, this manuscript would not have been possible. Returning to my childhood neighborhood in South Miami, Florida, became about much more than routine family visits because I became a pilgrim again. Visits to Swamiji aroused deep sentiments for the greatness of India's soft power culture and what it means to be a yogi!

I want to also thank and offer my sincere respects to Swami Tyagananda who, during one of our many meetings over the last several decades, shared with me the four Ls: Listen, Learn, Love and Let Go (surrender), which I adapted to the four branches of yoga. These concepts have been indispensable treasures in my spiritual evolution. Over the years as this book began to take shape, the connection that the four L's have to the four branches of yoga became clear to me. I came to understand how they present a very simple language and framework through which to understand the mystical concepts of integral yoga and Vedanta. The insightful editing of the manuscript is credited to Diana Mullins who helped with major restructuring of content and helped to simplify the mystical Sanskrit-Vedantic concepts into a more fluid arrangement.

All the hand-sketched artwork within the book was meticulously drawn by Baani Sekhon as well as the cover art of Goddess Lakshmi (Bhumi Devi). Other creative images and research on certain illustrations were prepared by Belinda Pearl. Natalie (Nataji) Levin was commissioned to hand draw the portrait that appears on the back cover. It was a pleasure working with all these individuals who added creative and tangible energy to the book.

Namaste,

Mas Vidal
(Maheshananda)

PREFACE

In my first book, *Sun, Moon and Earth,* I ask the question, What is health? And I present the ideal viewpoint regarding health as per the holistic perspective of the Vedic wisdom traditions where mind and body are unified. When a synergistic relationship between the mind and body is cultivated, healing can take place. In that book, I present a perspective of how yoga and Ayurveda can be applied in an integrated manner to address the health dilemma of mind-body fracturing. A healthy mind and body can evolve toward spiritual freedom, a unification with higher consciousness. This evolution toward enlightenment is one of the central themes of ancient Eastern or Asian thought.

With this second book, I elaborate on these wisdom traditions in order to explore the concept of individual evolution. I prompt readers to ask questions such as, Am I evolving? What does it mean to live an evolutionary life? Am I living a life that is segregated from nature or one that embraces the entire world as a reflection of my own consciousness? What is success? What is happiness? These questions have intrigued me for decades and I share my insights and experiences regarding how those individuals aspiring for enlightenment and a better world might live in a manner that will afford them greater health, harmony, and happiness.

One of the grandest questions any individual can ask is, Am I evolving? This is not the same question as, Am I happy? Because the concept of evolution goes beyond the typical societal markers for achieving success marked by material wealth, marriage or accumulating accolades for various achievements. Over many years, as I learned about the lives of people I met on my travels as an Ayurveda practitioner and Yoga teacher, and even more as I developed greater understanding of individuals through my practice in Vedic astrology counseling, I witnessed how markers of success do not correlate to happiness. I had students and clients from all socio-economic backgrounds, billionaires, corporate executives, entertainers in Hollywood, schoolteachers, stay home mothers. Their accumulation of things that seem so essential, cars, 401ks, health insurance, televisions, iPhones, and clothing, was not making them happy.

So, I asked myself the question, Do our modern ideologies, the striving for riches, education, getting married, climbing employment ladders, maximizing business profits have anything to do with being happy? My conclusion is no, not much, unless we are evolving spiritually. Vedanta, the great philosophy of India, presents a fascinating perspective on happiness: happiness is not something we are seeking or trying to attain, but rather our true state of being is happiness and it lies within us. To live daily in our true state of being, we need to remove fear and the mind-created obstacles that inhibit us from experiencing it. I have always wondered how ancient societies did it and how we have diverged from true happiness to arrive at a state of living in the way we do now. The further back we go in historical time, and the fewer possessions people had in general, the more we see people living simply, evolving toward an eternal love, the true richness of life, and the quest to attain immortality.

For many, the journey into evolutionary living is ignited while on sojourns to sacred places, in yoga classes, in healing workshops and retreats; however, it is spiritual books that sustain us, that become our most intimate partners. Our scriptures guide us to answer the burning question, "Who Am I".[1] The wisdom of the East was always powered by the value of the moon's energy, its symbolism of the inner mysticism of life. *A candle's light only shines as long as there is wax to support it.* In this book I will present an exploration of the moon, its symbolism and subtle nature as a significant force for promoting societal change and integral evolutionary living. Although the moon and its feminine qualities were once revered in many cultures, they have long disappeared from humanity's quest for healing, solace, and abundance. As the sun rises in the East, perhaps this has naturally encouraged us to turn towards it, like a guiding light, an attractive symbol for healing and the expansiveness of life.

The very pertinent questions we have finally begun to ask are, What is behind the rituals and practices of the East that are so relevant today, so transformative? Why is it that the world is turning to the wisdom traditions of Yoga and Ayurveda to find greater balance and peace today? Abundance and material prosperity are not enough. We need to make spiritual happiness the 'new rich' and the basis for true success. Perhaps life was not so much more difficult several thousands of years ago without the scientific and technological advancements of today. More so than ever before, the great adage, *simple living and high thinking*, is being embraced – not necessarily by choice, but rather by societies and individuals living in contrast with nature and having nowhere else to turn but within. *Turning inward* is precisely what yoga means; one turns inward in order to be united with the soul.

---

1   Atma vichara or Who am I? was the central teaching of the south Indian sage Ramana Maharshi (1879 – 1950) who brought global recognition to the holy town Tiruvannamalai and the Arunachala Hill.

Over many years of maintaining an ayurvedic counseling practice, I have recognized that the issues disrupting health and wellness are two-fold: 1) a lack of education or understanding of nature's principles; and 2) the inability to follow through consistently on recommendations and practices that would lead to balanced health. Every human being has great potential to enhance their capacity to transcend the dimensions of time and space awareness and potentially link themselves to the only constant, that of eternal consciousness. My intention with this book is to demonstrate the correlation between the power of human potential and evolutionary living.

The Dawn of a Cultural Revolution

Anyone who has lived during the last few centuries will have been part of a world experiencing a massive shift in consciousness. When we witness the events and motives of our global communities, we need to ask ourselves, Are the major religions working? Are they truly providing what they originally intended? Do the religious practices of our times effectively promote harmony, love and compassion for all life? As a spiritual aspirant I am inspired by the human quest for transcendent happiness and higher consciousness, and how each of us might choose a different pathway to freedom. To 'be free' simply means that our happiness is not determined by outer circumstances, but by how we work with our karma as it unfolds.

Karma manifests in each life in such peculiar ways. It is often daunting how distorted our vision of life's deeper meaning is, clouded by our association with outer forms (people and things), names (titles) and many societal influences. Perhaps the world in chaos outside of us, that we are witnessing, is an indication of an inner revolution that is taking place, a dissatisfaction with who we are and what it means to be alive. Inner discordance is characterized by a purposeless life, low self-worth, and insecurity, and is reflected in the outer rebellions taking place throughout the world. However, the war is within. The growing numbers of people who are interested in ancient traditions such as those that consider natural or wholistic living as a type of original religion is evidence of the material world shifting. The early spiritual movements (pre-religious era) included sacred worship, music, dance, and rituals that were performed in accordance with nature.

We must understand what distinguishes the evolutionary living principles of India from the teachings of the three Abrahamic religions, Judaism, Christianity, and Islam. Understanding the distinctions will shed light on the impetus behind our current revolution. India's evolutionary living principles embrace three primary factors that are absent from Abraham and the patriarchs[2] of such movements. The first is the law of karma, the second is reincarnation (rebirth), and lastly is the concept that Divinity exists in all living things, with nature playing the role of the feminine aspect of the Divine. Both karma and rebirth explain that everything is cyclical and that the events of one's life are not at all by coincidence or misfortune.

The monotheistic belief system tends to endorse patriarchy and thus eliminates or perhaps diminishes the role of femininity in Divinity and the importance of the human relationship with the natural world. The emergence of Abrahamic and the earlier Semitic religions gave rise to what eventually led to the change in the calendar that extracted the moon's importance in event timings. With this change, humans were segregated from nature, and this led to many perverted concepts regarding what it meant to live a spiritual life. In other words, the relationship one shared with the living world was not as important as the relationship a person might be having with their lord as defined by monotheism, whomever that may be, Abraham, Jesus, or Allah.

While polytheism is not incorrectly defined as the belief in many gods, it is important to point out that the wisdom of Hinduism supports belief in One God with many aspects as depicted in the Trimurti concept of Brahman, Shiva, and Vishnu. The ancient Semitic religions were polytheistic like that of the Canaanites and Babylonians. As nature has many beautiful aspects, so does God, and thus worshipping the varied forms should not be interpreted as meaning that many Gods exist. The Hindu tradition embraces one supreme consciousness as symbolized by AUM, the cosmic sound that supports the trinity of life as body, mind, and soul as influenced by the planetary vibrations of the earth, moon, and sun.

The brainchild of Vedic wisdom is the soli-lunar intelligence. Our knowledge of how planetary energies influence when and how our karma ripens, helps each individual live in harmony with shifting circumstances and changing health. Living harmoniously with nature, or the lack of harmony, is correlated with the level of self-care each person can engage in. In other words, **how we**

---

2   The Bible mentions three: Abraham, his son Isaac, and his son Jacob, who is also named Israel, as the ancestor of the Israelites.

***live in the world and the relationship we have with nature (Mother) is
a reflection of how we care for own body as our miniature ecosystem.***
I would like to proclaim that we have entered the dawn of a grand spiritual
revolution. One indication of this is a new and growing reorientation with
who we are as individuals regardless of gender, religion, or race. A new type
of inquiry is being undertaken about male-female relationships, institutions
of religion and marriage, what we want for our children's future.

Although the average life expectancy across the world has increased over the
last several centuries and during the recent scientific revolution, it has been
accomplished as a result of very superficial means and a tremendous code-
pendency on doctors, drugs, surgery and an entire medical and educational
system that undermines self-empowerment. Our societies have begun to
teach people ***what to think***, instead of ***how to think***. Americana, as a culture,
in particular, positions the outside world as the cause of American problems,
and places responsibility for our health in the hands of doctors, institutions
or the government. Our modern cultural norms make it very difficult to slow
down, self-reflect, and take responsibility for our thoughts and actions. Many
people live in fear, revealing their ego in prejudice, criticism, and harmful acts
against living nature; they are not thinking about spiritual evolution. My hope
is that this book will help support a shift toward new cultural norms where
Vedic wisdom can lead the way in answering your question, Am I evolving?

SUPPORTING QUOTES FOR MAS VIDAL (MAHESHANANDA) AND THE BOOK

This book is portable magic, it gives insights into India's Vedic culture with exceptionally easy to understand concepts about the mind, Mother Nature, spirituality, Ayurveda, and Yoga. Study it and experience the magic!

   ~ **Dr. Gunvant Yeola** - Professor & Principal of Ayurveda at D.Y. Patil University

A teacher is greatly pleased when his student is able to gracefully place "well-aged wine in new bottles"–to convey ancient truths in fresh and engaging ways that promise to enlighten the hearts and minds of today's and tomorrow's eager aspirants. In his newest book, The Evolution Revolution, Sri Maheshananda (Mas Vidal) has succeeded in doing just that by shining new light on Yoga, Vedanta, Ayurveda, and other ancient–yet revolutionary–religious and philosophical teachings of India and other Eastern and Western traditions.

   ~ **Sri Swami Jyotirmayananda -** Founder of the Yoga Research Foundation and the last direct disciple of Sri Swami Sivananda Maharaj

Engrossing and spellbinding, an intriguing display of how India's soft power culture and more explicitly how the use of ayurvedic herbs, diet, meditation, and natural lifestyle are fueling a global revolution. Mas Vidal presents the four classical paths of yoga as Listen, Learn, Love and Let Go, a truly thought provoking methodology for healing our relationship with the world.

   ~ **Dr. Sunanda Ranade** - Consultant TanMan Ayurvedic Research Center, Vice-Chairman, International Academy of Ayurveda, India

Having set the table with his powerful first book Sun, Moon and Earth: The Sacred Relationship of Yoga and Ayurveda, Mas Vidal now takes us on a magnificent, deeper exploration of how India's ancient wisdom offers a practical roadmap for all who aspire to evolve. This well-crafted and thoughtful book is a profound gift for anyone seeking true connection to Spirit, Nature and integration.

   ~ **Peter Rader** - author, screenwriter

How delightful is the author's fresh approach to the ancient sciences of Integral Yoga and Ayurveda! In this new book, Mas Vidal casts a sweet and inspiring new light upon these Divinely inspired teachings and provides highly effective tools for sincere spiritual seekers to realize the highest attainment through the health of their psycho-physical personalities.

   ~ **Swami Umananda** - Yoga Research Foundation

An evolutionary mystic from the Yoga and Ayurveda Tradition, Mas Vidal's innovative work, Evolution Revolution, is simply nectar for a new humanity. In this book, he explores Vedic wisdom tradition through the lens of Mantra, Meditation, Yoga and Ayurveda with well tempered cadence to guide the urgent global awakening in process. Skillfully integrating the ancient Vedic teachings into accessible form, Mas pays homage to this ancient tradition; notably to its resurgence of Sanatana Dharma - more recently referred to as, Soft Power, the timeless wisdom practices intended to unify and serve the whole of humanity.

~ **Maya Tiwari** - World Peace Humanitarian & Ayurveda Pioneer

Evolution Revolution is a valuable addition to the bookshelf of everyone who aspires for greater inner contentment. It wisely takes an integrative approach to the core teachings of Vedanta and Yoga, bringing together not only the diverse threads of those venerable traditions but also ancient and modern, inner, and outer, and spiritual and scientific. If you're committed to ongoing growth, you will be well served by this illuminating book.

~ **Philip Goldberg** - author of American Veda, The Life of Yogananda, and Spiritual Practice for Crazy Times

Mas Vidal does a remarkable job of bringing the sciences of Yoga and Ayurveda into alignment with Indian cosmology and spirituality, inspiring a worldview and future that we can all work towards. Mas reframes our religious traditions, our disconnect from nature, the land, our animal friends, and the cycles of time - offering solutions that we can and must adapt if humanity is to thrive and flourish into the future. In these transformative and troubling times Mas Vidal, in "The Evolution Revolution" offers us a great opportunity to take a step back and see not only where we have been but where we could be going.

~ **Sam Geppi** - Vedic Astrologer Founder of the American Academy of Vedic Art and Science, Author of "Yoga and Vedic Astrology".

Having travelled to 77 countries as a teacher of Ayurveda and Yoga, I concur with the author's opinion that major change is in the air with regards to spiritual evolution occurring globally through the soft powers of Indian culture. Readers will definitely find his newest book fascinating, very intriguing and thoughtfully written.

~ **Prof. Vaidya Ranade Subhash** - Chairman, International Academy of Ayurveda, India, Ex. Prof. and Head, Dept. of Ayurveda, Pune University, Director, Maharishi Vedic Research Foundation.

Chapter ONE

A New Relationship with Mother Nature

I believe that life should be lived so vividly and so intensely that thoughts of another life, or of a longer life, are not necessary.

Marjory Stoneman Douglas

Nurturing the Power of Mother Nature

Many today are beginning to feel that religions, in their current form as organizations that present a monotheistic approach to happiness or salvation for humanity, may not be the answer. Instead, what is being embraced is knowledge, devotion, and a lifestyle that embraces harmony with nature. In short, *natural lifestyle* is becoming the new religion that supports the power of individual consciousness to find a sacred relationship with nature, ecology, and progressive living. Religions have lumped humans together to loving God one way, to seeing God as appearing one way (usually masculine) and interpreting scriptures in one literal way.

However, we have forgotten about the great metaphors that give humanity the power to transform our thinking and explore truth in the way each person chooses. The promise of the Vedas, the ancient wisdom traditions of India, and those that have lived an evolutionary life that culminates in enlightenment, tells us that there is no "One" way to freedom. Similarly, the idea of truth in plurality is also found in the ayurvedic approach to health and wellness (homeostasis) in that there are no fixed standards for addressing diseases of the body. Every "body" is considered unique and distinct as a result of the consciousness and karma it holds.

It is evident that our modern culture is striving for a new approach to living on the planet earth. This includes environmentalism, vegetarian and veganism, animal advocacy, and, in the broadest sense, *a lifestyle* that becomes a new form of religion. This spiritual revolution is derived from the most obvious relationship all humans share with Mother nature herself. These ideals are based on a nurturing relationship with Mother nature, the moon, family life and the entire concept of what it means to be experiencing a human life.

The Systems of the Sun and Moon

As sun and moon systems, yoga and ayurveda continue to grow in popularity. There are several ways in which the sun and moon can be regarded as fundamental to humanity's developing relationship with Mother Nature, and these teachings have both literal and metaphorical implications. Specifically, yoga provides a systematic approach of dissolving contrasting dualities. In the practical sense, this means seeing the world as either black or white, male or female. Through its rituals and countless techniques, yoga dissolves the mind and its conditions. This dissolution reduces a person's karmic debt and enables him or her to recognize their soul nature as the first and foremost purpose of the human experience.

Yoga is born of the sun and aims to kindle the fire of aspiration and to inspire understanding of the interconnectedness of life events as a means of promoting greater evolution. Yoga is referred to as a "sadhana" tradition that embraces the importance of self-discipline; that is, the management of one's thoughts (mind), words (speech) and actions. In them, is reflected an awareness of one's relationship with all aspects of the living world. Ayurveda, as the science of life, is born of the moon. Its prime energy supports restoration, immunity, and cultivating a harmonious relationship with nature. As the moon is the closest planet to the earth, so should her children maintain a close relationship to the forces of nature. Gradually, what emerges is a growing recognition of the Divine. Although those forces may seem obscure, as we come to recognize them, they grow equally within us as formidable powers for self-healing.

Ayurveda teaches us the value of timing and cycles, thereby strongly underscoring the monthly feminine cycle of fertility, iterative creativity, and mindfulness with respect to the mind-body relationship. Timing and cycles related to systems within the female body; additionally, these systems allow us to become aware of cyclical processes applied to everyone. While yoga is singular and aims to unite every individual with their higher Self, ayurveda is focused on embracing multiplicity through adherence to the principles of natural living. Nature's cycles are never the same, they are ever changing precisely for one primary reason, to learn the art of adaptation.

A growing number of aspirants (sadhakas) who desire to follow the wisdom of ancient traditions like that of yoga and ayurveda, are beginning to view the living world from a more transient perspective by recognizing that the flux of life exists as reflections of light from one source, consciousness. Although the practice of yoga remains very physical, particularly in the Western countries, its deeper spiritual side is emerging as a lifestyle and through its relationship with ayurveda. In exchange for the stale promise of the major religions, people and are willing to take greater personal responsibility for their health and lifestyle even though ayurveda is still an infant in the crib of mainstream society.

Integral Yoga and Meditation for Evolution

There are four main paths of Yoga (Karma, Bhakti, Jnana, and Raja)[3] for establishing the individualized consciousness within the cosmic or eternal consciousness. Cosmic or eternal consciousness exists beyond the realm of time and space and is the source of intelligence that pervades all living things. In a practical sense, following these four paths means to live in a manner that embraces the fundamental law that all of living existence is interconnected by one source of energy or consciousness which upholds it. When this connection is made with the pure source of existence, then happiness exists, and you realize that your life does not exist solely or independently of the grander world you see around you.

The integral yoga system can be integrated into one's lifestyle, regardless of any factors such as age, culture, religion, or education. The very commercialized system of postural yoga has been misconstrued as a form of fitness, but

---

3   For a full description of the four paths, see pages 45-46 Note to proofreader:

integral yoga actually has much more to do with connecting with our inner being rather than simply improving the body and its functions. The use of the term integral can be viewed from several levels. Primarily, it implies the importance of integrating the ideals of yoga into one's life and not merely performing them as separate regimens. Secondly, integral implies that yoga should be practiced in its four forms as right activity (karma yoga), love and devotion (bhakti yoga), study of wisdom teachings which enhances one's reasoning capacity (jnana yoga), and the exercise and development of will or inner power (raja yoga).

Some aspects of Vedantic meditation practices have been misinterpreted and limited to seated and silent forms. In fact, Vedantic meditation techniques have many forms, thus providing alternatives for those who may not find sitting still so easy. Learning how to meditate can be one of the most difficult things any person endeavors to do in their life, although, with a natural lifestyle and a positive attitude, the practice of sitting still or calming the mind can become one of the most rewarding aspects of our lives.

Exploring the deeper aspects of the integral yoga tradition allows one to work with more subtle forms of energy and presents an approach to living that promotes attaining a transcendental consciousness. When understood fully, postural yoga and meditation is a deep process for detoxifying the body and disciplining the mind. The actual practice of the postures has much more to do with concentrating the mind than doing anything to enhance the body. By slowing the mind, we can gradually increase our capacity to concentrate.

Concentration, or the power of attention, is the solution to the many of world's problems as it increases our moment-to-moment awareness. The power to concentrate allows each person to witness, to have awareness of their breath and sensory feelings. Practicing moment-to-moment attention enhances the mystical sensitivities that come by way of greater love and compassion. Concentration enhances the individual's path towards evolutionary living. Through integral yoga, we can enhance the power of our concentration, thus taking us beyond the limitations of the material mind and expanding our attention to the treasure of the universal mind.

Meditation can be practiced by everyone. Just as physical or Hatha Yoga encourages those who are not flexible to practice postures, so too will those who have a monkey mind be encouraged to give their monkey the fruit of meditation. Calming the mind opens one up to attaining the essence of balanced life: great peace, contentment, and happiness. The unfocused monkey mind develops because of misuse of the five senses, poor discipline, and fragmented health habits. For example, think of the many times you have eaten beyond what is necessary, or late at night just before bedtime, or perhaps you watched television and gossiped until your mind became exhausted from the intoxication of meaningless ideas. Often, sensory abuse is experienced because of abusing stimulants such as alcohol and social drugs that lead one into the trappings of sexual promiscuity. Meditation can become an effective management tool for the mind, ego, senses, and intellect, and if practiced deeply and consistently, meditation can bring results even within the short period of time of several weeks.[4]

There is a sweet parable that Swami Vivekananda told in 1893 at the World Parliament of Religions about two frogs in a well. This parable makes a very relevant point about the nature of the mind and humanity's ongoing struggle experienced now for countless ages, especially in the modern era. I will recount it here in a brief paraphrase:

> One frog who lives in his well thinks that this well of his is the entire world and that nothing can compare to it, that there can be nothing bigger in the world than this well of his. Well, suddenly another frog, which is from the sea, jumps into the first frog's well. A discussion begins between these two frogs. The frog with the well questions his new visitor about how big the sea is and wonders about how it can compare at all with his little well.

> Surprised, the frog from the sea rebuts by saying, 'How my friend can you compare your little well to the sea?' The frog with the well, having never seen or experienced swimming in the sea, believes his well to be very large and believes, based on his judgement that the other frog is a liar. He believes that the frog from the sea does not know what he is talking about with such a preposterous idea that the sea well might be bigger than his little well.

---

4   A research study published December 11th, 2014, from Harvard University Medical School and Massachusetts General Hospital determined that meditation literally rebuilds the brain's grey matter in just eight weeks. It was the very first study to document that meditation produces changes in grey matter over a short period of time.

And so, this is the perpetual story of life and explains the nature of the divided mind. Each of us holds on to our story and believes our perceptions of life to be the end all and the truest thing. In this way, we forget the Divine energy that gives us all life, and instead go on believing only what we can see and have been exposed to. We are limited by our sense of perspective, thus reducing the opportunity to develop trust, faith and surrender to something beyond what we can experience with our senses or within our own little wells.

The metaphor within this simple story is that we must evolve beyond the limitations of our senses, the ego, and our intellect, otherwise life merely exists on a fractured level, divided from the realization that we are like bubbles that have floated apart from the sea[5]. The journey of evolutionary living begins by recognizing the limitations of the material mind, as it only perceives the world through its sensory instruments. Integral yoga provides powerful methods for shifting the mind beyond the traps of time and space thinking and expanding it to dwell in the boundless sea of eternal joy.

Unfortunately, yoga has been stereotyped as exercise, and reduced to merely stretching and sweating to attain wellbeing. Although postural yoga can bring us many benefits, its practice has much deeper implications for transcending the mind beyond egoistic tendencies. Wellbeing from the integral yoga perspective is much more subtle than just feeling good in your body because of various physiological enhancements. ***Yogic transcendence is measured in the attitude of the mind and its capacity to adapt to any environment;*** but, at the same time, one must recognize when certain people, places and things are neither harmonious nor supportive to one's own energy. Yoga has been given to the world to awaken it from its long slumber of unconscious living. Yoga is designed to prod us beyond the mundane life of the masses, that follow one another like ants trailing a bread crumb.

Balancing Inner and Outer Activity

Creating balance between our outer material responsibilities and our inner spiritual longings requires good company (sangha), a community of aspirants. This is because one's environment is more powerful than they are and what the mind is impressed with the most is ultimately what one becomes. Without

---

5   A reference to a song from Paramahansa Yogananda's, Cosmic Chants, entitled "I am the bubble, make me the sea."

positive associations, few achieve true success unless it was already developed to such a degree in a past life that nothing can impede it from manifesting. This balance of inner and outer activity is what Vedantic wisdom points to as a victory of the mind. This balancing, when reaching for the highest ideal or the dharma of life, is also called liberation.

"A brilliant ocean of light, the ocean of heaven." [6] In this ancient Vedic hymn, the ocean of light is a metaphor that refers to the attainment of awareness of the unified field of existence that exists within our own body as the light of lights in the forehead. The ocean presents an aspect of nature that is profound and vast as is the realm of enlightenment. When this illumination occurs the inner and outer worlds become unified, the sun and moon as forces of nature and within human existence are annihilated, and only pure consciousness remains. As the sun governs the light and moon governs the oceans, yoga is the amalgamation of these two aspects of life, leading to perfection of right activity. In physics, this is referred to as the Unified Field Theory (UFT), a term coined by Albert Einstein. The modern exploration of physics, which has developed over the last two centuries, brings together two concepts known as fields and forces. A field is finite and made up of eternal forces. The forces are distinct types of energies such as neutrons, protons, and electrons, as well as finer elementary subatomic particles which are distributed across a field. The field and force aspects of the theory can be correlated to the inner and outer domains of consciousness described in Vedic thought. The inner domain is eternal, and the outer domain of the material world is finite.

The central idea within the myth of Indra (one of the principal Vedic Gods) is the importance of destroying the negative aspects of one's personality. This destruction is a necessary step in evolution and leads to the blossoming of Divine virtues. Because all the other Gods had abandoned him, Indra, alone, slays the dragon who withholds the waters (soma or nectar). Indra releases the waters being held inside the dragon and the waters flow into the ocean. This action symbolizes the overcoming of the ego, as the ego is symbolized as the dragon. The ego limits our consciousness to the sensory level, but overcoming the ego allows the nectar of our individualized cosmic consciousness to flow into the ocean of unconditioned intelligence. Through this process, the yogi becomes a *jivamukta*, liberated while living responsibly in the material world.

---

6   "tvesah sa bhanur arnavo; divo arnam" Rig Veda, Chapter lll.22.2-3.

There is a great statement of Krishna's, in the Bhagavad Gita, that says, *"A person who does not disturb the world and who cannot be disturbed by the world, who is free from jubilation, jealousy, apprehension, and worry are very dear to me."*[7] We have come into this world with the intention of fulfilling all our desires; however, along the way, we discover that we keep repeating an illusionary idea, 'When I complete this task or attain my goal, then I will have everything I need, so then I will be free to listen to my consciousness or the little voice that is wise'. This illusion keeps us in ignorance and prevents us from gaining wisdom. The illusory force is very strong and pulls the senses outwards, creating a sense of "mineness" or ownership. It makes us believe that we need things outside of our own existence to feel contentment.

Krishna's statement refers to how wise it is to live in this world with an attitude of neutrality and surrender. We must also come to understand that we are not completely in control, that there is a grand force in place that governs all the operations of nature's cycles. It is this same force which operates all biological and psychological functions of the mind-body complex. Living with such an attitude allows us to become synchronized with the more subtle energies akin to the higher function of the mind. Through a process known as mental conditioning, the senses brainwash us into believing that life's events are a result of serendipity, when actually, we are the masters of the moments in our lives. This mental conditioning can be seen in the form of belief structures, concepts, and perceived limitations, all of which inhibit the mind, causing us to remain attached to names and forms (namarupa).

In a simple parable often shared by Yoganandaji, the soul becomes like a bird that has lived in a cage for too long. Even though originally born free in nature, after such a long time in the cage, when the cage door is opened, the bird does not fly away. This parable tells of how the soul has become imprisoned within the mind and body, as if a bird in a cage. This is a result of dependence on the senses which builds the ego's identification with the cage of the body and mind. For this reason, Krishna encourages the aspirant to remain even-minded while living in the world. When successful, this even-mindedness will limit the power of the ego. This allows the power of consciousness to be preserved as energy directed towards our Real existence.

---

7   From *God Talks with Arjuna: The Bhagavad Gita,* by Paramahansa Yogananda (Self-Realization Fellowship, Los Angeles), Chapter 12, verse 15.

When a serendipitous event occurs, it provokes inquiry into the nature of that event. We question ourselves, asking, How is it that such things can occur in such a synchronized manner? As we realize the source behind such experiences, we begin to develop greater devotion to the source, trusting the Divine hand is guiding us in the right direction toward fulfillment of our highest ideals (dharma). However, sometimes the outcome of such serendipitous events is not what we would prefer or perhaps is not what we may have expected. At these times, the mind experiences negative emotions of the ego, like anger or jealousy, and these can lead us into worldly entanglements, especially when we make decisions from an emotional state of mind. Alternatively, if we choose to cultivate compassion for ourselves, the negative emotions can be converted into heart-centered compassion (daya).

With greater compassion, we develop the inner sensitivities of the mind that can bridge the heart-mind relationship. Unifying the heart and mind is a powerful practice for overcoming emotional obstacles, obstacles that can lead to failures, or place us in positions that are not aligned with who we really are or what we truly enjoy. Unless emotions are converted into positive energy, they become obstacles, preventing us from overcoming bad habits. Emotions support the world of projections while devotion encourages us to move away from them. This moving away from projections represents an evolutionary movement.

Devotion and compassion are requisite to living a purposeful and evolutionary life. The Divine hand, as pure consciousness, takes the energy behind any emotion directed outward at another person or event of life, and transforms the energy by directing it towards the soul, the portion of the limitless creator within us. I once expressed to my spiritual counselor the pain I was feeling with regard to a personal and emotional circumstance in my life, and he said, "Turn all that pain (emotional energy) that you are feeling towards God." I did so, and it transformed my life. As a result, I grew tremendously in my relationship with God.

Human Mind as Equivalent to Monkey Mind

When we speak of a mind that is unfocused, controlled by fluctuating emotions and the desires of the ego, we often use the expression, 'monkey mind'. It invokes a simple allegory that implies the mind is fickle, jumping around like a monkey, always looking for something to attach itself to. We all have experienced this, thousands of times. We start something and never finish it. We have ideas or insights that are barely explored. We find pleasure in some object, a person, place, or thing, only to discard it after some time and in exchange for another new thing. We are mesmerized and blinded by the idea that these things are new, when, in fact, we have actually possessed or experienced most things before in this life or in past lives. The feeling of something being new is actually our becoming reacquainted with something that is familiar to us.

The monkey mind energy is motivated by the promise of sensory pleasures; however, it lacks loyalty, the highest virtue. Loyalty is the highest virtue because it leads us to love and devotion. Human love cannot truly exist without loyalty to Divine love. A profound insight is that love is not limited to a name or form (namarupa). Love is not something we give or receive, it is the experience of being in the presence of the soul, in contact with that source of pure consciousness that is not disturbed by the restless mind. The human dilemma is Self-love deprivation, and one must recognize the inner resource before distribution can occur and in order to recognize this resource the mind needs to be calm, concentrated and still.

Yoga has the ideal remedy for this in a concept called sadhana, spiritual disciplinary practices. Sadhana is the practice of controlling the monkey mind in order to purify the intention and efface the ego. It is the ego that is our narrative; the story we tell ourselves that perpetuates drama after drama. In order to awaken to our higher consciousness and subdue the monkey mind, one must first make the commitment to practice. Then, practice must be consistent, and most importantly, sadhana must be done with the power of concentration.

The following is a basic introduction to what I call the three Cs of success in sadhana. In chapter twelve, I expand on these concepts. Firstly, *Consistency* in our sadhana is a process of evolution that gradually transforms our outer desires into spiritual desires. Continuity of effort, abhyasa, increases the power of *Concentration* which inevitably determines the quality of our lives. Thirdly, sadhana also requires *Commitment*, which means being true to yourself. Staying committed to what is important to oneself helps to avoid the monkey mind drama. Drama of the monkey mind is like riding a sensory Ferris wheel that keeps us experiencing and believing the same thing, round and round again. It is a complete distraction from dharma, our purposeful living.

The 'monkey mind' expression has its roots in ancient Hindu-Buddhist traditions dating back thousands of years and thus reflects that a restless mind is nothing new to humanity. Krishna also mentions the fickleness of the mind in the Bhagavad Gita. I would propose that it is more evident today than ever before as in this current ascending Bronze Age (Dwapara Yuga) people have become hitched to the equation of speed = efficiency = evolution. Many believe that speed and efficiency are necessary for evolution, for attaining what they want and need, or for any desired transformation.

However, Vedanta challenges this notion with a foundational idea: increasing speed for the sake of efficiency is an indicator of how we believe in the illusion of the limited time and space paradigm. In fact, increasing speed in the hopes of contributing to our efficiency is actually perpetuating our karma, and because every action has an equal reaction, our habitual karmic behaviors keep us from evolving. ***Vedanta aims to direct us toward experiencing our true being and dharmic path of evolution, a coming to know how to un-do our selves.***

We may begin by asking, Why are we speeding up? Or What is it that we are increasing our efficiency for? Efficiency, the speed and accuracy with which we accomplish tasks, is measured by looking at how one performs various tasks in the world. However, because this world is illusory, we are living in *maya*, the tasks we perform are separate from, and can separate us further from experiencing higher consciousness. To live in higher consciousness is timeless and cannot be measured using the same scale one uses to measure efficiency in the objective world. Objectivity of any kind is an illusion and termed in Vedanta as *maya*. Therefore, any practice that perpetuates objectivity is a form of selfishness or egoism (asmita), in that it creates an association with conditioned consciousness. Conditioned consciousness creates obstacles that delay or prevent our experience of presence within pure consciousness.

The concept of efficiency is relevant when conceiving of experiencing pure consciousness. In the practical sense, there are ways to efficiently improve our lifestyle through ***mind-body synergy***. This is a concept I examined in my first book entitled, ***Sun, Moon and Earth***. Efficiency requires the power of attention, focusing the mind, and disentangling it from the senses to attain the power of surrender. This is all mind work, and the mystical meanings of efficiency and success have everything to do with the power of surrender. This is in stark contrast to the ego's drive toward material wealth, fitness, and physical health.

One unfortunate phenomenon that takes people away from the Vedantic path of evolution is the commercial globalization of postural-Hatha yoga. This is a colossal movement that does not seem to be slowing down, and it is mostly focused on the fitness of the body, by way of flexibility and balancing in various circus-like positions. As practiced today, postural-Hatha yoga does not emphasize the role that the mind plays in maintaining a balanced physiology, the systemic functions of the body, its role in a strong immune system.

With integral yoga, a mindful practice of asanas (poses) can be an effective means for healing the mind-body relationship and improving aspects of the mind that are vital to success in living an evolutionary lifestyle. When beginning, the practitioner correlates the body with the mind in a limited fashion. The body is simply a place for the mind to place its attention, similar to how one uses a map, the mind, to navigate terrain, the body. However, with consistent practice, the mind can transcend the body. Initially, evolution begins with nurturing the mind-body relationship as a foundation for developing what Sage Patanjali referred to as the Yama (social behavior)-Niyama (personal behavior) principles for raising consciousness. We should not disregard the importance of the body and skip onto higher practices because evolution relies on the body as the temple for sustaining prana, the life force energy that consciousness expands from.

Even though this is a primary stage to the evolutionary path, the relationship one has with their body and breath have profound effects on the later stages of development. For example, the entire aim of Hatha Yoga is on centering the prana (samana-vayu), wherein the currents of the left side (ida-nadi) and the currents of the right side (pingala-nadi) must be balanced. If not balanced, the doshas become either weakened or dominant. The practices of both asana and pranayama play an important role in this balancing process. The inhaling breath controls prana's upward flow (udana) and the exhaling breath controls prana's downward flow (apana). After consistent practice and the development of the capacity to concentrate one's attention, the breath becomes slower and more heart-centered. This creates gaps between inhalation and exhalation, thereby providing the mind with the ability to ascend beyond itself. When the mind can ascend beyond itself, the mind is no longer an obstacle to experiencing the feeling of serenity which comes from the heart.

Evolution then progresses on a secondary level where cultivating a unified mind and heart relationship is felt as awareness and devotion. While one works at the primary stage of balancing mentioned above, it is also important to reach for this secondary level of unifying the mind and heart. This can be accomplished through practices such as engaging in creative pursuits through the arts, spending time with Mother nature by gardening, promoting healthy ecological behaviors, and engaging in charitable activities, which is the greatest of all services. Devotional (bhakti) yoga practices includes chanting mantras, dancing, and intimacy rituals that bring out the sweet sensitivities within one's personality.

Today, the meaning of success for most people has been reduced to a narrow meaning. To many people, success means being financially rich and accumulating accolades that celebrate the ego-based contributions to the world. Although great achievements in the world that improve the welfare of humanity are very positive and should not be discredited, these achievements in and of themselves will not enhance one's spiritual evolution. It is the effort that a person directs towards carrying an idea to its fruition, what we can call developing one's will power, that at some point in the person's evolution can be positively applied to spiritual practices. This will power will enhance one's evolution.

From the perspective of spiritual evolution, we must consider the entire person on the level of mind, body, and soul. In order to elucidate this perspective, I will share with you some of the teachings of a barely known early twentieth century Indian Swami-saint named Rama Tirtha and also the teachings of Swami Jyotirmayananda, with whom I have had the honor of spending many years studying Vedanta and integral yoga. Both individuals share a practical approach to teaching Vedanta, applying its trademark concept that one truth exists, God alone. Their use of simile, simple stories, and examples from scriptures provide greater understanding of the mystical implications contained in Vedanta's profound teachings.

When I first met privately with Swami Jyotirmayananda, I had at that time already been a long-time devotee and consistent practitioner of the Kriya Yoga system as taught by Paramahansa Yogananda. I expressed my concerns to him that I perhaps was being disloyal to my guru or lineage. With an emanating aura of love, he sweetly remarked, "That is perfectly fine, the world is your guru." That simple gentle remark not only enhanced my relationship with my lineage and guru, but also penetrated my entire consciousness. It taught me something very new, how to listen to the world as my guru, making the entire world a living scripture.

'The world as your guru' means that in order to understand success beyond the mere material viewpoint of our times, we must begin to redefine what success is. We must understand the laws of nature, rediscover the relationship between mind and body, and embrace life with a unified vision that can allow us to see beyond the veil of life's ever fluctuating complexities. "Simple living and high thinking," is an age-old saying that can actually work when it is applied. The fascinating Meher Baba once taught this lesson, "What is the meaning of God-Realization? It means to become one with God. By thinking and imagining, one can never become one with God. Union is possible only after the death of thoughts and imagination – the mind must die."

Education regarding the values that define true success is imperative today and necessary for overcoming the monkey mind. At some point in human evolution, we became a clever type of human called homo sapiens. However, it seems that many of our human behavioral patterns have regressed to the restless nature of a monkey that jumps from tree to tree. The monkey is restless until it gets its banana, at which point it sits and begins to peel it. As the monkey peels one section at a time, it becomes calmer and calmer, and its mind becomes more focused on eating this fruit. So too, the human mind, as taught in Raja Yoga, becomes calmer as one's consciousness becomes more concentrated on the true existence of our joyous being, known as pranava.

Similarly, as taught in Tantra Yoga, the mystical energies of the secret spine, referred to as chakras, are centers that vibrate at various levels of consciousness. Each of these chakras resonate according to one's level awareness and determine what a person sees and experiences in the "the world." Each of the chakras emanate light and the mind projects the quality of that light, whatever it may be, out into the world. This projection creates our destiny. However, this does not mean that our fate is destined, indeed, quite the opposite. Each person can change the vibrational resonance and then our awareness shifts so much so that the dramas of life and the lessons of the world shift. Practicing integral yoga removes the limitations that have been encumbering the mind. The limitations are a result of past negative impressions and conditioning.

In our Western societies, our educational systems are focused on teaching people how to make money, and, because of this, success is largely measured by how much we earn. However, our American ideals promote innovation, freedom, and individuality. These higher levels of consciousness are what launched the revolutions to abolish slavery and colonial rule throughout the world. It was an initiative started by Lincoln[8] with the Emancipation Proclamation that gave momentum for a global search for truth. By no coincidence, while Abraham Lincoln was fearlessly asking America to uphold moral and ethical values likened to the great dharma king Rama of Ayodhya[9], so was Ramakrishna Paramahansa (1836-1886) afire on the other side of the planet in northeastern Bengal, India. Ramakrishna was reviving the yoga tradition and Mother worship (Shakta) practices that revived the lunar tradition and led to the reformation of relevant societal practices such as respect and honor of women as the Goddess. Ramakrishna worshipped the Goddess in the forms of his wife Sarada Devi and Divine Mother Kali. Much of his work held the purpose of promoting equality between men and women. This is one fundamental principle necessary for spiritual evolution.

Yoga explains that, as an individual increases their awareness, as the soul continues along its inherent path of ascension, the petals of the chakras open proportionately, one by one. The human banana is the spine, and the fruit of liberation begins to show in their enjoyment of quietude. Their moments of stillness expand their awareness like light reflecting off the vast ocean. For example, self-inquiry (vichara) is a technique of meditation that explores the nature of our thoughts, words, and actions to aid in dismantling the conditions of the mind, and the patterns that lead much of the world to pain and suffering.

From the physical perspective, the self-care branch of ayurveda becomes the best healthcare approach because it promotes discipline and individual responsibility which produces greater management over our lifestyle choices. In terms of the three dosha types, for vata (air) types it leads to greater consistency in a practical sense, for pitta (fire) types it emphasizes moderation, and for kapha (water) individuals it leads to an inspired attitude in all activities. The greatness of Hatha (postural) yoga is that a healthy life is a result of a healthy spine, and a newborn connection with the spine then expands the mind to new vistas of confidence through quietude. Success needs to be defined from an integral perspective that considers the trinity of mind-body and spirit evolution. In other words, a happy person is what defines a successful person if it is reflected in a balanced body, a peaceful mind, and compassion towards all living things.

---

8   Abraham Lincoln was elected 16th president of the United States of America in 1861, and served until his assassination in 1865. Lincoln was considered a great yogi from India in his past life.
9   The birthplace of Rama and setting of the epic Ramayana

The Human-Animal Lifestyle Paradox

Humans have inhabited this planet for many millenniums and beyond the point that history or even science can record. Countless civilizations have come and gone, from the Incan, Mayan, and Aztec of the West, to the Greek, Egyptian, Roman, Atlantis and Lemuria of the East, each with their unique aspects that most humans today know very little about. The few things that I have found consistent in all these ancient cultures include 1) a fascination with the mystery of life and a reverence for the powers of consciousness that uphold this creation through worship and rituals to honor the forces of nature – air (wind), fire (sun and light), and water (oceans and rivers); and 2) a daily life that is informed by a close relationship to nature, agriculture, and the animal kingdom. This last point is important because in my view, animals are the vehicles for revealing the consciousness that exists within nature. They teach us how to see the Divine powers hidden – and often not so hidden – in nature and the vital role these powers play in our evolution.

Today, the fascination, reverence, and higher consciousness of these ancient cultures are absent from modern societies. Instead, what compels humans toward evolution is limited to trinkets, the power behind corporate logos, bank accounts, and stock markets. This way of living reduces life to a multitude of struggles for a very distorted definition of happiness. We massacre millions of animals yearly, using them as commodities for human consumption and selfish pleasures. Additionally, humans are literally working themselves to death to attain currencies that purchase goods and services that perpetuate the illusion of happiness and success. Large populations continue to live in geographical areas with diminished natural resources, such as water, that is vital to life, but people push ecosystems to their limits and beyond.

An accurate account of history is rarely found, and humanity's general level of education is limited, with most maintaining a geographical orientation that does not go much beyond their own neighborhood or their immediate family of origin. The patterns of recent history[10] create the conditions of hu-

---

10   The idea of a recent history is referring to the astrological cycles of consciousness known as Yugas in Sanskrit. The last two cycles (descending & ascending) are known as Kali Yuga (701 BC to 1699 AD) which reflects the darkest periods of humanity and spans approximately 2,400 years. The Kali Yuga accounts for the creation of religions, countries, empires, dictatorships, countless wars, and devastation to the earth's ecosystems. The Atharva Veda states, "A hundred to you, ten-thousand years, two Yugas, three Yugas, four we make." (AV V111. 2.21).

man nature and are what drive societies into the monkey madness we see today. The evolution of humanity through its many revolutions and eventually to the most recent scientific era, shows how the human impetus is now beginning to change from revolution to evolution. In other words, during the revolutionary eras, humans followed doctrines produced by centralized figures such as kings and queens, with each culture seeking to acquire various types of commodities from precious metals, silk, spices, tobacco, sugar, and other natural resources.

Gradually, over thousands of years, the world has developed through innumerable civilizations, religious movements, the development of the nation state, the colonization of empires, and most recently in the last century, communism, socialism, and the fascism of Nazi Germany. Societies all over the world have swallowed the promise that government, or some centralized form of rule imposition, will keep order and provide everything they need, like health care, safety, and protection from viruses and foreign invaders.

In the early to middle part of the twentieth century, German and American physicists like Max Planck, Albert Einstein, and Niels Bohr, to name a few, were exploring the mystery of life from the perspective of science and light. They were studying the properties of light and its emission in order to try to understand magnetic energy, and even perhaps to arrive at a clear concept of the nature of Reality. However, these efforts have not arrived at any conclusion except that time and space are limitations of the earth plane and other astronomical views of how this world came into being. In contrast, the ancient yogis had already developed profound understanding of the vast domains of consciousness, through their direct experiences with the light domain that exists directly within the human physical body. Yogis penetrated these realms by learning to control the mind, mastering the breath, using mantras as sacred sounds, focusing on geometric images (yantras) and offering prayers to the Gods.

If consciousness is what upholds creation, how can it be measured? Our modern history is based on scientific findings, a collection of material evidence that leaves us with many unanswered questions along with a limited scope of the purpose of human life. Alternatively, our ancient history is bathed with the spiritual depth of rituals to the sun and moon, fire ceremonies, communities that celebrated the changes of seasons and astrological movements and most of all the ancient civilizations that had a profound relationship with the natural world.

In the Hindu-yoga teachings, the Gods and Goddess are often associated with an animal that is symbolic of an inner potential of our consciousness. Animals such as Shiva's bull (Nandi), Durga's tiger, or Krishna and the colorful peacocks, deer, and cows represent the quality or nature of the Divine in relation to our own inner being. The Gods or Goddesses are part of metaphorical stories that aid in unlocking ego-bound consciousness. Animal archetypes can also be found in the eastern Greek and Egyptian mythologies and the western Mayan and Incan teachings. Sadly, animals are a commodity for humans today, something that is here to serve us, entertain and feed us.

When the famous guru of the Hare Krishna counter-culture movement, Srila Prabhupada was asked what his teachings were about, he said "To awaken God consciousness in the human being. The human being is distinguished from the animals in that the animals cannot understand what is God. And if the human being also does not understand what is God, then he an animal." [11]

This points us to the interesting paradox between humans and animals. We have much to learn from the way we are similar to and different from animals. Humans, like animals, have senses, protect their young, and recognize energy in its various forms all of which develops the function of the brain. Humans have become like animals in that our behavior mimics fight, flight, or freeze survival mechanisms of animals, and the Darwinian theory of evolution or natural selection shows us the links between behavior, environment, and biological consequences.

So, we all come into life following the patterns set in place by our parents, family environment, societal influences and more…and then we begin seeking to fulfill our unique individualized desires. Animals operate purely from the instinctual plane, their patterns of behavior are relatively fixed, and they cannot create karma because of this. Humans, on the other hand, operate through three planes of consciousness: the instinctual, intellectual (reason) and intuitive (spiritual). As a result, we do determine the fate of our lives through the laws of karma, also known as cause and effect. The lower the plane upon which we operate, the greater the suffering. For this reason, we see so much suffering in the animal kingdom and their lifespans are mostly so short.

Humans are born with free will, and the choices a person makes determines

11   Stated during an interview in 1973 on a local news network in San Francisco, CA.

their fate. If a person lives a very destructive life as a human, it is very likely and possible their soul returns in the form of an animal. Sadly, this is a regressive form of life known as involution. When humans live like animals, killing each other and protecting their territory like a pack animal or a dog, it reflects a total denial of their potential higher soul nature. As a result, after having ignored their spiritual essence and the intuitive plane, the soul reincarnates in a form to experience the lifestyle that reflects one's behavioral choices in their past life. Swami Jyotirmayananda explains, "Animal embodiment is called bhog-yoni and is meant for experiencing the fruits of past karmas only. Animal embodiments are a kind of hospitalization of souls."[12]

Everything in nature has a soul and this includes plants. Even bacteria are alive and have visible and measurable energy. The wisdom of Vedic culture expands on this idea to support humans evolving through a synchronistic relationship with nature. This is because the same energy that upholds the trees, plants and animals is the same one that sustains our very own physical body.

Personal Primers for Success in Evolutionary Living[13]

Below are vital qualities for operating on the higher planes of consciousness. They can be considered prerequisite factors necessary for creating an evolutionary lifestyle and overcoming the modern mindset. These points represent personal aspects, qualities and characteristics of mindset and behavior that one can apply daily for evolutionary living. One's lifestyle can be enhanced if the positive aspects are integrated and the negative aspects are reduced. By focusing on these concepts, one can begin the process of self-transformation.

- **Work**

Work is not defined as a job; work is about living a life of dharma. Without work, one can never succeed because according to Vedanta, work is rest. This means that when the body and mind become fully absorbed to such a degree that the idea, "I am working," becomes entirely abolished, one is at rest in their true nature. This means that one is no longer ignoring their Divine purpose because their work is for a higher purpose and not merely for monetary gain. Diligent work can be a wonderful form of mental purification of the ego; it

---

12   Response given to a question asked by a devotee of Swamiji.
13   An adaption of Swami Rama Tirtha's Secrets of Success, In the Woods of God Realization.

increases will power and promotes dharma. Where there is dharma there is victory! And that victory is truth. According to Vedantic wisdom, the fundamental factor behind the development of the monkey mind and suffering, is ignorance. By ignoring the true essence of our soul nature, we forget our Divine nature. This occurs life after life until the greatest result of suffering is felt as a lack of purpose, a lack of understanding of the true meaning of life (dharma).

Forgetting our dharma can also be referred to as our acquired nature. Over lifetimes, we may develop a divergent and untrue sense of purpose for our existence as perceived through the senses. In this way, life becomes reduced to the instinctual plane of living like animals. Thus, having spent countless lives living for the senses, we are like ants marching single file, each one following another without ever acting independently of one another. Such group or tribe mentality denies us the opportunity to think independently, to question or inquire. Therefore, classical yoga endorses the primary importance of *satya*, living in truthfulness. Satya promotes questioning the world, its existence, and our thoughts.

- **Selflessness**

The Bhagavad Gita explains, "Therefore, always conscientiously perform good material actions (karyam) and spiritual actions (karman) without attachment. By doing all actions without attachment, one attains the highest."[14] Selflessness implies performing all actions without attachment to their outcome. When we perform material actions as a necessary part of living a responsible life in a selfless manner, it purifies the mind and body. This is because these actions promote the flow of life force (prana) to flow and strengthens one's mastery over personal energy. Prana animates all of existence. Selflessness in spiritual actions, such as yoga practices and austerities, leads one to higher sentiments, attaining affinity for the Divine which, in turn, promotes success in wellbeing and evolution. Often, many assume that living a spiritual life requires poverty and harsh physical conditions. This is far from necessary; in fact, a balance of selflessness in worldly activity is just as important as spiritual activities themselves. The combination of worldly and spiritual activities promotes an exchange of prana as positive energy between the outer and inner life.

---

14   From *God Talks With Arjuna: The Bhagavad Gita*, by Paramahansa Yogananda (Self-Realization Fellowship, Los Angeles, CA).

- **Compassion**

Cultivating compassion includes the process of transitioning from thinking and feeling exclusively about oneself into feeling for others. The thinking mind is vulnerable, at risk of being entrapped by the ego, but feeling is a quality of the soul. Compassion is a quality that develops out of being in love, not with another, but by abiding in the very essence of the soul. Cultivate compassion through random acts of kindness that are spontaneous expressions from the heart. ***Compassion is the wave and love is the ocean.*** Compassion brings a very fluid and Venusian nature to life that both attracts others and promotes inner contentment (santosh).

- **Cheerfulness**

"Sarve Bhadraani Pashyantu,"is a wonderful line from a Sanskrit peace chant that means, May all see what is good. When we focus on the good in people and in the world, it promotes cheerfulness. When too much attention is placed on our physical body, we are more likely to become moody, which makes sense, because the body is heavy by nature, filled with elements and gross impurities or malas (feces, urine and sweat). The body is constantly releasing. However, a natural landscape or nursery makes us feel positive and cheerful, especially fruit trees. Natural grocery stores bring out a cheerful mood in all just as positive company (sangha) does.

- **Fearlessness**

Fearlessness is requisite to spiritual evolution; it promotes life success and spiritual success. Deluded are they who divorce one from the other. The greatest feats in life are accomplished from a total absence of fear. Fear is expelled from the mind through sadhana, and spending time in nature because positive associations help one to gain discipline over the mind. Fear is the opposite of love, and is the most crippling emotion, retarding spiritual evolution potentially for lifetimes. Fear is an emotion of the lowest level of consciousness. Fear promotes violence and destruction. As Gandhi said, "Cowards can never be moral." To live an evolutionary life, fear must be eradicated in thought, word, and action.

- **Self-Reliance**

Swami Rama says, "When we depend on others we say go, go away and everything runs from us, and when we rely on our true Self, through trust and faith…all things flock to us." Vedanta points to the soul for self-reliance because the soul is the source of pure consciousness that exists within every human being. The aim of yoga is to manage the mind and its worldly conditioning so that all obstacles can be removed. One can then rely on the qualities of the Self that emanate in their purest forms as contentment, peace, cheerfulness, and love. Self-reliance is also inner reliance on the qualities of the indwelling spirit within.

The greatest ambassador of this Vedantic ideal in the West was Ralph Waldo Emerson. His writings in an essay entitled, ***Self-Reliance***, represent many of the central ideals of Vedic culture and spawned within me, while in college, the very movement that eventually led me to evolutionary living. He writes,

> "Society everywhere is in conspiracy against the manhood of every one of its members. Society is a joint stock company, in which the members agree, for the better securing of his bread to each shareholder, to surrender the liberty and culture of the eater. The virtue in most request is conformity. Self-reliance is its aversion. It loves not realities and creators, but names and customs. Whosoever would be a man, must be a nonconformist."

This is a profound statement that defines the evolutionary life and demonstrates the importance of discovering the inner Self. The inner Self is buried beneath names and customs and conditions of the mind. They paralyze our natural capacity to inquire, wonder, and observe the world. Learning from the world requires a ceasing to conform.

- **Purity**

Purity begins at the level of the mind and is promoted with simple living. When the mind is pure, one has attained sattva, a clarity of consciousness, a mental field that is free of impure thoughts and emotions that cloud the sky of the mind with endless desires. Mental purity, shaucha, is one of the fundamental steps of classical Raja Yoga's niyamas. Purity of mind is attractive to God consciousness because it allows for prana to expand without encumbrances. A pure physical body can also promote expansion of prana because it does not weigh the mind down. For prana to expand, one must make space or do some spring cleaning.

Broadening the Scope to Supplement the Primers

- ### Enhance your Prana

Prana is enhanced and sustained in the human body through fresh foods, clean water, and natural air. These three elements constitute the primary channels[15] of the body-mind relationship. If you ask any integrative healer what some of the main causal factors of chronic diseases are today, they will point to the toxic elements found in foods, water, and the air we breathe. They will also say the number one cause of chronic disease is stress. These toxic factors and stress create disturbances in the ayurvedic doshas[16] that lead to disease and disorder in the body. So, if the elements that surround us are toxic and our mind is stressed, how, then, can we pranify the mind and body?

Yoga teaches us that prana is also the energy of our thoughts, the intention of our words, and the momentous power of our will in all our activities. As the saying goes, 'Prana goes where the mind goes.' This means that if the mental focus is disturbed, the mind sends these disturbances to the body via the central nervous system. Because the mind's energy is not focused, the energy trying to reach the body areas that are experiencing discomfort is not strong. The disturbances and weakened energy result in a mind-body fragmentation. When the mind is not focused, the energy it sends to heal areas in the body that are ailing is inconsistent. Will power is weak and intelligence is lacking. Proper healing requires a reciprocal relationship between the mind and body, so when an area of the body has blocked energy, it can affect the mind adversely. An apt metaphor is a poor internet connection that makes it difficult to open a webpage that you have typed into the search bar; you can keep waiting, but unless the communication is clear, the data will not be transmitted. So too, we see that with mind and body, unless they are in harmony, healing on an integral level will never occur. This lack of mental focus is the reason so many people resort to artificial means of healing through prescription medications and surgery.

---

15   According to ayurveda, the primary srotas (channels) are Anna-Vaha (food channel), Prana-Vaha (respiratory channel) and Ambhu-Vaha (water channel).
16   According to ayurveda, there are three primary energies or elements that govern and influence all biological and psychological functions, namely vata (air), pitta (fire) and kapha (water).

- **Reduce Stress**

Society imposes certain pressures, viewpoints and concepts that distort our sense of purpose. Humanity is over-worked, over-populated, and over-loaded with stress and toxins. Humans, today, create unrealistic goals that lead to a very stressful life. When the goal of life is the accumulation of wealth and we are subscribing to materialism, stress is bound to occur because one object creates the desire to only want another one, over and over again. However, if one changes their goal to be the creation of a simple lifestyle, one that cultivates a more intimate relationship with nature and its purifying elements, stress will be reduced. Focusing on the elements, we will find that the Earth element is grounding, the water element is soothing, fire is transformative, air uplifts us, and ether promotes understanding through expanded awareness.

- **Family Values**

The lack of family support for the youth in our world has created emotional deprivation, which results in a type of suppression and dysregulation that can lead to the abuse of drugs, alcohol, and sexuality. Children, in particular, need to learn how to direct (sublimate) their emotions in a positive manner otherwise it leads to many distortions in their behavior.

The family unit has been broken to pieces as the divorce rate continues to climb, the support of the family unit is virtually non-existent, and many children today live without a father or motherly support. Love and proper guidance have been absent, driving children away from embracing their feelings and being forced to discovering their suppressed emotions when it's too late. Not only do children need attention and guidance, but they also need discipline, and, in fact, so do the parents. This is where yoga comes in. As yoga continues to spread into our modern societies, not merely as fitness fad, but as we are experiencing now in a cultural lifestyle revolution, yoga is restoring the dharmas, the universal truths and purpose of life.

Family life, as described in the Vedic ideals or four aims (purushartas), when balanced, should have a fourfold structure, namely social, practical, intellectual, and spiritual. In the later chapters we will explore the how the four yogic branches expand on this four-fold system to profoundly align family life and promote evolutionary living.

- **Spiritual Ecology**

This principle is founded on the idea that nature is Mother Divine in the form of the five elements of earth, water, fire, air, and ether. Mother nature is found in the rocks, minerals, earth, water, plants, and animals as expressions of her creative presence or **prakriti**. Humanity must begin to recognize that Divinity is not limited to a monotheistic approach to evolution but points us towards the capacity of appreciating and experiencing the Divine in any of the myriad of ways that her all pervasive beauty can be found in this world.

In this tradition, being spiritual is characterized by living in daily awareness of this world, felt as an intimate and ongoing relationship with all living things. This book is an exploration into the current revolution that is expanding into a new relationship with God, Guru, and the entire world process as our teachers, guiding all souls towards an ever-expanding unified state of consciousness. The outer stories and dramas we witness each and every day can become potentials to greater detachment and compassion and provide new opportunities for knowing Him, loving Him and serving his children.

- **Reviving the Lunar Energy**

This revival begins with understanding the importance of the moon's positioning and cycles in relationship to the sun and earth. Embracing the lunar traditions includes rituals that encourage humankind to live on the planet with greater compassion, while at the same time promoting selfcare. Selfcare is the backbone of ayurveda and reflects the moon's gentle quality. Lunar energy is restorative, while the suns presence can be over-bearing and produces excessive externalized energy that can lead to depletion if not moderated. Essentially, the balance of the sun and moon energies promotes cultural harmony, productivity, and evolution.

Introduction to the Four Paths of Yoga

Every person is imbued with aspects of these four virtues, also referred to as paths. The yoga tradition provides various methodologies according to each path to suit the qualities of the aspirant. These four paths will be become adapted into an integrative model referred to in the last chapters of this book as Listen (Karma), Learn (Jnana), Love (Bhakti) and Let Go (Raja).

Karma Yoga

- Karma Yoga represents the practical action-oriented aspect of one's personality and allows us to use our activities as gestures for improving the world. Every gesture can become Karma Yoga if done with the right attitude. For example, gardening and tending to the welfare of house are chores that practically everyone must do, although few people view them in a purely positive light. However, if a person takes the attitude that God is sustaining the body to perform these actions, then one's perspective shifts, erasing the idea that You alone are doing this activity. Karma Yoga teaches you to give everything back to God by embracing the understanding that it is He who is supporting you in doing whatever it is you have to do, or want to do, at any given moment. Any action can promote spiritual evolution if is done with a selfless attitude. Service to humanity in any form is one of the most purifying forms of yoga because it promotes equality. Service benefits you as well as everyone else involved as givers or receivers of the service.

Jnana Yoga

- Jnana Yoga is the power of reason that develops into intuitive intellect or pure wisdom. Jnana is experienced through the study of scriptures and maintaining a resilient focus on the truth. "I am Brahman" (Aham Brahmasmi) is one of the great utterances of the Upanishads and is the culmination of Vedantic thought. It is the Realization that you are Divine.

Bhakti Yoga

- Bhakti Yoga is the path of love and devotion that is cultivated through opening the heart. Bhakti, as a practice, is usually developed through mantra, dance, and shifting one's emotions into devotion toward God. It is also experienced as our enhanced sensitivity with all living things.

Raja Yoga

- Raja Yoga is the fourth path and is founded on the cultivation of will-power through various disciplinary practices including the other three yogic paths. Continued practice produces an internalized state of mind that eventually becomes anchored in absolute consciousness.

Evolution Begins with Non-Violence

The very first thing we all need to embrace when beginning our evolution is the idea that we share this planet equally with all of humanity, animals, and nature. Everything living is divine and should not be harmed or exploited for selfish motives. The entire planet is an embodiment of consciousness that continues to expand and contract through the many planetary epochs.

Evolutionary living is founded on the yogic principle of ahimsa or non-violence and can be understood in a very practical manner. If we hurt others, we hurt ourselves. If we take from anyone for some personal benefit, we are only taking from ourselves; unless the exchange is mutual and there is conscious consent. It is important that both persons are mutually supportive of each other. So, when a thief ignores this principle, he is thinking and acting in ahimsa and says, "When I steal from others, I gain for myself." Sadly, this is the fundamental thinking of many humans today. Many are just simply stealing from each other and nature with the idea that they are gaining for themselves. As a result, we can look at the where the world is today, with much chaos and disharmony.

One might ponder if there was ever a time in human history when the world process was not so full of disharmony, and if so, is this not what yoga helps us to return to? We, instead, live in a world filled with clever people and massive corporations that generate billions upon billions of dollars and yet hundreds of millions of people, live in poverty. Even those who have amassed such great fortunes cannot claim they have attained supreme happiness. I'm not specifically professing a distribution of wealth through forced tax laws nor limitations to anyone's capacity to be innovative and creative while not be rewarded for hard work. This is about recognizing the law of karma, in that all actions have an equal reaction.

When a person begins to understand the subtler laws that exist on earth, they begin a slow process of expanding their awareness beyond selfish desires. They begin to balance their activities and desires in a more moderate manner and that is more self-aware, not so externalized. This moderate lifestyle creates a compassionate approach to living that embraces ahimsa by proportionately spending our energy on enlightened pursuits. In ayurveda, this shift occurs through balanced time management and living a pace of life that adheres to nature's rhythms. When you live this way, you can see it physically in the body, because it radiates with light. Ayurveda, as a science, supports our evolution in an empirical manner. Even after a short time, you can see the results within the body and mind. As a complement science, yoga supports our evolution by increasing our intuition. Yoga should not be viewed in such a quantitative manner because yoga works by changing the way the brain functions and in turn influences how the mind adapts to the living world. These results are difficult to measure with empirical tools. Yoga practice transforms aspects of one's karma that may never come to fruition in this lifetime even though the karma has been lying dormant like a seed in the soil waiting to sprout. Yogic disciplines remove the seeds of our desires (samskaras), but often the transformation is too subtle to measure.

The Jewels of the East

I have written this manuscript not as an academician, but as a sadhaka, a spiritual aspirant who is enthralled with exploring the deepest truths behind human existence and the fulfillment of the supreme purpose of life. The practice of meditation has been one of the cornerstones of my exploration along with many other modalities that pertain to the yoga tradition and Vedantic philosophy. I have concluded that the cost of thinking is a figure that can never be measured. What we think can help us and it can harm us as well. For this reason, humankind must be careful and spend more time sorting through the various array of thoughts before acting on them. Thoughts are extremely powerful and are the roots of all that we reap for better or worse.

Vedantic texts, such as the Bhagavad Gita and the Yoga Vasishta, present profound teachings through allegories expressed in a dialogue between the Guru and disciple. These teachings counsel us to have ongoing discretion when becoming overly associated with our thoughts or our senses. In our own life, we can reflect on the many instances when a thought has been born and has led us into a series of actions that have led us astray, far away from what happiness is. We have been fooled millions of times and have chosen to eat unhealthy foods that disturb our digestion. We have spent unconsciously on material objects that do little to promote evolution.

Many are aware of the negative qualities of their lifestyle choices; however, they keep choosing them repeatedly until a terrible habit develops. Nobody imposes anything on us, we make choices that either support our wellbeing or not. Our choices are mostly motivated by our conditioned mind and based on the environment and circumstances that are habitual.

However, one practice that supports our wellbeing is meditation. Meditation comes from the mystical teachings of the far East that many all over the world have turned to as a treasured practice for overcoming the pain and suffering of repeated karmic cycles. These cycles come from the misuse of our instinctual and intellectual planes which entrap us, whirling our lives upside down and inside out. Eventually we begin to explore our third faculty of intuition, existing on a higher plane, which unifies and balances the physical and spiritual domains of life. Meditation allows our intuition to develop and is the most precious gem born of the teachings of sages and seers of the Vedic golden age. Meditation is the secret to successful evolutionary living. It arrived in the West in the late 19th century and has been a priceless gift to the Western world. India has shared the gifts of yoga, ayurveda, astrology, mathematics, architecture, music, dance, martial arts, and sacred language as aids to evolution.

During this longer cycle (yuga) of materialism that is expanding itself, resulting in the discovery of finer energies such as electricity and solar power, we have experienced scientific advancements. More importantly, we are potentially becoming more altruistic. This can lead us to discovering the techniques of meditation that enhance our capacity to be less disturbed by the complexities of life. Our Western world, and many urban societies, have no mythos or dharma to live by, therefore, people measure success from a mundane perspective. However, one measure of success through meditation is the ability to live simply and identify with the living world. ***Success is where one begins to exist in a manner that seems inseparable from every moment and all that surrounds their life.***

It is fascinating to consider that meditation has been a major element in the lives of many great personages from Gautama the Buddha, Jesus Christ, Mahavira[17], Guru Nanak and other historical personages like Mahatma Gandhi[18], Leo Tolstoy and Ralph W. Emerson. We now see that meditation has influenced the lives of many CEOs in the corporate, finance, and media worlds like the founder of Apple computers Steve Jobs and Ray Dalio, the founder of Bridgewater. Additionally, mothers, children and the elderly are

---

17   Born in India about 599 BCE, Mahavira also known as Vardhamana and considered a reformer of the Jain Monastic community. Mahavira was a monk and followed a highly disciplined spiritual life and attained kevala, omnipresent consciousness.
18   Mahatma Gandhi was initiated into Kriya yoga meditation by Paramahansa Yogananda in 1935.

learning meditation and it is creating a church inside the hearts of all types of practitioners. Meditation is gradually abolishing what Swami Rama Tirtha and Sri Paramahansa Yogananda referred to as "Churchianity" and, instead, is slowly creating sacred temples in the hearts of all aspirants. ***Our body is our temple, and we can learn to make it a sacred space for contemplation and stillness of the mind.*** Meditation, overtime, produces a state of awareness that is portable and not limited to when you are sitting in a pew or on a cushion. In the Vedantic meditation tradition, the pew is nature where one is exposed to the elements that calm the mind and slow the heart, allowing consciousness to expand beyond the ego's constant craving for something outside. Higher consciousness is all inside.

Chapter TWO

Evolution on Earth

*Evolution is a suggestion of God in the human mind, and is
true in the world of relativity. Actually, everything is taking place in the present.
In Spirit there is no evolution, just as there is no change in the beam of light.*

Paramahansa Yogananda

The Concept of Evolution on Earth

The topic of evolution is probably the most vast and complex topic one can ever explore. The exploration varies depending on the perspective one takes, whether it be historical, scientific, religious, or spiritual. Perhaps the five systems of human thought, mythology, religion, theology, philosophy, and science, developed because of humanity's struggle to understand the world and our search for happiness. One thing is clear regardless of the perspective, and that is **nothing remains the same, all things born of this worldly manifestation must change.** Geology, geography, cultures, kingdoms, governments, human beings, and especially religions are bound to the cycles of grander forces governed by the planets and higher laws that are only vaguely understood by science at this time. These evolution topics all deal with manifest creation as fabrications of the human experiment. They essentially exist as objects and concepts based on our limited perception via the five senses, the intellect, and the ego.

Evolutionary living often begins with a change of attitude, a willingness to recognize that what we have become is based on the conditioning of the mind as a result of family, culture and the relationship we have with the entire world process. A change in attitude is typically spawned by a subtle awakening of consciousness that spurs inquiry into the nature of the world, our existence, and the purpose of life. From this spark arises new types of desires that purify old conditions and desires, and we can change physically, mentally, and spiritually. When these new desires emerge, they inspire us to cultivate self-discipline, self-reflection, and the power of surrender. These three principles are major cornerstones of yoga's royal path.[19]

To understand what it means to live an evolutionary life, we must completely understand the natural and spiritual laws of this universe. This includes the laws of karma and rebirth, the magnetic laws of attraction, the energetics of the seasons and other life cycles, and, most importantly, the three levels of embodiment: physical, astral, and causal or soul-level. Each embodied soul maintains a causal body, a mind or astral body, and the gross physical body. There are many terms that can be used to describe whether a person is evolving or not. However, on a mundane level, spiritual evolution is occurring when a person is beginning to feel a greater connection to their surroundings, to the energy in all things. They feel their own individual energy becoming synchronized to the life force (prana) that upholds the material world. For example, consider the many times you have visited a certain place, perhaps it has become a favorite destination. There is something magical and distinct about the way you feel inside when you are there, it feels familiar, and the place brings out a sense of comfort. What is it that brings in this feeling? Is it your awareness becoming more connected to the subtle vibrations at this spot, or is it a place you visited in your past life, or perhaps both?

The concept of evolution as defined in the Vedic wisdom traditions recognizes that in each lifetime, a person has the capacity to reduce their karmas and desires, or conversely, the opposite, the same person can regress toward greater suffering. It all depends on the choices that person makes. When on the ascending evolutionary path, one gradually feels less compelled to pursue desires within the material world. There is a growing realization that any lack of contentment or lack of peace is a result of a fragmented relationship between

---

19   Raja Yoga Sutras enumerate three principles tapasya (self-discipline), svadhya (self-reflection), and Ishwara Pranidhana (surrender or faith).

the mind and body, a recognition of how one's current lifestyle makes one unable to transcend the fragmentation, and an increased awareness regarding the faults in one's character. If the mind and body are not in harmony with each other it is unlikely a person can find complete contentment. The search for truth begins with removing the obstacles that inhibit higher consciousness from abiding within the mind and body. Disharmony with the body is usually a result of a character flaw conditioned and embedded because of egoism. As a result of the laws of karma, the mind is always responsible for the relationship it shares with the body. The body's health reflects the extent of the mind's fragmentation.

Teachings related to evolution and enlightenment have been embedded in the Vedic traditions of India for countless millenniums. Having changed somewhat from the original methods, particularly in the West, Vedic wisdom is being assimilated into many diverse cultures of our times. The wisdom is inspiring people to live a better life, beginning with the basic understanding that if you "do good", you will "be good" [20] which is the basis behind the practice of Karma Yoga. The common expression, "good karma," refers to seeking to live beyond the pitfalls of modern society that limit human experience. Typically, we see these pitfalls as the desire to accumulate tangible objects, or the association with names and forms, titles, and entitlements. Living beyond these pitfalls by choosing to live according to the laws of karma includes cultivating the relationship we share with each other and the natural world. This, in turn, leads us to look for something deeper inside of ourselves, and we realize that the experiences of our lives are pointing us back to one place: our own consciousness.

This universe that we all live within provides us with a language that every soul can understand. Although it is an obscure and hidden language, it is rooted in an inner knowing that we are not separate from the world and that our individual existence is simply a magnificent expression of a vast eternal consciousness called by many names. True language goes beyond thought and emotion, and until one can live fearlessly, evolution will elude us.

To evolve is to experience a growing realization that you are the soul, a reflection of the eternal consciousness that pervades all living things. On a practical level evolution is increased when the mind and body area synergis-

---

20   An adaption of a quote by Sri Swami Sivananda Maharaj.

tically more attuned to each other, this includes feeling the shifts within the body that may be mimicking the shifts that are occurring within nature. The evolutionary path is characterized by a mind that is more reflective and less reactive, allowing the outer world process to exist just as the clouds float in the sky while the sun keeps shining above them. Evolutionary living is best symbolized by the sun, a radiant source of light, and the warmth that gives us awareness, energy, understanding, and the compassion to coexist on the planet.

Practically speaking, this shift to evolutionary living involves a reorientation with our body, seeing it as our own personal ecology. ***How we manage our own inner landscape is often how we manage ourselves in the outer landscape of society and nature.*** Mentally, this requires a growing awareness of our thoughts, words, and actions. Spiritually, we acknowledge there is no one way to truth or self-realization, but instead, there are many paths to truth, although every person must find their own way. This is a theme the yoga tradition has carried with great integrity through its various branches (Karma, Bhakti, Jnana, Raja, Tantra) to meet the call of every type of aspirant.

Let's explore more about what we mean by managing our inner landscape. For example, when your mind and body are in synergy with each other and you feel thirsty, you are sent a signal through the body's nervous system telling you that you need water. The thought appears in your mind, so you become conscious or aware of this need and perhaps even an image of the type of fluid you may prefer. Then, you respond to the body's need by fetching yourself something to drink. Unfortunately, I have heard numerous stories from my clients about how they ignore these needs, especially the urge from the body to use the bathroom, the feeling of hunger or even some pain. Sadly, when people ignore these signals repeatedly and the habit persists for months and even years, an associated chronic condition often manifests.

The question many ask about chronic conditions is, Who or what is responsible for this? Science says the propensity for diseases comes from your genealogy or the result of some deficiency in the body. However, Vedic wisdom explains that the mind dictates to the body. The body is merely a reflection of our psychology and is shaped by our associations, environment, and the countless number of lifestyle choices we have made over many lifetimes. Therefore, synergy between your mind and body is a primary step to evolutionary life. When a person does not have a good mind-body relationship, it is because they ignore the organic communication that takes place between psychology and biology. In addition to biological needs, our ego aspect of the mind is the source of all desires; however, the evolutionary path includes becoming aware of our desires, discerning them from actual needs, and having the capacity to make wise choices with respect to our responsibilities and lifestyle.

Discerning Between Needs and Desires

On a more positive subtle level, the mind begins to refine its capacity to intuit by discerning between needs and desires, making our lives much more efficient. Most modern urban societies live according to the demands of desires produced by the ego and the senses. This is largely due to the collective societal consciousness, in that a majority of the choices individuals make are based on the conditioned mind, the socially accepted habits and patterns of the past. However, when a person begins to question the mundane world and aspire to resolve the mystery of life, the desires lose their power of influence over our lives. The practice of integral yoga and ayurveda is the greatest boon to humanity in this regard. Both the yoga and ayurveda traditions aim at improving mind-body synergy, thus increasing our capacity to live in accordance with natural laws and guide us to the heights of enlightenment.

Learning to live an evolutionary life begins with some aversion to the patterns of the ego. One begins to cultivate a growing awareness of what is essentially good for us, although for a period of time a person continues to perform actions that contradict their inner conscience. This may go on for months, years or even lifetimes, until enough discipline is attained to say, Enough! And then those actions are obliterated for good. So much of the world is filled with people living out of harmony with their inner consciences, in that they know that something may not be good for their wellbeing, but their actions continue to contradict what they know. Alternatively, many people know that certain things like postural yoga, meditation and so on is good for us, but they lack the discipline to do it consistently. They live in the back and forth of starting and stopping spiritual practices (sadhana) even knowing how important these practices are to spiritual evolution. Even arriving at such a state of inconsistent practice is still a blessing, regardless of difficult it may feel. Every effort made in sadhana is never in vain and will eventually lead to victory as the soul continues its constant craving for liberty.

Consistent practice is supported by the idea of keeping things simple. Living simply is one of the cornerstones of yoga and can be defined as living a balanced life between our inner consciousness and our outer responsibilities. This is particularly important today in the fast-paced societies humans have created where the human brain is impressed with very high level of sensory impressions. The brain's neuro-receptors are stimulated by the sensory impressions and activated by neurotransmitters like serotonin, dopamine, norepinephrine, and histamine which support communication between the brain and the body. The more complex our lives become, the greater the potential for disturbing communication between the mind and body.

Slowing down the pace of life is necessary in order to reduce the hyper-stimulation imposed onto the mind, which, in turn, taxes the instrument of the brain. Disciplinary practices like yoga balance these hormones. Neurotransmitters like serotonin and dopamine are referred to as "happy hormones" because of the feeling they produce in the brain and throughout the nervous system; however, this is not the Real contentment that yoga aims to create. Hormones create a sensationalized feeling, often interpreted as happiness, although this is precisely what makes the mind so unreliable and unstable. Yoga practices promote transcendence beyond these superficial secretions, anchoring the mind in devotion toward the true source of everything humans seek, the Self. In order to live simply, we must slow down and reduce the schedule of outer oriented activities. While doing so, we must increase the amount of time spent on yoga, exercise, meditation, spiritual discourses (satsanga), and rituals to promote harmony with nature.

The Vedic teachings recognize that a balanced life includes seeking to balance the four aspects, Purushartas, of every individual person. These four aspects are kama, artha, dharma, and moksha. We may speak of these aspects in familiar terms like practical, sentimental, intellectual, and spiritual. The practical aspect of each person needs to be blended into activities that align with one's personal interests. Talents and skills can be associated with any craft (artha). The sentimental aspect is aligned with the importance of integration into the right community and good associations (kama). The intellectual side draws one towards meaningful tasks or endeavors that support the principle of reciprocity (dharma). One's spiritual qualities are developed in sadhana and lead one toward the goal of liberation (moksha).

Personal (Kama) – includes social life, family life, friendships, and intimate relationships. Touch and affection are essential for emotional balance. Kama can be correlated with the devotional branch of yoga called Bhakti.

Vocation (Artha) – includes work, jobs or a career that provides monetary support for all of life's responsibilities. Our work should be connected to our talents and capacity to enjoy synergizing the mind-body relationship. When we are truly working, we lose our separate sense of "I" and this produces a tremendous power of concentration. In Sanskrit, this is referred to as *artha* and can be correlated to the branch of yoga that deals with activity or Karma.

Kama and *Artha* both deal mainly with our outer life and how we live in the world. Their effectiveness and success are dependent on good mind-body synergy.

Purpose (Dharma) – Every human being has a duty in this life to serve this world with the wisdom they have been endowed with at birth. Each person has a unique responsibility to serve this world in their own way that best suits their capacity, talents, and karma. To have purpose in your life, to find meaning and value in every experience is for the higher good of your spiritual evolution and benefits others. When your life has purpose you expect nothing in return and surrender your actions to the Divine force that upholds the existence of your breath and life. Living your *dharma* (purpose) is an inner practice of surrendering to a higher power, higher intelligence, and guidance, that allows things to manifest just as they should be. This can be correlated to the Jnana branch of yoga that reflects inner wisdom of the mind directed outward as will-power, action that harnesses the initiative of moving towards freedom beyond the limitations of names and forms (namarupa) of the conditioned mind.

Liberation (Moksha) – To be free of desire is the ultimate level of evolution-ary living that culminates in the consciousness that unifies spirit and matter. The state of liberation is *moksha* and reflects a life of disciplinary spiritual practices, self-reflection, and trust and surrender in the Divine intelligence or God. Liberation is attained through the gradual calming and concentrating of the mind in that state where the mind no longer fractures the individual identity of the Self or inner spirit from grander consciousness that pervades all living things. This principle can be correlated to the Raja branch of yoga that represents an integral system of yoga.

Dharma and *Moksha* deal mainly with our inner life, the culture of medita-tion, stillness, silence, and solitude. Dharma ignites our willingness to work and serve as a result of becoming aligned with truth.

Spiritual Immigration

The Western world, from a modern historical perspective, is made up of an immigrant society, a people who migrated, certain brave individuals who explored and discovered greater resources and opportunity, or perhaps were just simply following the tribe, so to speak. Many may also argue that world history, and the founding of what we refer to as nationhood, is founded on migration from one place to another in search of truth. Those who migrated were seeking something outside of themselves and wanted to obtain something that they felt they didn't already possess. This is not a reference to the basic needs for survival (food, water, shelter, etc.) but is based on the idea that there comes a time when we begin migrating away from identification with geography, or association with a religion or any cultural identity that inhibits us from understanding our true nature. People create cultures, cultures create countries and countries create governments that breed pride, all of which perpetuates belief in the world process. This world process is filled with vicious cycles of life and death, health and disease, and joy and suffering until the soul eventually begins its spiritual migration towards oneness.

From the perspective of spiritual evolution, we must be willing to migrate away from ideologies created by the limited ego of the human complex that has conditioned our thinking, resulting in the fragmenting of our minds and bodies, and that perpetuates violence and destruction of anything that appears to violate the credo of "I". As the sun rises in the East, so does the wisdom of the ancients as part of the modern East-West story, and thus the metaphors of history (time and space) inform us that the soul's search for the sun bears many names and faces. The far East (India) has been associated with spiritual customs and ancient practices that to the common thinker are mysterious, and perhaps with only a partial glance, judges them to be obscure. However, to the aspirant, what looks like obscurity reveals itself, through the nuances of awareness, to be the grand vision of consciousness, and increases our curiosity. It is not coincidental that India has been the jewel of the East for millenniums. Many have looked to India's wisdom teachings as spiritual mentorship, especially as a fractured global community searches for harmony and peace. Just as the great American civil rights revolutionary Dr. Martin Luther King Jr. once said, "To other countries, I may go as a tourist, but to India, I come as a pilgrim."

The many customs of Eastern societies once considered taboo, carried over by the pilgrims on the trails of spiritual immigration, are becoming necessary cornerstones for healing mind-body fragmentation and the consequential patterns that perpetuate disease, suffering and unhappiness. From sitting cross-legged on the floor, to wearing loose clothing, open sandals, beaded necklaces, the global yoga movement – including its stereotypical physical aspects – to chanting, meditation, and the free-spirited attitude that began to inspire authors, philosophers and naturalists in Europe and the Americas in the mid 19th century, many cultural expressions have taken us beyond the limitations of history and the current crisis of humanity to coexist on the earth in harmony and peace.

Historical Perspectives on Spiritual Evolution

Is wisdom ancient or universal? The term universal implies that inherent wisdom buried within human nature is applicable for all and not limited to timing, culture, or limited to any religion. Often Vedic wisdom is spoken of as ancient, but is it really? Is it not universal? Originally, it was referred to as eternal and known as sanatana dharma, the eternal tradition. In one respect, Vedic wisdom has recognized the evolution of humanity as being cyclical and moving through four main ages, yugas, where the rise and fall of consciousness on the planet is witnessed through its civilizations. However, Vedic wisdom has been applied during any age and has produced the promised result of enlightenment.

Alternatively, the modern viewpoint categorizes human life as having evolved through four major revolutions or ages spanning of thousands of years, namely, Cognitive, Agricultural, Industrial, and Scientific. Political movements, known as empires, have ruled much of the world for the last several thousand years. The British empire was finally fractured with India's independence in 1947. Empires are classified by their political form of leadership such as monarchy or oligarchy. The Roman Empire is probably the most well-known but moved mostly from East to West, aside from Egypt.

Notably, the Rashidun Caliphate influenced the invasion of India. The Rashidun Caliphate began after the death of the prophet Mohammad who died in 632 AD and spawned Islamic rulerships in various areas of the world such as the Abbasid Caliphate and Umayyad Caliphate empires. Out of Europe came the long-enduring Portuguese movement spanning the years 1415-1999. Others, out of Asia include the Yuan Dynasty and Qing Dynasty, China's last dynasty.

Out of Europe, many more developed such as the Roman, Greek, Spanish, and eventually the British Empire which was the largest the world has ever seen, covering regions of land from east to west.

Many more empires exist and reflect the barbarous consciousness of the last several millennia. For people who want to learn about Vedic wisdom traditions, there is one positive consequence that came of British rule. This was the spread of English throughout the world, making it the most popular language of our time. The translations have supported a conceptual bridge, connecting the material efficiency of the West with the spiritual wisdom of the East. While this brings balance to the world, it came at a price of great human suffering that came with the colonial dominance of British rule. This uniting of the East and West was a point emphasized by both Swami Vivekananda and Paramahansa Yogananda. India's independence from British rule marks one of the clear turning points of the collective consciousness and a renaissance for Vedic dharma in the modern age. The original impetus behind this global spiritual movement was initiated by Sri Ramakrishna Paramahansa and others, much of which is explained in my first book, **Sun, Moon and Earth**.

The latest shift in consciousness began in the year 1800 A.D., when the actual cycle of human awareness began its second epoch, the Iron Age (Dwapara yuga). The Iron Age reflects the age of technology that is attributed to the Piscean age. Although many in recent times have celebrated the Aquarian age, this is mainly a result of astrological errors that have had the world embracing a hybrid zodiac that combines both a tropical[21] and sidereal zodiacs. This miscalculation as well as other lost truths such as the long dark age of humanity (Kali yuga) and other misinterpretations of historical events such as the Aryan invasion theory of India, the Christian interpretations of the bible as literal as opposed to allegorical and the incomprehensible acts of racial prejudice and slavery that has segregated humanity for centuries.

The scientific achievements of the Iron Age follow a linear schema that does not embrace the cyclical laws of karma, rebirth, the three energetic bodies (physical, astral, causal). Nor does it embrace the unity consciousness or cosmic arrangement of mind-body-spirit. Generally speaking, science adheres to the

---

21   As a result of the procession of the equinoxes, the actual placement of zodiacal signs has shifted approximately 24 degrees backwards across the sky from the original calculation at the time of the adoption of the tropical zodiac. Thus, any person who has followed their birth (sun) sign (in the Western world) would, in all probability, have a different ascendant (sign).

idea that ancient cultures where poorly developed and lacked the intelligence to develop the technology and the advances in medicine that we have now which according to science defines an evolved culture. This view couldn't be more incorrect although the integration of Vedic wisdom has seen better days this is a result of the cycles of human consciousness which rises and falls. However, the current resurgence in global awareness is beginning to challenge the scientific advancements as a result of what is compromised in health, wellness and true evolution. Advancement of a society is not defined by science or technology but rather it is reflected in the relationship humans have with living in harmony with nature and aids in the expansion of one's consciousness. Even though science has provided remarkable developments against diseases, surgery, diagnostics, and tele-communications, the world is still deeply mired in violence and destruction. If science is to become an aid to spiritual evolution it will need to embrace the laws of karma and rebirth and demonstrate a capacity to unite us.

Vedic wisdom has taught that every human being is equipped with seven wheels or levels of consciousness, each of which reflects the capacity of one's awareness. Similarly, this can even be seen eloquently expressed in Shakespeare's famous monologue, All the world's a stage[22]... which refers to the seven potentials of the human being. A similar expression is found in the Christian bible when Jesus referred to evolution by saying "In my Father's house are many mansions." [23] The seven centers are the mind's capacity to expand the light of consciousness that empowers every human to live in their true existence. We can think of each of the seven centers like a distinct house with a unique design, furnishings, and containing a certain amount of natural light. The light comes from the sun, soul, and if it is blocked, the ego predominates, perpetuating its foolish whims and selfish desires. When the light enters a distinct house, the individual aspires to know the truth that comes in seeking God (Brahman), the creator and executive director of the light. The stage of the world is where the projections of these seven centers are manifested, where every human plays out their roles based on their own consciousness.

---

22   *All the world's a stage, and all the men and women merely players; They have their exits and their entrances, and one man in his time plays many parts, His acts being seven ages.* William Shakespeare's play "As You Like It" published in the early fifteenth century.
23   John 14:2.

Over the last two millenniums, multiple generations have been trapped in the cycle of worldliness with a linear viewpoint and a lack unity consciousness. The modern mind has been driven into darkness and despair. We have seen the multitude of wars, diseases, and the destruction of our ecology. Whether it be the rich and diverse wisdom of the ancient Eastern world, the determination of the Roman and Greek empires, or life in rural Africa, the story we can comprehend is similar, it is a story on a canvas that societies continue to paint over and over again. The canvas does not really seem to change much; it does not matter where in the world these images are being drawn, what matters is that we begin to understand how these stories can help us to transcend the world process. As long as we continue to become entangled by the images and experiences of life, we miss the subtle messages they contain. Transcendence requires creating a new path to enlightenment while living in the world of time and space.

Stories upon stories are being interwoven within each other, creating layers of psychological complexities, and covering what is actually the truth, the real story of our cultural history and that of our global history. The world of time and space consciousness is an ever-evolving story of illusions that have strayed far from the real purpose of life. In one sense, life has become one big game filled with many ways to play it. The rules or laws change from one country, culture, or religion to the next and all have winners and losers, heroes and villains and the only difference really is the names and faces keep changing over time. In many ways, the game is driven by one desire to acquire more money, materialism and the superficial (misleading) sensations of power and greed. Changing the canvas begins with erasing the pictures and stories of a very distorted history, that has conditioned us into denial of the true essence of our existence.

Why is it that humanity worships things that we create…be it religions, symbols, people, doctrines, brands etc.? However, if it's something created by God, as in nature, plants, animals…we destroy it. We kill and pillage this planet as if God has nothing to do with natural existence. What is natural or loving about religions that are so distorted and misinterpreted that, people are killing each other over what they mean or what was said? How were supposed to follow the doctrines, especially with governments imposing their own prescriptive viewpoints?

Many, particularly in the Western urban technologically advanced societies, have found refuge in drugs, alcohol, and many other types of sensory addictions as well as countercultural revolutions that reflect a struggle with individual freedom. The world has measured its value and quality of life based on external phenomena, laws, access to health care and economics. However, the social revolutions can be viewed as reflecting our struggle to surrender, pointing out a lack in self-trust and the unwillingness to claim responsibility for one's own life; or alternatively, as an impetus to search for something beyond the perplexing world.

In some ways, modern technology has become the new drug that will eventually lead to newer and more complex diseases, and this seems to have already begun. The stories of those individuals living this dilemma are plentiful. For one reason or another, perhaps they didn't have good parents, or they felt neglected, abandoned, not heard, people have become narcissistic with egoistic cultural value. Many of them have influenced the culture in America, so it has become the country of consumerism, grandiosity, and efficiency. When there is a lack of support from family, people do not cultivate self-awareness and are more prone to seek support in toxic friendships, social groups or substances and degrading acts that diminish a person's inner dignity and self-worth. When we observe the outer world today, we see it caught in the musings of gadgets, fashion, video, music, media, finances, dramatic stories, drink stimulants, and intoxicants.

Today in America and in most large urban societies, we seem to have created a divided mind with one side of our consciousness (outer) completely absorbed in what we see and only what we can actually see. This determines how we think, how we make choices, and how we communicate with others. Video screens have replaced our imagination and everywhere we go we literally don't have to think anymore, the screen provides all the answers we need. Our schools and parents are teaching kids what to think instead of teaching them how to think. When our thinking is properly managed, the mind becomes a very useful instrument. Alternatively, misguided thoughts, of the monkey mind disconnect us more from the heart of life and the truth of our existence. Our thought processes are one of many tools granted to us. Thinking can be likened to a knife. When we need to cut something like food, we use it, making it easier to digest and enjoy certain foods. Then we clean it and put it away back in the drawer; however, the same knife used incorrectly can injure us or even kill us. Today, thoughts of loneliness, the fear of being left alone, is one of the greatest fears and it leads many to creating very destructive life circumstances.

Technology has its capacity to enhance many aspects of our lifestyle and commerce, however it is slowly becoming the greatest obstacle to health and wellbeing for several reasons. For one, the average attention span has been reduced to its lowest levels, making it difficult to even sustain a conversation. Secondly, human error is increasing, especially at the corporate level where basic things like day-to-day responsibilities are being programmed into a computer or machine. Because people do not have to focus or endure through any task that requires them to concentrate until that task is accomplished, training in concentration is not part of daily life.

The second half of the divided modern mind is the inner side which is rarely explored. People are vaguely aware of its deeper dimensions like the capacity to reflect, decipher and explore the energetic value of existence. The practice of inquiry into the subtle aspects of life such as…Why am I here? What is spirit? Why am I experiencing this in my life? What can I learn from it? What is my purpose? And What are the universal ideals for living a balanced life? Are not being explored. Thus, the mind's potential is not being activated.

Sadly, many religious systems, the off-shoots with Judeo-Christian origins, do not encourage its members to introspect because the religious practices are supposed to work for you, solve our problems, and lead one to salvation (so they say). For many in the Western world, there is an aversion to religious practices tailored to hide its confining orthodox structures, like those found in commercialized Christianity. Many seeking spiritual practice within Christianity find only the promise of conversion and strict dogmatism, which diminishes the importance of free will, discipline and diverse pathways for discovering truth. As a result of this aversion to the confining and quite often divisive religious dogmas people seem more inclined to label themselves as "spiritual" with the idea that being spiritual is a type of lifestyle or attitude, rather than actually following something that moves them in a spiritual direction sparked from their own inner awareness. Indian mystics who ventured over to American and European shores have repeatedly expressed a message of unity, truth, and a brotherhood of mankind.

The modern world has many constants that remain unchanged regardless of time and location. People enjoy community, food, music, comfortable places to live, and beautiful places to visit. This is because the basic needs and functions of the human body will never change, for example, humankind needs sustenance to maintain the body for its energy and longevity. Humans have always been attracted to warm places and most of the ancient world's population and civilizations have existed near the equator. It is only in the last two millenniums that we have seen substantial population increases in colder areas north of the equator because of improved insulated dwelling structures. As a result, people living farther from the equator were exposed to less sunlight and so their skin had less melanin. Prior to these population increases in areas further from the equator, humans had always had darker skin. Ancient civilizations living close to the equator, like Egypt, Greece, Rome, the Arab kingdoms, and the Mayans all sustained dense populations, and this reflects the human pleasure of being stationary and social.

In the last 2,500 years, we have witnessed the creation of world religious movements that engage the majority of the world's population. These are Hinduism, Buddhism, Islam, Judaism, and Christianity, although other religious movements exist, such as Sikhism, Jainism, Bahai, Taoism and countless other indigenous systems. Most of the world's cultures have been influenced by individuals who intended to serve the world with their wisdom teachings, but their practices, particularly in the modern interpretations, have been distorted. The teachings no longer integrate the natural laws of living, but religion and natural living must go hand-in-hand in order for spiritual evolution to take place. Humans must inquire within themselves asking, What is my truth? The Christian tradition, which started in Israel and was developed in India, is the largest religious movement in the world. It is interesting that so few who follow the Christian faith know that their founder and savior spent most of his short life in India studying Buddhist and Yogic practices of meditation. Meditation is mostly absent from current Christian religious practices. The similarities shared between two distinct cultures evolve and change over time because of cultural changes and politics, even though, in the case of Christianity and the Vedic traditions, those similarities were initiated by a major figure like Christ. The original essence and purpose of a great teaching can get lost and misconstrued.

In looking at the same historical points within ancient civilizations, we see parallel cultural and religious practices taking place. For example, the Egyptian culture had its fascinating pyramid burials and its Nile River ecosystem. Egypt was a great civilization steeped in the mystery of the afterlife and the occult energies of spirit and thrived from early 3,000 B.C. to approximately 300 B.C. Egyptian culture was well versed in astrology, sacred geometry, and was most famous for its grand architecture and mummification. Just a bit further East beyond the Arab peninsula is India, where spirituality reigned during the same time. The spirituality of India presented worship of the divine in many forms, God, Goddess, animals, rivers, and nature along with many living Gurus.

These two parallel cultures, Egypt and India (Bharata), had thriving civilizations that spanned thousands of years prior to their golden heyday where cultivating devotion for God was a primary part of life. In India, music was sacred, as was architecture, dance, and ayurveda, along with six major philosophies that allowed India to expand its forms of worship into many more diverse forms. However, these two ancient cultures present a stark contrast in their view of death and the afterlife. According to Egyptian beliefs, mumification was used to prepare the body for an eternity in the afterlife. However, in India, the body was cremated, marking the end of the body and the release of the soul to the domain of light (astral plane) where the soul transitions before entering another body.

Eygpt: Sphinx and The Great Pyramid of Giza, Great Sphinx is dated at approximately 2500 BC and built for the pharaoh Khafre.

Ecology and Spiritual Evolution

Ecological factors and climate changes have affected the cultural differences among peoples. Aboriginal people are the original inhabitants and indigenous people of Australia. Their culture is said to date back some 50,000 years and extends into areas of Papua New Guinea and Tasmania. It is also recognized that sea levels rose some approximately 11,000 years ago and separated Tasmania from mainland Australia further isolating a particular sect of Aborigine. The same rise in sea levels is also recognized in India and this great flood is no myth as it was accounted for in many other cultures. In India, it was referred to as Mahapralaya and is interpreted as "Great Dissolution" and the term can also be defined as non-existent.[24] The literal and figurative flood has both literal, as noted above, and allegorical implications. Allegorically, the flood signifies that all things are born from water, or the womb of creation – *prakriti* – and all things must return to the water. All lands (earth) are being held together by water and this element supports fertility, life, and beauty. Water, as an element, can be correlated to the cosmic power of preservation as symbolized by Lord Vishnu.

Like the Biblical Genesis flood, the more ancient Hindu mythologies mention Manu as the original human being, a king who was saved from the great flood by Matsya, one of the main Avatars of Lord Vishnu.[25] Matsya, having informed Manu of this disastrous flood, promised to carry Manu and his family to safety, along with the Vedas (ancient books of supreme knowledge), seven sages, seeds from all plants and a pair of every animal. Historians and academicians have explored why multiple stories with the same plot may have appeared within different cultures. They question if the flood was an actual episode in human history or purely mythological. The answer is that ancient texts such as the epics of Vedic-Hindu culture, always infused actual earthly events

24   Pralaya is a term which appears in the Samkhya Karika, the main text that expounds the famed philosophy of ayurveda in 72 slokas (statements). Samkhya Karika was authored by Ishwara Krishna (350 CE) and was a disciple of the great sage Kapila. Samkhya philosophy, second to Vedanta, has greatly influenced Indian history. The text was also translated into Chinese around 550 CE, a period when Chinese culture was influenced by the earlier Vedic traditions.
25   Lord Vishnu is part of the triad of Hindu gods and is considered the preserving or restorative force of cosmic consciousness. Shiva is the destroyer and is symbolic of the destructive power of wind. Brahman is considered the creator, the creative capacity of life and symbolic of the fire element. These three elements, or powers, control the entire world process. Equally, within the physical body, these forces are recognized in ayurveda as the three doshas. Their balance is required in order to maintain homeostasis as general health and wellbeing.

with allegorical meaning for the purpose of teaching. The flood is no myth. It actually occurred, probably as a result of global climactic changes that are evident in all major continents around the world.

For example, the western part of the United States, most specifically California, which is now mostly an arid desert was a sub-tropical region thousands of years ago. The same occurred in the north-western area of India known as Rajasthan (land of the kings), which is now a desert. Rajasthan was the site of the Indus Valley Civilization and the sacred Saraswati River. The river dried up several thousand years ago and so did the civilization.

Geography changes and cultures adapt according to the fluctuations in global energy, the main energy sources the world relies on. Oil is slowly being replaced with electric, solar and wind. Today, scientists and weather researchers claim the world is getting hotter as a result of human activity; however, looking only at our activity does not allow us to understand the true nature of the world. What we need to understand are the implications of our relationship with nature. The human relationship with nature creates a biosphere that grows out of the exchange between thought energy, as our consciousness, and material existence. Thus, what we see in the natural world is a reflection of human consciousness. As the yoga teachings explain, it is the collective consciousness of the world that influences all aspects from geography, weather, trends, and mental stereotypes. This world cannot be destroyed because it is Divine and will always reflect humanity's consciousness as does a projection on a screen.

Because the world is impermanent, the temperature of the world will always rise and fall over long cycles of time and should not be the primary concern of the human family except for very practical purposes. For example, if a person's body is more comfortable in a more humid climate, then they should consider living there. Similarly, in the historical record of civilizations, when a geographical area began to lack water or crucial resources for life, then people migrated to another area. Many believe this is one of the primary reasons why the Mayan Civilization ended because of a major environmental event such as drought. The entire world process is ever in flux, change is its essential nature, and Vedanta teaches us to enjoy the change, allowing it to entertain us and inspire us to flow with Mother Nature's grace.

*Matsya Avatara or the fish god is one of the ten avatars of the Hindu God
Vishnu. Manu is saved by Matsya during a devasting flood.*

The Rise of the Soft Power Culture

Much of the ancient civilizations remain in ruins and continue to perplex as well as fascinate humanity through exhibitions at museums, while Yoga and Ayurveda are in renaissance. The practices and rituals of the Vedic-Hindu-Yoga traditions are now mainstream throughout the world and gather people of all races, nationalities, and ages. The importance of gathering for spiritual purposes is witnessed in India with the Kumbha Mela, the largest festival in the world where aspirants gather to practice, study, and aspire to attain enlightenment. Festivals of an awakening consciousness are appearing in many parts of the world as the power of community is recognized. In yoga this is known as sangha.

It is not likely that the global awakening of human consciousness is merely a fad. On the contrary, humanity is slowly cultivating a new relationship with nature, and instead of being religious, our lifestyles are becoming more spiritual. Even though 'being religious' and 'being spiritual' can be defined in similar ways, the terms reflect stark differences in the way that people live and the relationship they have with the natural world. Religions have created such deep stereotypes associated with traditional religious doctrines. We have witnessed many controversial events related to religions. As a result, many people are adapting their religious practices and would consider themselves to be spiritual, living a natural lifestyle as their new form of religion.

One of the basic tenets of this spiritual lifestyle is the recognition of the Divine in abstract forms, perhaps as an animal, or an aspect of nature, or even as intelligence. Even use of the word "god" has become too religious and unscientific for many millennials. Instead, bringing their attention to phenomena that can be measured using scientific methods feels more comfortable, more natural to many people, as they tap into nature's vibrations, like the seasons, ecosystems, astronomy, and so forth. Another substantial factor emerging from this spiritual movement is the concern about gender inequality that exists in many aspects of our societies. The lack of respect for women and the decreased emphasis on Divine Mother (Goddess) worship are directly connected. This inequity exists within the major religious movements of the last two millenniums that have male figure heads. One exception to this is the Tantric yoga tradition which worships the Goddess in many forms. The

Vedic traditions, as seen in what is now called Hinduism,[26] is founded not only on polytheism, but strongly emphasizes Divine Mother (Goddess) worship in various forms. This wisdom indicates the importance of connecting our worship and devotion to nature in all her magnificent forms.

History has continually demonstrated how destructive it is to force people to follow a certain religious path while discriminating against others. Such a divisive approach leads to exclusion and prejudice, perpetuating fear and worry. The clearest indication of a true spiritual movement is in its capacity to produce great peace, love, and compassion for all living things. The current spiritual movement is changing the world in this way. However, the world changes in accordance with how we, individually, change. We must change our attitudes, our character traits, and replace our singular focus on our own personal desires with efforts that serve others. When we engage in acts of reciprocity, we see the world changing and reflecting our inner consciousness.

Vedanta teaches us to recognize that what we see or attract in the world is simply a reflection of our individual consciousness. Our perspective on the world changes when we observe all matters with the single eye of awareness that is without criticism or judgment. Our awareness simply enhances the power of observation. Ants appear to be blindly following each other, but when they recognize what nourishes them. When one ant finds the treasure of food, the rest follow along to get a taste of that same treasure. The Perfected Yogi (Siddha) Mahavatar Babaji once exclaimed to Swami Sri Yukteswar, "For the faults of the many, judge not the whole. Everything on earth is of mixed character, like a mingling of sand and sugar. Be like the wise ant that seizes only the sugar and leaves the sand untouched."[27]

Over the last millennium, India has endured a devastating subversion of its dharma, its spiritual laws. Through ruthless acts by colonizing powers, the people of India have endured religious conversion, and the destruction of precious indigenous cultures and their wisdom traditions. Some have called it cowardly to choose to ignore their right to defend themselves; however, I want to call attention to a profound principle called ahimsa, nonviolent

---

26   The term Hinduism is a misnomer and is derived from identification of a group of people within a particular valley region of northern India called the Indus. The original and more appropriate term that correctly defines the Vedic wisdom traditions is Sanatana Dharma, which means the eternal tradition.
27   *Autobiography of a Yogi* by Paramahansa Yogananda (Self Realization Fellowship, Los Angeles, CA).

defense. Ahimsa is a form of soft power that was boldly enacted through great freedom fighters within India that sacrificed their lives to attain the freedoms of democracy. In global mainstream history, Mahatma Gandhi is mostly credited for this; however, countless others such as Vinayak Damodar Savarkar, Subhash Chandra Bose, Sri Aurobindo and many others played a vital role in the transformation of India's nationhood from empirical rule to a country that now thrives because of its complex cultural and religious diversities. Many great yogi's such as Aurobindo, Yogananda, Vivekananda, Rama Tirtha have demonstrated the importance of upholding the dharma and have spoken out publicly on the social and political issues that have ravaged India for centuries.

India shares its powerful wisdom traditions with our ailing world. These tremendously important wisdom traditions can be referred to as a "soft power" and are part of a national movement sweeping across India. People are re-embracing their spiritual heritage, pluralism, humanism, and unique worship of Mother Nature. India's soft power renaissance is about harnessing the culture's attraction and appeal to the Divine. The inner soft power culture of India's ancient wisdom traditions has emerged as an evolution revolution. People are focusing on developing higher knowledge as attained through intuition by way of integral yoga and exploring its vast Sanskrit scriptural heritage as well as many other complimentary systems like ayurveda. These universal soft powers are guiding humanity to discover, within their own being, a capacity to self-heal the body and its relationship with the mind. In this way, people are developing an inner contentment that is reflected in simple living. A person experiences love and devotion for God in whichever way one feels attracted, and, most importantly, people are cultivating the capacity to live a purposeful life that leads to enlightenment. In order to discover that these powers exist within every human being, all that is required is a yearning for truth

Juxtapose these practices with the limiting belief systems that follow strict doctrine or one holy text that has been incorrectly interpreted and distorted many times. These belief systems have no scientific bases or any aspects that reconnect a person to nature and her laws. Because of their limited nature, they stand to divide the world. Such religious doctrines are hard-pressed to demonstrate to humanity their interconnectedness to the living world. Perhaps it is for this reason that Vedic systems are thriving as cultural practices and in systems of yoga and ayurvedic education. Vedic educational principles are spread throughout countless texts, allegorical stories, and compilations (samhitas). There are many options for an individual to explore in order to find and develop their own unique path with divinity. India has, for millenniums, been referred to as **Vishwaguru,** the universal teacher. This is because it has a unique and vast spiritual heritage that much of world can learn from. At the same time, it is a great boon for India to continue rediscovering its wisdom traditions suppressed for so long by Mughal rule (Muslim), British Raj, the Portuguese, Communism, and even Christian missionaries.

The Mughal Empire was founded in 1526 and lasted until 1761. It was largely taken down by the Maratha's, a warrior group led by Chhatrapati Shivaji and this change in rulership ushered in a formidable movement called Hindutva[28] Swarajya, meaning "self-rule of Hindu/Indian people." However, this movement remained somewhat dormant and obscure as the country transitioned into empirical British rule that lasted almost 200 years. Both Muslim and British rule over India undermined the yoga and ayurveda traditions leaving the country and culture in shambles until, finally, India gained independence in 1947, when the country was partitioned into two separate states, Hindustan (Republic of India) and Pakistan and subsequently also Bangladesh.

However, to this day, a large majority of people in India, including current yoga leaders like Yogi Adityanath,[29] agree that the partition of India has resulted in creating more problems than any single event in India and perhaps even the world. This separation segregated the people, preventing them from learning to live together and getting along with one another. The geographical divisions have been associated with certain types of religious ideologies and cultural identities, again creating cultural division and alienation. In the case of Pakistan, there are many regions there that have become havens for extremist religious practices. Note the similar effects that nation-state partitions had on Israel and Palestine. Also, imagine if Lincoln had allowed the union to split into separate nations of North and South, thus giving slavery a place to thrive? Partitions based on religion or racial inequality create conflict, and loss of cultural and spiritual traditions. Our world history is messy and there will never be a time when all countries get along until a universal spiritual outlook is embraced. We must all learn to see our earth, countries, and cultures as different spiritual vehicles. The conflicts and crises have the capacity to transport humanity toward an evolutionary pathway. We can attain a common enlightenment and the peace and happiness that comes with higher consciousness.

---

28 A term revived by Vinayak Damodar Savarkar in the 19th century which became a nationalist philosophy that helped influence the Independence of India.
29 Chief minister of the largest state in India, Uttar Pradesh.

Christianity's Link to India's Vedic Culture

Epic Vedantic scriptures like the Bhagavad Gita, Ramayana, and the Yoga Sutras of sage Patanjali each present a unique perspective for understanding the mind, its multifaceted nature and the secrets to mastering it for the attainment of liberation (moksha dharma). From metaphors and allegory to abstract aphorisms, each great teaching provides us insights to reflect on in order to expand our knowledge (jnana). In the Rig Veda there is great saying ***ekam sat vipra bahuda vadanti***, "Truth is One, but the sages speak of it by many names." For most of those born in Western world, they have been influenced by the Judeo-Christian traditions. For example, when Thomas asked Jesus, "Lord, we don't know where you are going, so how can we know the way?" Jesus answered, "I am the way, the truth and the life." [30] However, for many, Jesus is not the only way to the Father and sadly, because of much misinterpretation, this teaching has undermined the value of other great teachings. In my view, the misinterpretations have played a major role in dividing our cultures and societies from living together in a more harmonious manner.

Much of the divisiveness found between religions today, and especially among Christians, may be the result of many circumstances regarding Christ's life and teachings. One circumstance was the short amount of time he presented his teachings, which was approximately three years. This was not much time to train disciples in a particular teaching that was considerably different from the existing Judaic practices. Secondly, the gospel was not directly written by Christ and the gospels were originally anonymous with the modern names (Matthew, Mark, Luke, John) added some time later, potentially one century later. Lastly, the lineage of Christ is also not clear, while many inside and outside the yoga tradition agree Jesus was in India for the eighteen missing years of his life. We still do not know who, or exactly what, he actually studied besides the natural assumption it was yoga and other Buddhist and Hindu practices. Without a clear lineage, the transmission of the teaching is fragmented, and does not support succession [31] to carry the teaching forward so it can be properly adapted to the coming ages without distorting it from its original intention. As a result, now, some two thousand years later, the teachings of Christ have been reconstructed by those in religious and political power. The

---

30   John 14:6.
31   Paramahansa Yogananda was commissioned to revive the lost teachings of original Christianity for the modern ages and bridge the spiritual wisdom of the East with material and business efficiency of the West.

predominant teachings carry a fear-inducing threat, namely, that if a person does something wrong, then they will be sent to a place called hell.

However, one can feel the deep wells of compassion embedded in Jesus's teachings when they are interpreted from the yogic perspective. For example, the concept of cultivating devotion is central to his lessons, and the expansion of one's unconditional love is his life's message. The role of spiritual evolution is embedded within the roots of Christian faith. I agree with the growing view that Christianity developed in India around the mid-first century CE, when Jesus made a long contentious sojourn to the country of India located along the famous silk road.[32] In the historical record, there is not an explanation regarding his whereabouts during this eighteen-year span of his life when he traveled abroad and returned with new religious perspectives. He is a person who has been so influential in human history, yet he only lived to the age of 33. In the case of other major religious figures, much is known about their entire lives with the intention of adding further value to the experiences that shaped their teachings.

Any follower of the Christian faith can question how politics and the Church may have influenced what is known about the roots of the tradition, but this lack of information about Jesus's life is a formidable stumbling block. However, concluding that he gathered Vedic wisdom is logical especially considered how much he taught in the short span of three years (approximately age 30 – 33). If Jesus did spend time studying in India, then the esoteric understandings of his teachings make more sense. Patanjali Maharishi's work, his timeless Yoga Sutras, were of vital importance, being studied by many people in India two centuries prior to Christ and most likely influenced him. Support for this comes from people like Nicholas Roerich and others, who began to crack open the mystery of his life and perhaps many long-held secrets of the Catholic Church. We can also go as far back as the discoveries made by Nicolas Notovich in the late 1890s, and again a few decades later to the discoveries made by Swami Abhedananda.[33] He was in charge of operations within the Vedanta Society in New York that was founded by Vivekananda in 1894.

---

32   An important route that was used for trade of silk and many other commodities which began sometime during the second century BCE. It was central to the economic, religious, and cultural development of many countries such as China, India, and Japan, and linked these Asian cultures with Europe. The Silk Road was not one road, but instead, a network of roads. Human movement across inner Asia dates to prehistoric times.
33   See Swami Abhedananda's, *Journey into Kashmir & Tibet* published by the Ramakrishna Vedanta Math.

The idea that Jesus studied Vedic wisdom spread like a wildfire among people seeking alternatives to religious doctrines. In fact, yoga's swift propagation in the West is due, in large part, to this exploration. The study of how Jesus's time in India influenced his theology and original teachings has gotten the most substantial support from Paramahansa Yogananda, who has been recognized as the father of yoga in the West. He wrote the most comprehensive compendium, or scripture, on the original teachings of Jesus.[34] Yoganandaji taught all over America during the 1920s and 30s. When his spiritual centers, "Church of All Religions" began welcoming patrons in the early 1940s, he placed Jesus on the altar next to Krishna along with his entire lineage of Kriya yogis. Yogananda explained that Jesus had been working closely with Babaji, the maha siddha (perfected being) of the Kriya Yoga lineage of gurus, all of whom recognized Jesus as a brother yogi. Yogananda himself confirmed having direct communication with Jesus through the super-conscious realm.

Swami Rama Tirtha also supported the idea that Jesus spent part of his life in India, and interestingly, Swamiji also died at the age of 33. The great Ramakrishna of Calcutta, a Brahmin priest who worshipped Divine Mother Kali also embraced the practices of Christianity and considered Jesus's teachings as a viable path towards freedom. Many great yogis of the last two centuries have embraced the teachings of Jesus as universal tenets, such as, Love your enemies, and, Judge not, that ye be not judged. Juxtaposed to these leaders' embrace of unconditional love and empathy, many practicing Christians continue to criticize Hinduism, labeling it as an idol worshiping religion. Many Christians even condemn the very practical postural yoga system as devious and perverted spirituality. This was especially prevalent initially when the wisdom arrived at the shores of America; at that time, in the early 20th century, there were countless accusations made which increased the prejudice felt by those who practiced yoga. The hypocrisy of this can be seen in the Christian conversion movement which was amalgamated along with the colonial invasions of India for the purposes of acquiring new territory for the Christian British Empire. By calling attention to this prejudice and persecution I aim to prompt deeper inquiry into the nature of any system that does not promote a spiritual unification of humankind, any system that may not answer all the practical questions that, today, many are beginning to ask.

---

34   *The Second Coming of Christ, The Resurrection of the Christ Within You*, by Paramahansa Yogananda (Self- Realization Fellowship, Los Angeles, CA).

The eighteen missing, or silent, years of Jesus's life were dedicated to spiritual practices in Buddhist and Yoga traditions that would eventually shape the gospels of Mark, Mathew, Luke and John. Originally, the Christian movement began as a small unorganized band of spiritualists who were enthralled with the promise of salvation after death through Jesus as the son of God. This took place over two-thousand years ago during a difficult time in human history when political and religious issues were experienced by those who were subject to the growing power of the Roman empire. There were also many who experienced strife due to the differences between Judaic principles and the polytheistic expressions of the Egyptian religion that embraced mythology, science, and spiritualistic rituals connected to astrology. Even Hinduism was distorted during this descending (Kali yuga) era of the world's collective consciousness. During the time of Christ, India was also continuing to embrace the very rebellious teachings of Gautama Buddha, who predates Jesus by approximately 500 years. Buddhism today remains primarily intact, thriving throughout the world because of its promotion of meditation, mindfulness, nonviolence, and its embrace of the core principles of karma and rebirth.

The early Christian movement developed directly from the teachings of Jesus within a short span of three years after Jesus, whose name is Issa in India, returned to Israel from India at the age of 29. Something for us all to consider is that perhaps his teachings never really had the time in which to properly develop. His teachings do not leave behind a clear set of principles aside from the Ten Commandments. Perhaps we see this reflected in the fragmented approaches in Christian doctrines and practices that first spread throughout Europe and then on to the Americas.

After the physical crucifixion, the religious movement of Christianity began to depart from the original principles and practices that were part of Jesus's original teachings, the concepts he developed as a student of Vedic culture. His teachings developed into different strains of religion as they were influenced by various societal and powerful political forces. As the various practices gained in popularity and became Westernized, his teachings continued to digress from the original. Their Vedic qualities were lost, in part, as a result of the development of churches as is seen in such mega structures as St. Peter's Basilica, Notre-Dame Cathedral, Sagrada Familia, and Le Mont Saint-Michel to name of few of the hundreds that were constructed during this Western movement.

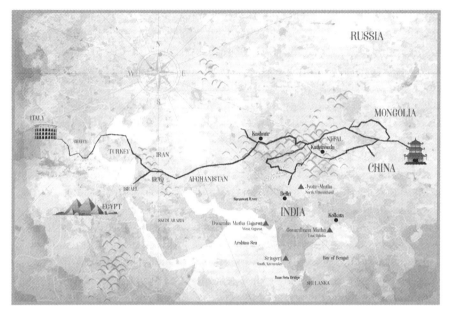

Ancient Silk Road, a probable path for Jesus on his sojourn to India.

Jesus was Asian, born within the customs and rituals of a Middle Eastern culture and influenced by the South Asian religious practices of Tibet and northern India. He spent the majority of his life studying principles central to Indian spirituality such as meditation, pranayama (breathwork), and mantra worship of the Divine in various forms. However, the teachings took a strong turn away from foundational principles of ahimsa (non-violence), karma, and rebirth during Constantine's Romanization of the Church, and even a stronger turn away during the Reformation and Europeanization of the Church.[35] By the time Christianity spread into different factions, church practices were reduced to blind faith, superficial prayers, and fear-based conversion methods, the threat of going to heaven or hell. This period is marked by a clear departure from the teachings of Vedic wisdom and the highest goal therein, that of spiritual evolution.

The Indian sage Patanjali who lived approximately two centuries before Christ,

---

35   Historians place the Protestant Reformation at 1517, with the publication of Martin Luther's *95 Theses*. The Reformation was a powerful political and religious transformation of Catholicism that turned against tradition by embracing the Bible as the sole authority of its teachings.

was given credit for developing the most practical compilations in three major areas of Vedic wisdom. These three are: 1) Yoga, in the now-famous Yoga Sutras and the eight-limbed path;[36] 2) Mahābhāṣya and a commentary on the grammar of Panini's classical Sanskrit, and 3) ayurveda. With his works, Patanjali expounded three very central aspects for the evolution of humankind.

Yoga is for the mind. His Yoga Sutras define Yoga as control of the mind, or chitta, and the disturbances, or vrittis, the outward modifications of the mind. This reference to the mind's fluctuating nature may have some connection to the similar earlier Buddhist thought, which commonly referred to the mind as that of a monkey and was also later adapted by Taoism.

Secondly, Patanjali connected ayurveda to yoga and established it as the science for healing the body. Thirdly, Patanjali emphasized the importance of the Sanskrit language for the purpose of soul realization in its sounds and speech patterns rooted in eternal vibratory energy, *pranava*. This trinity of integral healing began with evolutionary living principles he called Yama and Niyama that can also be equated with the ten commandments of original Christianity.

Patanjali's influence on yoga, ayurveda and Sanskrit, are revealed in more detail when we consider the emphasis that he placed on two concepts, Tapasya and Svadhya. **Tapasya** or austerity is the physical discipline that is developed through ayurvedic regimens. **Svadhya** is the study of spirituality through texts and scriptures. As one increases their wisdom and understanding, they share it with others by speaking, as we usually speak about what we know. This practice of sharing knowledge invokes the austerity of speech and importance of language in the attainment of spiritual knowledge. Spiritual knowledge provides purification from negative or gross forms of speech. As one evolves, their speech becomes penetrating and gains the power to influence those intrigued by the mystical life, inspiring others to begin the spiritual path. A third important concept is **Ishwara Pranidhana**, surrendering to God, and this invokes mental austerity. These three principles of thought, word, and action, provide the foundation for spiritual transformation as taught in classical yoga.

The spiritual wisdom traditions have gone through inevitable changes that no one could not have ever anticipated. Faith should not be blind. It is important

---

36   Chapter Two, *Sutra* #29 which enumerates the famous eight limbs of yoga.

for any person to discover the lost bridge of spirituality that connects one to the wisdom of the East as well as to the efficiency of the West. These two sides of the world, one very solar based (West), and another more moon based (East), must come together to bring balance on earth. Perhaps one Eastern wisdom tradition, The Noble Eightfold Path[37] of Buddha's teachings. They are principles for evolutionary living and commonly symbolized as a Dharma wheel (Dharmachakra). This is similar to the concept of the wheel or yogic chakras of the mind that pertain to the astral body. Other symbols of spiritual evolution include the serpent. Patanjali was regarded as an incarnation of the thousand-headed serpent-king named Shesha or Ananta, whose coils are said to support the God Vishnu, the sustainer of life. The spiritual symbolism of the serpent appears in both Shavism and Vaishnavism paths and serpent symbols are used in different contexts to explain various mystical teachings.

Few Christian followers have visited the Asian world, and most have not been exposed to the cultural customs that shaped early Christianity. This leaves Western cultures to discover and pass on adaptations of Jesus's teachings that were influenced by politics, patriarchal culture, and profit-minded economics. All these forces undermine the Indic culture that shaped the early spiritual movement of the West. While many around the world who have become practitioners of yoga in some form or another, they have also become pilgrims of India, embracing her as the mother of spirituality. The legacy of India is not founded merely on its fascinating and colorful culture but more so on its capacity to embrace an eternal tradition that transcends time, history, and the eccentric behavior of a select few in positions of power. Now, thousands of years later, it the light of pure consciousness endures, continuing to guide humanity toward spiritual freedom.

Evolutionary Mind and Brain

For millenniums, the yogis and scriptures of India have taught us that the mind is a powerful instrument that can influence the material world. For example, the great Indian text the Yoga Vasishta is one of the most profound texts ever written. Its content includes time travel, airplanes, telepathic communication, embryonic cloning, and sex changes. To gain its mystical understanding, one

---

37   The Eightfold Path consists of eight practices: right view, right resolve, right speech, right conduct, right livelihood, right effort, right mindfulness, and right samadhi 'meditative absorption or union'.

should study the Yoga Vasishta from an allegorical perspective, regardless of how these concepts have become very progressive when viewed from our modern perspective. Within the text, Sage Vasishta is encouraging his disciple Rama to utilize features of the mind that are helpful in overcoming the evils of the world process. The human brain is simply an organ conditioned by the mind. If the mind is devoid of its Divine virtues, then the brain's function is doomed, it will fail to connect us with the world's beauty and sacredness.

How the mind and brain are engaged plays an important role in evolution for the attainment of Self Realization. If one is consistently preoccupied with worldly objects, technologies, and moody experiences, when one is eager to resolve problems or attain goals in some outer form, then the mind is distracted, and this dulls the brains capacity. However, when an aspirant repeatedly exposes his or her mind and brain to inner worldly truths, when one listens to the teachings about the Self and then reflects on what they have heard, one's consciousness can focus on moving in an evolutionary direction.

The scientific discoveries of the last two decades have provided greater understanding of the functions and connections between the mind and the brain. Modern scientific studies of the brain have led to findings about how its structures can change over time, and how various uses of speech, sound, and visualizations play a major role in brain function. As many people today are complaining of stress, poor concentration, and disturbed sleep, new methods for treating these symptoms have been devised. Neurofeedback[38] is one of these methods. Measurements taken of brainwaves, electrical impulses inside the brain, reflect how one's thoughts and emotions are directly connected to one's level of stress. Once aware of the cause and effect of stress, one can begin to reduce stress by changing thinking patterns and regulating one's emotions. Daily life stress has become more prevalent with many people behaving with touch screen sensitivity and reacting to even the smallest of circumstances that leads to creating unfavorable situations in work, family, and social life. Stress creates an inability to cope with the basic aspects of life, such as work and responsibilities and is the largest contributor to the chronic diseases

---

38   Neurofeedback is a therapeutic intervention that provides immediate feedback from a computer-based program that measures the client's brainwave activity. Neurofeedback is also known as EEG (electroencephalogram) biofeedback. While it does seem to provide incentives that motivate a person to engage in therapies that promote health and wellness, unfortunately, the science, by itself, does not include the inspiration to promote self-realization.

we see today. This is one of the most practical values of yoga meditation, it makes the mind more resilient to the stresses of the world because it expands the mind beyond ego, emotions, and excessive thoughts. When the mind becomes highly reactive, frequently triggered, it is an indication of how it has become corrupted by negative impressions. These negative impressions lead to emotional turmoil and an instability in one's personality.

While many turn to modern scientific methods for understanding the brain and healing, the ancient systems of Vedanta, yoga, and ayurveda provide an integrative approach to preventing the imbalances of the modern human. Vedantic philosophy, with its many entertaining allegorical stories, provides the opportunity for one to gain insight into the hidden domain of consciousness. Ayurveda teaches us how to care for the body-mind complex by awakening consciousness in the form of prana. Blocked prana creates disorders referred to as doshas and yoga provides the tools and practices for attaining the freedom from the ego, our conditioned consciousness. Thus, flow of the life force energy (prana) between mind and body becomes a primary factor in health and wellness. Additionally, the flow of prana awakens the higher mind linking a person's consciousness with the original source of pure existence which leads to an expansion of awareness.

From the scientific perspective and Western view of the mind, the brain has developed through empirical knowledge, collecting information through the senses. Empirical or sensory development increases intellect which operates under the guise of ego. This type of mental technology increases the rate at which we associate with the world. This means the modern human brain is operating at faster speeds than ever before to keep up with the pace of technology, interpersonal communication, and general lifestyle. However, from the spiritual perspective, intellect and this faster firing brain becomes a limitation, a superficial power that keeps us focused externally and entraps the mind in time and space dynamics. The mind must instead become refined, or as some say purified, serving our inner focus on the intuitive level, promoting greater feeling in the heart. Anything else is a misuse of the mind-brain relationship. Awakening the intuitive power as sensitivity in the heart demonstrates a progressive step in spiritual evolution.

It's important to differentiate between how the mind works and how the brain functions. The mind is an active instrument, in that it determines how we live in the world. The mind is not who we are, it's simply an instrument, a component of the body. The mind and body are not separate entities, they are part of the same complex, coexisting as a result of consciousness which upholds them. We use the mind to think, process concepts, and make daily life decisions. The brain, however, operates in a passive manner because it simply takes on the signals it receives from the mind.

In yogic teaching, the mind is measured through the gunas or three qualities,[39] and the quality of the mind one develops all depends on one's choices, the impressions of their environment, the teachings of the culture. The mind, at any given moment, reflects the total of a person's karma. Both the yoga and ayurvedic lifestyle emphasize one's attention to this topic because what we do the most on a daily basis determines how we evolve within a lifetime. The mind is subtle, and when it is connected to the spiritual heart, it develops a sensitivity that can help link us to the vast domain of pure consciousness. We need to stop looking at the mind as separate from the body, but rather understand it as an *extension* of the body, **This is what pure meditation actually does, it transforms our awareness from the limiting capacity of the senses to a limitless domain that is liberating.**

The ideal goal of yoga is liberation, in that a person becomes free of associating with the body and the oscillating tendencies of the conditioned mind that bind us to the world process. Yoga is essentially mastery of the mind to attain the powers that exist beyond it. **The powerful methods of integral yoga allow us to observe the world with compassion and joy while witnessing the Divine hand of energy that supports its destructive, creative, and preserving qualities. This also means that yoga allows us the capacity to observe our emotions and thoughts without being controlled by them.** The entire world is made up of layers of consciousness and the five great elements, earth, water, fire, air, and ether[40]. The foundations of the great ancient healing systems such as Ayurveda, Traditional Chinese Medicine, Unani, and Siddha are built on five elements as forms of consciousness.

Understanding the five elements as vibratory fields helps to harness the mind to awaken specific domains in the brain's function that are mostly dormant in humans today, like imagination. Imagination is one of those capacities that

---

39 The gunas can be considered forces of energy that reflect the quality of one's consciousness: 1) tamas – dull; 2) rajas – active; and 3) sattva – spiritually harmonious.
40 As enumerated in the Samkhya philosophy.

has been stripped away from the average bystander who uses tech gadgets in a passive manner; this is juxtaposed with the medium of radio or podcasts which allow one to listen and reflect as an act of will power. Imagination exercises the brain and cultivates the capacity to be creative and, most importantly, cultivates one's capacity to learn. Imagination is a subtle expression of will power because each of the five elements are layers of the mind that influence all the organs and functions of the body on one side. On the other side, imagination leads to expansion of consciousness. Imagination can draw a person toward very gross levels of the body and senses; alternatively, it can be used to visualize Divine images like nature, guru, or gods and goddesses, creating positive impressions that heal the brain and free the mind.

Earth (prithvi) – represents the entire physical body as a manifestation of planet earth and creates the sense of smell. The earthly soil parallels the general quality of the physical body. The earthly vibration allows objects to take shape, making the material domain functional and practical. Its basic forms exist fundamentally as mineral, rock, plant, animal, and the human body that houses the soul. Prithvi, operating our sense of smell, gives the brain its actual heavy earthly like quality. The earth is to the brain as the moon is to the mind.

Water (jal) – all liquids that support the fluid functions of our inner organs depend on water; in fact, the entire anatomical system does. Just as most of the planet earth is made up of water (rivers, lakes, and oceans) so is the human body. After conception, the fetus develops in a womb of water. Water controls our sense of taste and the brain's capacity to absorb ideas, thoughts and receive all types of impressions. Think of a sponge, when it is dry, its hard and cannot absorb much. When a sponge is moist, it is expansive and can hold a good amount of water within it.

Fire (agni) – life exists mainly because of the warmth of the sun. The penetrating rays of sunlight enliven all functions of the physical body and give light to life. Primarily, fire governs digestion, is the light of conception and the destruction of cells, and the breakdown of muscle tissues and atoms with their tiny particles called protons, neutrons, and electrons.[41] The warmth of the body is a direct result of the fire within every tissue (sapta dhatu) of the body. Fire controls our vision and the brain's capacity to cognize.

---

41   Protons are positively charged, neutrons are uncharged, and electrons are negatively charged.

Air – oxygen, our breath, is the energy of circulation that gives life to all the systems and functions of the body. Air animates our expressions and the sense of touch.

Ether – also called space, relates mainly to the energy of any area, and any sound, and governs the sense of hearing. Ether is both the founding source, the origin of life, and the culmination of the other elements. The entire world's atmosphere is made up of gases and is the domain where the time and space paradigm transitions into the vast field of silence.

Life force (prana) – is subtler than space-ether and supports all living things. Prana is delivered to the body via natural foods, spring water and clean air. Shiva, as the great teacher-guru of yoga, is the supreme master of prana. The maha-prana enters through the roots of the medulla oblongata, in other words the root of human consciousness is at the head and thus making humans upturned trees. The metaphor of being 'rooted' is a misconception because tapping into higher consciousness is not about having both feet on the ground, but instead, can be more appropriately described as having our head in the right place.

Light (Tejas) – is the vast domain of consciousness beyond the limitation of time and space. Chit is also the light of our innermost being or atman. We could say the inner light of the soul is a portion of the grandest light of creation (Brahman). The planets reflect their light on the earth, influencing the process of karma as it unfolds over the course of our lives in its various forms.

Will power (Ojas) – is the most subtle of all energies and exists as the prime energy that sustains us. Our autonomic nervous system is sustained by ojas, for example, our heart continues beating during sleep while all other organs rest. This is an involuntary form of ojas, where we see the effects of the mind working in the subconscious domain and the heart relies on ojas to sustain its function. Ojas drives us to live, to accomplish and maintain balance of the doshas to support ideal synergy between the mind and body. We can also define ojas as the very essence of will power, the energy that each human being exerts to control their body in a voluntary way. It is important to recognize the functional purpose of the five elements that are all derived from the cosmology of the universe. All living things share a relationship with an energy source. The same energy that sustains the human body is the energy that sustains the movements of the planets, constellations, and allow the moon and earth to move around the sun. The five elements are the material forms of these more subtle energies all controlled by the mind.

If we change the mind and our mental attitude, then we naturally can also change the brain, and then both can work together to promote evolution beyond the limitations of each independently. This is where the five elements can play a therapeutic role and understanding them can promote a harmonious mind-body relationship. Working with the elements can help us to unfold profound levels of imagination in order to free our consciousness to dwell in higher realms. Learning about the elements is not intended to focus on their worldly limitations just because they are considered natural forces. It is best to understand the five elements as energies, vibrations of consciousness that can help us connect to everything in the world as a teacher, to our body as a vehicle with which to enjoy life, and as powers that can unlock the mind so that we can imagine and experience what is beyond all of this. Just as Swami Anubhavananda Saraswati says, "A great guru will never bind you!" Similarly, a great mind will never bind you, and should work efficiently to dismantle the limitations of the ego, thoughts, intellect, and emotions. Yoga teaches us how to manage the mind and how to move beyond it by slowing it down, cultivating awareness, and developing concentration, all of which we will explore later in the book.

Vedanta's Concept of the World Process

Rivers have been used as powerful images and metaphors of Vedic thought for millenniums giving us rich stories for understanding the movement of the mind. In ancient India some rivers flow directly into the ocean like the famous Saraswati while others puttered out into a valley or desert. The sacred Ganges River of India is known for its long history associated with holy rituals to cleanse oneself from the karmas that bind us to the body, creating pain and suffering as a result of the world process, as life and the inherent search for happiness. The term *world process* is used to describe the practical reality of human existence. The world process implies that a soul is born into a body, known as reincarnation or rebirth, and the soul seeks to attain fulfillment of their desires. According to Vedanta, desires are endless and perpetuate human suffering and the cycles of birth and death until a person awakens to the true reality. The true reality is that only God, pure consciousness, exists. God alone exists, and it is everything every human being is seeking. Anything else is maya, an illusion of time and space dynamics.

Practically speaking, water is a natural cleanser for the body, and mentally, water symbolizes the flowing attitude of remaining detached from life's unpredictable circumstances. Therefore, sweating is so important for our health because it is not only beneficial for removing toxins from the body, but there is also a neuromuscular feeling of relaxation that occurs when the body sweats. In my counseling practice, I have noticed a pattern in individuals that do not sweat regularly (weekly) are often mentally stuck and hold on to things in their lives either materially or experientially.

Often, when a person harbors emotional resentment without ever exploring non-violent communication around an issue, it creates an impetus for imbalance or dosha. Similarly, the body without sweating begins to increase kapha as increased water weight. This excess dampness in the body increases body fat and exists as a type of psychological layer of resistance to shield them from what they are experiencing inside. This is typically the case in kapha dominant constitutions, pitta types do the same thing by increasing muscle mass, and vata types go into denial, avoiding the issues and ignoring their relationship to the body. The basic fact is that ***the quality of our consciousness shapes the body and acts as a mirror to the inner aspects of the mind.***

In life, we can either choose to proceed down the river that leads to a dry and superficial life, one that is controlled by the ego, thoughts, senses, intellect, and emotions, or alternatively, we can choose to flow up the stream that leads to spiritual liberation achieved through non-violent communication, mindful living, and yoga meditation. It all begins with control of our thoughts and how we use the mind, and this brings up the importance of sangha or good association. Community (sangha) is one of the cornerstones for moving our consciousness upwards and who you spend time with determines whether your life will proceed towards the dry desert or flow towards the ocean of bliss. One's environment is more powerful than most people realize, and unless you are a saint, you must choose your associations carefully. If a person is developing spiritually and has a strong mind, they will naturally attract similar people of like-consciousness into their life through the power of the soul's magnetism.

In order to overcome the world process, we must make our homes spiritual hermitages for living an evolutionary life. All yogic disciplines (sadhanas) are supportive in moving our consciousness to the ocean of liberation because they help us to embrace an integral approach to overcoming the conditions of the mind. In Patanjali's Raja Yoga Sutras[42] importance is given to both detachment (vairagya) and consistency of yoga practice (abhyasa) to diminish the ego's association to names and forms (namarupa). As less attention is given to these superficial outer forms, the indwelling feeling in the heart is exposed, opening it wider and wider until the power of the soul is revealed. I want to define, in more detail, the Vedantic concept of the "world process" since it provides a foundation for understanding the objective of living and evolutionary life. The world process and its various layers perpetuate the cycles of birth and death (samsara). Below is a brief introduction to its seven components.

1. **Ignorance (Avidya)** – created by a life of indulgence of the senses and falling into the trap of maya (illusion) that develops belief systems that support the idea that the world is real.

2. **Impressions (Samskaras)** – all experiences that have been absorbed into the mental field.

3. **Subtle impressions (Vasanas)** – the seeds of samskaras that have been planted and are being watered with intention as will.

4. **Desires (Kama)** – impressions that have been cultivated and are now circulating the through the mind.

5. **Thought waves (Vrittis)** – outgoing, mental activity, movement of the impressions in the form of thoughts.

6. **Actions (karma)** – manifest activities as exchanged between the head and the limbs of action.

7. **Embodiment (Shariras)** – physical, astral, causal bodies.

As my spiritual counselor often said to me, swimming up the river takes time and much effort. As we swim past others in society who continue swimming downstream, sometimes we pause and question, Should I follow them again? This process provokes the ego to question our newly embraced motives and sometimes we do, and unfortunately end up in more severe situations than when we started. Everyone has their own experiences they can relate to this, ranging from involvement in unhealthy relationships or marriages, to decisions

---

42   Samadhi Pada (Chapter One), verse 12 Abhyasa vairagyabhyam tannirodhah.

that lead to more addictions, or even the desire to be recognized or accepted. The ego influences our decisions, bringing such grandiosity that it pushes people away. It is natural for our consciousness to flow outwards because of the senses, that is their purpose, to prompt us to experience the world process; however, through the practice, consistent yogic practice of detachment (vairagya), the consciousness (chitta) is given greater inward momentum, away from the senses and into the subtle astral centers of awareness in the spine.

Within Vedanta, the concept of **vairagya** is relevant to our understanding of the two streams of consciousness. In a basic sense, vairagya is defined as being more detached and less reactive to dramatic moments of the material life. It restrains the mind from reacting and supports its reflective practice. We see this similar teaching in the Bhagavad Gita when Krishna gives counsel to Arjuna so that Arjuna can be successful in overcoming the restless or fickle nature of the mind. We will discuss this further in the book in chapter eight when I share with you a practice of learning how to respond to circumstances as opposed to reacting to them. Initially, when one learns to respond to circumstances the process can feel delayed, like there is a pause. However, this perceived delay is the mind activating its capacity to reflect and respond with great insights to the problem or situation. This is the mind preparing to flow toward spiritual enlightenment. Reacting using conditioned patterns of thought and behavior perpetuates the cycles of samsara that proceed to the dry dessert. Samsara means *the cycle or wheel of life*, the repetitive cycles of birth and death, pain, and suffering, and is one of Buddhism's central concepts. The concept of the world process is likened to the wheel of a wagon that carries the body, mind, and all its conditions that keep spinning over and over again. Vairagya is one of the Vedantic concepts and choices that provides a way to get off the wagon.

The Heart and Consciousness

As spiritual values become more integrated into one's personality and lifestyle, a natural balance between reason and feeling is developed. In one sense the mind becomes more concentrated, producing greater efficiency and in other sense the mind grows closer to the heart, the region of feeling. The yoga term *chitta* refers to the heart as the spiritual center of our consciousness and is where one comes into being with their true oceanic essence. Overcoming the ego begins with transforming our mental processes so that we focus on increasing our feeling and connection with our heart center. This can be done through meditation or mantra, and other devotional rituals. The insight one gains from connecting to the heart is a major step towards evolutionary living. Greater compassion for all living things, a growing desire to spend time in nature, making time for reflection, and enjoyment of meditation, are all qualities of the expanding heart of awareness. Prana, our vital energy, expands if we are mindful and the body vessel in which our soul abides is worthy of holding it.

Practicing pranayama (yogic breathing) can also be very effective even for persons living an idle life and can lead to transcendental inner experiences. However, living an idle mindless lifestyle, one that does not integrate the mind and body, will take more than breathing practices. Be honest and be careful, adhering to practices that are within the scope of your awareness. This means avoid performing techniques and yoga practices without having integrated natural or ayurvedic lifestyle principles. Vedic wisdom is founded on a relationship with nature as an eternal relationship that should not be segregated or fragmented, but as an authentic approach to living that calms the mind, heals the body, and opens the heart. Evolutionary living is founded on these threefold ideals of balanced healing between the head, hand, and heart, and is aligned with three main branches of yoga that encourage us to develop the entire being, physically, mentally, and spiritually, through jnana (wisdom), karma (practicality) and bhakti (love and devotion).

A person does not suddenly transform from being unconscious to becoming fully conscious or awakened (except in very rare cases). It is a slow and gradual process that takes place over many lifetimes. Consciousness, and its various levels (gunas), is like the energies of the ayurvedic doshas in that it cannot be molded to appear a certain way. The same is the case with the signs of the zodiac. When a person is born on the cusp of another sign, it is likely they will carry influences from both signs. The energies of Consciousness cannot be contained to fit inside a specific context, they will always have points where they overlap.

In Veda Vyasa's commentary on the Yoga Sutras, he recognizes fives states of consciousness or chitta[43] where the mind of humanity mostly dwells. These states vary depending on a person's karma and reflect various qualities of the personality and levels of aspiration toward living an evolutionary life. It may be easy for those of us who practice yoga, meditate, and claim to hold a newly awakened consciousness to criticize others for not living naturally or living in accordance with the dharma (spiritual virtues). However, it is important to remember the concept of maya (illusion) and how each person's spiritual awakening is more varied and complex than we may understand. Persistence through obstacles and consistent practice over a long period of time is important.

In the Samkhya philosophy, the concept of prakriti is understood as the womb of creation and the concept of Mother Nature. From prakriti, three modes of consciousness arise as the gunas. Sattva expresses itself as maya or illusion, rajas as ignorance, and tamas as matter. All these aspects of creation appear to curtail one's effort towards self-improvement; however, they can all be transcended through integral yoga as the yoga of perfection. This pathway to perfection of one's personality will be a blend of selfless action, devotion, deep meditation, and intuitive wisdom. This perfection leads the aspirant to the heart of pure consciousness, the Self. As the mind is dissolved and purified, the heart awakens, although this comes with repeated challenges.

An aspirant, while striving to live and evolutionary life, occasionally experiences dull states of consciousness (mudha). These states often negatively influence health symptoms like poor sleep, fear, and laziness. At times, one may even experience feeling distracted (kshipta) and experience worry, mental fickleness, or selfish actions. Regardless of these changes, the true aspirant (sadhaka) is not dismayed by these experiences, the outgoing thought waves (vrittis). Instead, they continue their spiritual practices (sadhana) and dedication to their path of truth, performing their practice without attachment to the action or its fruits, enduring the never-ending dismay of the world process. The practices of integral yoga transform these outer fluctuations and shift

---

43   Five states of the Chitta are: Mudha (dull), Kshipta (distracted), Vikshipta (partial concentration), Ekagrata (one-pointed), and Niruddha (controlled). *Raja Yoga Sutras of Patanjali* 1:4.

the mind's state into a sharpened level of concentration that manifests as joy and happiness (sukham), the inner most qualities of the heart.

In time, with continuity of disciplinary spiritual practices (sadhana), good associations (sangha), and selfless service (seva), the mind becomes more purified and develops towards the state of one-pointedness (ekagrata). This one-pointed state of the mind (chitta) produces heightened levels of detachment from the ego, thoughts, emotions, intellect, and the entire world process. This allows one to view life like a spectator at the arena and leads to a controlled mastery (nirodha) of their own individualized consciousness. Over time, this eventually leads the aspirant to liberation (samadhi). I often refer to this movement towards liberation (samadhi) as a growing awareness of sameness, a realization of the one pure consciousness that pervades all existence and the intelligence that flows into all living things. This progressive movement is what defines evolutionary living and helps us to surrender with grace.

Chapter THREE

The Planet's Role in Evolution

Such is the great influence of Time which governs the universe.
No man can overcome this influence except him who, blessed with pure love,
the heavenly gift of nature, becomes divine.

Swami Sri Yukteswar

The Calendar's Influence on Society

Today, we follow a calendar that is based on our movement around the sun, giving priority to the sun as our timekeeper. But what about the twelve exact lunar periods that occur within this solar cycle? How are they important? We do not focus on the months and their relationship to the moon. There are two important cycles that need to be distinguished, one is the cycle of earth moving around the sun in 365 days, which produces two solstices and two equinoxes. The second cycle is that of the moon moving around the earth, representing the monthly periods of time. Originally, in Vedic India, these two cycles were integrated and referred to as the soli-lunar cycle. The soli-lunar cycle provided for accurate timings of spiritual events and the new year, and this integrated calendar helped their ancient civilization to thrive in harmony and balance for thousands of years, a long time before the Egyptian, Greek, and Roman civilizations. Over the last two millenniums, as a result of the development of European political power, many practices extracted from India and Asian cultures have been changed. Vedic wisdom has been misinterpreted for political and religious reasons related to the spread of Christianity. The calendar that the world now follows only recognizes the earth's cycle around the sun. This leaves us with a fundamental problem for the balance and evolution of humanity.

The sun represents the soul and how we search for truth and the moon represents our inner feelings, emotions, and our mind. Following a soli-lunar calendar is an important step in harmonizing our relationship with nature and promoting a global spiritual movement which prioritizes the regular cycles of the moon's phases in relationship to the solar year. Below are some benefits of aligning with a soli-lunar calendar. Our ascension into the higher ages depends on integrating the correct calendar approach that embraces both the sun and moon cycles, thus recognizing the important balance between these two aspects in every living being.

Integration of the soli-lunar cycles will:

- prompt us to perceive how the celestial movements of the two most influential planets are synchronized with life on earth.
- call for adjusting our health routines according to the proper seasonal regimens.
- promote a cruelty-free approach to our human diet.
- synchronize the earth with the moon because every soli-lunar month ends on a New Moon (amanta).
- conceive the great metaphor of emptiness of the mind since each New Moon is when the moon is aligned between the sun and earth. This is symbolic of attaining a state of consciousness beyond the limitations of the mind and the disturbances of thoughts.
- increase greater acuity of consciousness and development of intuition.
- for those who have not begun Vedantic practices, allow for feeling more connected to nature and their own physical body, thus improving all aspects of lifestyle scientifically referred to as circadian[44] rhythm.

---

44 Circadian rhythms are found in most living things that influence the mind and body's response to light and darkness. Circadian rhythms influence sleep patterns and the mind-body relationship. Yoga and ayurveda synchronize these rhythms to increase the capacity of life force-energy necessary for expanding human consciousness.

- discover enhanced periods of inner silence for meditators.

- encourage humans to adapt to nature and her changing cycles as passive shift towards learning the yogic art of surrender to those forces that sustain our ecology.

Since the world began following the Gregorian calendar, our societies have been alienated from the earth, ecology, seasonal change, animals, and the natural world. In addition to resulting in an overall lack of compassion for all living species on earth, disregarding the moon's cycles within the calendar has resulted in our living with greater dependency on scientific and logical constructs of communication, lifestyle, diet, and religion. The Indic culture has always recognized the purposes of using a calendar that embraces the primary planetary trinity between the sun-moon and earth. However, the soli-lunar calendar that is still being used in India today is limited to Vedic-Hindu spiritual practices and is not embraced on a civil level as the world has adapted to using the Gregorian calendar for the sake of convenience.

Another cycle that often confuses people with regards to their birthday and profound aspects of their personality is that of the zodiac.[45] The zodiac demonstrates the Western world's disconnection from the moon's importance. For example, when a person in the west is asked what their astrology sign is, they will likely answer based on the sun's position in relation to one of the twelve signs of the zodiac on the day of their birth. If they understand the tropical zodiac, they may interpret their personality and life events using the sun's placement; however, few understand the deeper implications of what this actually defines. The sun, generally speaking, is the most masculine planet of the seven major ones and represents the father, ego, and how the world views us from a superficial or external perspective. Although, on the positive side, the sun also represents the soul and how we search for truth, and it is probably for this reason that the ancients of all major civilizations have always worshipped the sun.

Originally, in Hindu or Vedic astrology, importance has always been given to the moon because it reflects the inner aspect of who we are, and often reveals many things people do not know about themselves. The moon is compassion, nurturing, devotional feminine energy. In India and in most Asian countries, a person is identified with their moon sign. It is the moon's placement in our

---

45   A circle (chakra) of stars (constellations) grouped into twelve different signs.

birth chart that matters when it comes to understanding our inner feelings, emotions, and how we will get along with others. For this reason, the moons placement in the birth chart of a potential husband and/or wife are analyzed by the family astrologer to see if they are a good match for marriage. The moon is of major importance in our lives and our relationship with it, how we understand its placement in the birth chart and its influence by transit, determines how we will behave on the earth.

Before I continue expanding on this point, I want to explain what I believe are some important points that should be recognized regarding the calendar and its influence on the world we are currently witnessing. We need to be reminded of this basic point: the outer structure of one's life and how one lives on the planet reflects of the quality of one's consciousness.

As we can see, we live at a time when humanity is truly distracted from the positive influences of the sun, our soul's search for truth, and most have fallen toward its negative egoist side of being overexposed to the light of the external world. This can explain why humans live out of accordance with nature and out of touch with the feminine aspect of life and the Divine. It is blatantly obvious that a feminine representation of Divinity is largely absent from Western spiritual movements and even much of Asia. Although the few remnants of God as Mother are mostly seen in India, a culture that has worshipped the feminine Divine for millenniums, demonstrating India's cultural connection to the moon.

In order to understand the importance of following a soli-lunar cycle, as opposed to a purely solar calendar cycle as we are currently following, we need to explore some basic astronomical calculations and examine history. This will allow us to understand the impact that a solar-dominated calendar has had on global evolution over the last two millenniums.

The scale of our concept of time is based on a measurement of the earth's orbit around the sun, which determines the length of a year in human life. Humanity plans their lives on this yearly cycle. Whether you are an accountant, or farmer, or in the family stage of life, this cycle serves us. The 24-hour day is a measure of the earth's revolution on its axis, and the 28 to 31-day month is measured roughly by the moon's orbit around the earth. These three cycles or movements (sun, moon, and earth) are what allows us to calculate the concept of time and the distinct feeling each seasonal shift brings each year.

It is apparent that humanity has struggled with understanding these basic cycles as our world has become very alienated from nature, treating it more like a commodity than as something sacred or Divine. The modern Julian and Gregorian calendars are riddled with errors of the dark ages (Kali-Yuga) and have been mostly influenced by religion and politics.

Over the last two thousand years, the Julian and Gregorian calendars have prevailed and overlapped with the two Kali yuga cycles (ascending and descending) which began approximately 700 B.C.[46] The current Gregorian[47] calendar, which most of our world now follows, is based on the solar cycle which tracks time using tropical years, the time between the two vernal equinoxes, which explains why a year on earth is 365.25 days in length. The earlier calendar (Julian) was initiated by Julius Caesar in 45 B.C. and was in place prior to the Gregorian calendar. Julius Caesar wanted a solar calendar that consisted of twelve months, and when first adopted, the Julian calendar shifted the beginning of the year from March 1st to January 1st.

The lunar year is measured by calculating the time of 12 moons, one for each month, and measures to an approximate 354 days. A solar year is 365, an eleven-day difference, and this difference, over a 33-year period, creates a deficiency of one entire year. To make up for this difference we currently have leap years, so those using a solar calendar add a leap day in February every four years. Those following a lunar calendar add a 13th month every three years. The basic point to understand with all this astronomy is that the solar and lunar cycles are different, and do not provide a fixed pattern, unless they are integrated. Therefore, to keep some consistency in the world, the calendars are supplemented with the additional day or month.

The question I have been asking for a long time is, Why have the solar and lunar cycles been separated in the calendar year? As mentioned, the spiritual traditions of India still follow an integrated approach. Additionally, most ancient Eastern cultures like the Chinese, Islamic, and Judaic traditions recognize the lunar cycles, and some still continue to follow the lunar calendar today. From the Western commercial and technological point of view, it is obvious that most of our global societies have advanced substantially, and we live with

---

46   Sun, Moon & Earth, Chapter Two, "Creation and Nature".
47   In 1752, the United Kingdom forced all its colonies to follow the Gregorian calendar. Since this constituted much of the world's geography, this current system has managed to endure until now.

greater efficiency, everything is a button or a voice command away; but does this equate to real evolution? Politically, just because countries and leaders are getting along, does not mean we have evolved from the perspective of yoga and ayurveda. Special interest groups and political action committees (PACs) continue to support the destruction of nature and slaughter billions of animals every year. From the agricultural side, our ecology is being controlled by corporations that support the use of genetically modified organisms that are destroying the soil and ruining the lives of generations of farming families, not to mention the effect GMO's have on the health of both humans and animals. Where has all this calendar chaos left us?

I believe that implementation of a soli-lunar calendar is a vital step for the evolution of the world community and healing Mother Earth. The integration will provide greater efficiency in our lifestyle, and will create a balanced relationship between the head, hand and heart, aspects of integral yoga expanded upon further in future chapters of this book. For example, in our yoga practice, the earthly year is represented by one entire breath in yoga (inhalation and exhalation) through the spinal energy centers or chakras and represents the connection each human being has with the cosmos. Each human body is a miniature cosmic body. Also explored in future chapters are traditions that honor lunar cycles and display how valuable it is to have an integrated sun-moon calendar. For example, each year India celebrates Navaratri[48], a festival for honoring Mother Divine, through meditation, prayer, and service towards others. Navaratri (nine nights) is a Hindu festival calculated by measuring the duration of lunar days overlayed with time of sunrise. One worships the Divine Mother in her three aspects, Durga (protective), Lakshmi (abundance) and Saraswati (wisdom).

The Effects of the Equinoxes and Solstices on the Human Body

The earth's cycle around the sun provides us with four important periods that occur each year. As these planetary bodies, the sun, moon, and earth move, they influence the human body on multiple levels such as one's digestion, circulation, and hormones. Vata, the primary (master) dosha, influences

---

48   *Navaratri (Nine nights) Hindu festival calculated on the duration of lunar days overlayed with time of sunrise to worship Divine Mother in her three aspects, Durga (protective), Lakshmi (abundance) and Saraswati (wisdom).*

the human body as a result of the two equinoctials,[49] shifts that occur each year, making the day and the night equal. The autumnal equinox occurs in September in the northern hemisphere, marking the beginning of autumn. The vernal equinox occurs in March, marking the beginning of spring. The inverse is true for those living in the Southern Hemisphere. Each equinox (and the solstices), occur sometime within a three-day span.

As a result of the sun crossing the equator during the fall season, the body's metabolism slows down. This is because the sun influences the internal heat or fire of metabolism in the human body. The slowed metabolism is why most people feel some disturbance between the mind-body complex. This may appear as a physiological imbalance months later. To those living in the northern hemisphere, the sun begins to appear much lower in the sky, a reminder that our digestive power is vulnerable or weaker and can make the body more sensitive when digesting certain foods. Understanding this important transition can be a remarkable preventative measure in health and creates a window of opportunity, a ***power point***, for the expansion of life-force (prana) energy. Power point is a term I originated that defines the increasing capacity for prana within the mind-body complex as a result of living an evolutionary lifestyle

These power points, as I refer to them, have a general influence on everyone but their effects depend largely on a person's unique astrological configuration (birth chart) and each person will respond differently. They will either have a progressive shift, if they are following an evolutionary lifestyle, or a regressive shift, if they are living predominantly according to their conditioned consciousness, what sage Patanjali refers to as *asmita*, egoism. In short, vata dosha gets pummeled twice a year in Fall and Spring as both seasons are characterized by cool and dryer climates. The Ayur-Vedic Sanskrit secrets outlined in the Atharva Veda and the later regimens in the pre-eminent ayurvedic text, ***Ashtanga Hridaya***,[50] provide a multitude of methods for using these equinox power points. We must use them to advance our evolutionary lifestyle, otherwise the world can easily throw us into more hustle and bustle.

The solstices (ayanas) are grand moments that shift twice each year, once in

---

49   The sun's crossing of the celestial equator.
50   Considered one of the primary texts of ayurvedic wisdom and is believed to be authored by Vagbhata; however, an enigma remains as to whether or not his son was also a contributor to the text. The text presents the eight branches of ayurveda and dates to 550-600 AD.

December and again in June, as a result of the earth's position in relationship to the sun. The winter solstice marks the sun's turning point for ascending into the sky and thus shines with an ever-increasing power to heat up that part of the world (northern hemisphere). Similarly, the body also begins to heat up, the inner fire (agni) begins to scorch viruses, metabolize food and push sweat out of our pores with greater frequency. As the northern course begins, we generally experience a stronger appetite, and as a result, we eat more, naturally increasing body fat. The extra increase in body weight (fat) is a normal part of the process and will vary depending on a person's constitution (prakriti). Vata types show the least, or no, increase in body fat, pitta types show gain in moderation of 5-7 pounds, and kapha types can increase as much as 10 pounds or even much more if they are not following a synchronized seasonal diet. Most types will naturally be drawn towards spicier foods as spices warm the body and calm the mind during the chilly winter months from December through March.

Once the sun reaches its culmination point in June, the start of summer, the sun begins its southern course (dakshinayana) and daylight naturally begins to diminish (hence the seasonal term "Fall"). Also diminished is the body's agni (digestive fire), which results in a decreased appetite and an increase in appetite for fluids of sweet and bitter tastes. Finally, the cycle is completed in the Fall season, when the digestive fire is weakest and most vulnerable. For those not living in accordance with the natural laws, their body can begin to "fall" apart, so to speak. Even though there is measurable and scientific importance to these cycles, it is more important to understand them from an allegorical perspective as they have profound spiritual implications for pranifying[51] our lifestyle.

I am grateful that I was trained in this manner, how empty these scientific concepts would be without understanding the important relationship they have towards supporting our spiritual lifestyle. I often like to use the common analogy of the wave and the ocean that I have witnessed during splendid moments while surfing under the sparkling rays of the sun at Swami's Beach in Encinitas. While most surfers sit focused on watching the waves, few are aware of the ocean and its vast presence which sends swells of love through all the little waves. It's always nice to ride the waves, but we must never forget the ocean of God's love that sustains us all.

---

[51]   A term I originated that defines the increasing capacity for prana (life-force energy) within the mind-body complex as a result of living an evolutionary lifestyle.

Winning with the Light of Awareness

One of the epic scriptures of India, the Ramayana, expresses through great metaphor and allegory that the vital essence of life is to follow our purpose, or svadharma. Rama, as the great dharma king, reunites with his wife, Sita, because of a great battle with the demonic Ravana. Like other great Vedic scriptures, the famous battle of the Ramayana, represents the life of Lord Rama and the essential human dilemma to understand our true nature. Such stories are meant to be applied to our own lives to encourage us to awaken to a higher purpose beyond the mundane concepts that have come to define a successful life. Rama's search for Sita represents humanity's search for balance, truth, and spiritual freedom. To follow one's higher purpose is to awaken Rama within us by cultivating greater awareness. When one begins to expand the light of awareness, they become an aspirant, a sadhaka, who is beginning to uphold the universal principles that Rama symbolizes.

While on the path of evolutionary living, **svadharma**, we develop a growing awareness of our inner obstacles and struggles. These obstacle and struggles are the result of the outer circumstances the ego experiences through its limited instruments of perception, senses, intellect, thoughts, and emotions. The path of Jnana Yoga teaches us how to cultivate greater will power through the light of the soul as the expanding light of our consciousness. The light of consciousness, in the basic sense, is wisdom, understanding, and the capacity to discern between needs and desires. This growing awareness is a transformational process and can be referred to as the ego's effacement or dissolution. Understand the ego as a small circle of awareness, with limited understanding, often reactive to circumstances because of our mental conditioning. When we transform our negative experiences or reactions into greater inner awareness, now the small circle of the ego begins to merge, expanding into the light of consciousness, bringing a greater connection to the heart, the center of feeling.

When a person's mind dwells in negativity, they become very disconnected from their own heart because the mind is clobbering them into an identity crisis. Conditioned consciousness works through the ego to further entrap the soul by keeping the mind associated with what is unreal. Humans are literally punishing themselves, hurting each other and the natural world in seeking to find contentment outside of themselves. The path of yoga, first and foremost, is an inward one that transcends the way we view the world. Happiness and inner contentment become a natural part of life as the traits of the ego, its small circle of conditioned limitations, gradually dissolves. What was at one time the gloominess of a cloudy day in your lifestyle, now has merged into the brightness of a clear day as clear consciousness. ***Take note of even the smallest changes in your personality as the movements toward the inner realization of the light of your inner sun (soul) grows brighter.*** You are becoming more resilient, rising above the battles of the world process.

Rama and Sita seated together signifying fidelity, devotion, and following our heart as the path of dharma.

This expanding light or awareness is symbolized by ***uttarayana***[52] (first day of winter), where the northern course of the sun represents the soul's victorious

---

52   Derived from two words, "uttara" (north) and "ayana" (movement).

ascension towards enlightenment. Indian culture celebrates this shift in our personality with a festival called Makar Sankranti. Many festivals celebrate the shifts during periods within each calendar year as reminders of these powerful transitions among the celestial bodies. They are power points in the sky that support our inner transformation.

As Vedanta proclaims, the Divine Self is Sat, Chit, and Ananda. This means our true essence, our potential, is threefold and defined as Absolute Existence, Absolute Knowledge, and Absolute Bliss. The expansive schedule of festivals in India mark celebrations of the different human potentials that are enhanced by these planetary cycles (or planetary alignments). The planetary cycles serve to propagate one's potential and inner transformation toward the Divine Self. For example, the Summer Solstice in June marks the start of the sun's southern course, referred to as *dakshinayana* (first day of summer) and signifies one's ignoring their true dharma, *adharma*. If one chooses to ignore their truth and live against the laws of natural living, there will be less light, less awareness. This is because the sun is beginning its descent. The sun is a symbol of the light of awareness and the search for truth. The southerly course of the sun is a metaphor for ignorance (avidya), a turning away from the true purpose of life. The sun's southern movement in the sky is an observable reminder of what happens in nature, the light of each day becomes shorter, days slowly becoming cooler, and nature enters a stage of death and decay, with leaves falling, animals hibernating and many plants and animals dying because of the brashness of winter. Even though the reduction of sunlight during the winter darkens the sky, winter never leaves us completely astray as it often presents the beautiful gift of powder white snow, reminding us that the light is just behind the temporary darkness of the clouds.

In India, the festival that marks the start of the northern course is called Makara Sankranti.[53] It is usually celebrated in the middle of January and marks the first day to celebrate the expansion of the light. As we just discussed, the actual northern course of the sun begins at the winter solstice around December 21st; therefore, the current date for celebrating the start of the sun's northern course is off by almost an entire month. As a result of the precession of the equinoxes, the time of this auspicious event is not correct. This is because it is

---

53   The term *Sankranti* refers to the sun's movement into a new sign. As the most powerful planet, the sun's movement can be unsettling. For this reason, meditation is highly recommended so that one can adjust to the movement and reflect on the lessons of the past.

currently being celebrated based on a time that aligned with an old positioning of the sun in sky, its position in relationship to the sideral zodiac of 1600 years ago. Vedic astrologer Sam Geppi explains this point very succinctly, "In the sixth century Indian astronomer and scholar Varahamihira[54] instructed that the northern course began when the sun entered the constellation of Capricorn in the sky. However, based on the procession of the equinoxes the current alignment of the winter solstice is no longer accurate with those ancient instructions, as the sun's entrance into "Capricorn" does not occur until January 15 using the sidereal based zodiac of India. The error occurred because emphasis was placed on the astrology sign, not on the northern course of the Sun. Meaning, the northern course Uttarayana is the solstice and nothing else is to be considered (including astrology signs, precession, etc.)."

The Gregorian calendar was introduced and enacted in 1582, by Pope Gregory XIII. This represents what, in my view, was the initial fracture that changed the world to becoming masculine. The moon's cycle was abolished from our time keeping and subsequently permanently removed from importance[55]; along with this calendar change came a political and cultural masculinity. The sun's dominance in our global societies is still evident with extensive political egoism, loss of women's equality, wars, and the most destructive relationship historically with ecology. Without the moon's influence we lack compassion for each other and even more so for our animal kingdom. The entire ecosystem and biosphere of this world is maintained and supported by Her direct stewards, the living creatures that interact directly with those elements in order to live and sustain themselves.

We live in a connected world where cultures interact because of technology, and this calls for a calendar that supports both feminine and masculine aspects in all cultures, the arts, and religion to unite the global community spiritually. Over time in many cultures, festivities surrounding the solstices and equinoxes of the wise East were slowly disposed of, creating a greater

---

54   Brihat Samhita of Varahamihira, Chapter 3 – V. 2-3 "At present, Dakshinayana (southern course—first day of summer) starts from the beginning of Cancer and the other (northern course—Uttarayana, first day of winter) from the initial point of Capricorn. This fact, which goes against the old statement can be verified by direct observation."

55   The original intention for reforming the Julian calendar was to bring the date for the celebration of Easter to align with the time of year in which it was celebrated when it was first introduced by the early Church. However, the Gregorian calendar reform also abolished the lunar cycle that was originally used by the early church.

disconnect between people and nature and the cycles of the sun-moon and earth. Ancient societies were connected to the movements of the sun, moon, and earth and were aware of how the stars influenced life on earth. Humanity needs to once again adhere to celestial events that support real points of importance and align humans to a higher purpose beyond materialism.

Materialism or outer achievements can no longer be defined as the only success that matters. India has an Eternal Tradition, originally known as Sanatana Dharma, but over the course of history, the Indian people were forced to ignore their spiritual heritage. However, in many aspects of India's society today, with its current democracy, a cultural renaissance is aimed at repairing and protecting the Vedic wisdom culture and the soli-lunar connection that has been indigenous to the Indian sub-continent for well over 7,000 years.

Take, for instance, an example of the soli-lunar connection: the history of sitting down. This was one custom common to ancient cultures, primarily in Southeast Asia, Africa, and Latin America. People socialized and cooked on the ground and regularly relaxed their back and feet in the fully squatted position. But during the Middle Ages, both peasants and those of importance, such as Kings, Queens, and Gods and Goddesses commonly use of benches and thrones. In art we see them drawn sitting in large chairs or thrones with ornately decorated backs and arm rests. Sitting seems to have been socially stratified by the time of European Industrial Revolution[56] and even much earlier. Chairs like Greek klismos, designed and built in the fifth century B.C. are still considered among the most beautiful chairs ever made. Sitting on the ground was a reserved custom for peasants, farmers, and slaves.

In India, however, sitting on the ground was always a cultural norm and considered sacred by yogis. Sitting on the floor is still widely practiced, especially in ashrams, temples, and shrines; even in homes, families still eat seated around a low table on cushions. A common practice for the learner was to sit cross-legged on the ground with the Guru who was also seated on the ground, with their back (spine) facing the trunk of the tree. Yogis promoted the importance of sitting cross legged under a tree to hear the Guru impart knowledge, and the tree acts as a conduit of energy between the earth and the heavens, symbolic of the human body as an upturned tree. In India, people of all types enjoy sitting cross-legged, and sitting on the ground is a gesture of

---

56   1750-1850

respect and humility towards those whom you are visiting. For several reasons, it is not considered important in modern urban societies. From the ayurvedic perspective, sitting on the ground cross-legged promotes healthy digestion as it relaxes the hips and sphincter muscles of the anus. When the feet are turned downward making contact with the earth it produces a calming or grounding effect on the mind and body. However, when the feet are turned away from the ground it is cooling and promotes prana to move upward (udana) which has a cooling quality. The effect on one's prana depends mostly on whether the body is vertical (heat) or horizontal (cool).

Why has sitting on the earth been, so to speak, culturally stereotyped as a behavior exhibited by those of low consciousness or those who are impoverished? Is the earth (child) not Divine and is it not the closest planet to the moon (mother)? Is this a result of the recent dark ages, that we have removed ourselves from sitting on the ground? In my view, revival of the moon's importance will bring us to respect and connect with the earth as Mother, and not seeing ourselves as Father or one who is above her, standing on her.

Another interesting example of the solar-lunar connection in ancient cultures is found in Teotihuacán, in South Central Mexico where the Pyramids of the Sun and Moon were built in approximately 100 CE. Their placement draws great intrigue because they are on the other side of the world from India. Also intriguing geographically, far away from Mexico in Egypt, are grand pyramids where mummification practices were upheld, mainly as a preparation for the afterlife. While pyramids do not exist in India where the body is cremated and viewed as a temporary form of one lifetime, one could say the architectural gesture of building such structures in Mexico and Egypt shows the intention, from the yogic perspective, of attaining inner heights of enlightenment. These structures were dedications to the Sun, Moon and the thousands of other Gods worshipped in Egypt like Osiris, Amun (God of Sun and Air) and Isis (Mother of the Pharaohs). The great mythologist Joseph Campbell used to say that the tallest structures of ancient times were religious, sites of spiritual pilgrimage, and the tallest modern ones are dedicated to finances and capitalism.

Meditation: The Royal Path of Evolution

When I first began to explore the broader yoga movement in the USA that existed outside of my own lineage, I was surprised to learn how many "spiritualists" or "yogis" did not meditate. What I discovered was that being spiritual was defined by a relationship they were having with their body. This baffled me because, having been trained in Vedantic thought, I discovered that the body is not who we are or what defines our character or personality. I learned that to understand the mind, one must silence it through meditation and its techniques, thus bringing it under control of the higher discerning power of the mind called buddhi (a major attribute of Gautama the Buddha). This allows one to access the mind's inherited will power, or borrowed energy, from the realm of pure consciousness.

Having the interest to meditate simply means that there is an aspect of your consciousness that has risen into present moment awareness and is beginning to question the nature of one's existence. This awareness gives rise to an aspect of the mind that has the capacity to inquire and journey into an exploration of life's biggest questions, most of which are often ignored and buried by worldly distractions. Such questions that begin to arise are, Why am I here? What is my life purpose? What does it mean to be alive, truly alive and in the moment? And, When will I go out of this body?

Meditation is something that everyone does but most do not realize they are meditating. Meditation is the power of reflection and introspection. In a basic sense, meditation occurs naturally when our mind shifts from identification with "I" am doing this or that, to becoming a witness of the "I". It is where one begins to question, Who is doing those things? It's simply a change of narrative. While the story remains the same, the perspective or viewpoint shifts. Vedantic meditation guides us into the source of energy or intelligence that upholds all life forms on planet earth. In this way, mankind can begin to see the wisdom in nature, the lessons hidden within our experiences, and develop a meaningful life. Vedantic meditation has a multitude of techniques and practices that rely on discipline as its cornerstone. Discipline can be defined as the regular effort put forth to manage the body, senses, thoughts, speech, and actions. It's a complete overhaul of the mind-body complex.

Meditation is probably the oldest practice of the Eastern philosophical pantheon and finds its boldest expression in Vedanta[57], the main teachings of the Vedas. India has given birth to most of the world's religions including the ancient Vedic practices, Hinduism, Buddhism, Jainism, Sikhism, and the

---

57   Vedanta is the core of India's ancient spiritual teachings and is considered one of the six main philosophical expressions of Vedic thought.

Vedas influenced both Zoroastrianism[58] and original Christianity. India, as the land of devotion, has provided a sanctuary for spiritual diversity to exist more than any other country in the world. The cultural ideology of *mi casa es tu casa*[59] is a well-known Spanish expression that welcomes all to stay at our homes has been embraced in India for millenniums and has always been extremely welcoming to all peoples much to its own demise. India has tolerated more invasions than any other country in the world. The gesture of offering our homes is a cultural anchor for the spiritual journey, in that support from family, friends and community is a necessary bedrock for balancing the emotional body an unruly factor of mind management. This cultural ideology of my home is your home is common in Latin or Hispanic cultures was probably influenced by Indian culture. The gesture of offering another your home is perhaps also similarly expressed in the very spiritual gesture Namaste that conjoins both palms of the hands together as a gesture of recognizing the spirit that dwells within you also exists within me.

The concept of welcoming diversity is not limited to India's culture, yet it is interesting to note that valuing diversity is included in the Vedantic approach to meditation and its spirituality.. I often say that we go to India not to see something, but rather to feel something. This is because subjective experiences are meant to be interpreted differently according to each person, and Indian culture encourages everyone to explore their own personalized relationship with the Divine. In contrast, an objectified approach to religion reduces the concept of an all-pervasive Divinity to a scripted experience and does not permit the mind to develop its own viewpoint based on a person's distinct affinity. Current religious interpretations teach people what to think instead of how to think, limiting a person's exploration of how they may find the Divine attractive.

True intelligence lies in learning how to use our thoughts and to inquire as to

---

58   A monotheistic pre-Islamic religion from approximately the 6th century B.C. The scriptures of Zoroastrianism are mostly found in the Avesta. Its origins were in ancient Persia and founded by Zoroaster. It carries universal concepts found in Vedantic texts such as the law of karma, maya (illusion), fire rituals and ahimsa (non-violence) which leads to vegetarianism, which Zoroaster himself followed.
59   This is a well-known Spanish expression that means, All are welcomed to stay at my home. It has been embraced in India for millenniums because the Indian cultural norms include being extremely welcoming to all peoples, much to its own demise, as India has tolerated more invasions than any other country in the world.

the nature of their existence. An inner revolution is ignited when one begins to meditate, and although at times one may feel internal resistance because of mental conditions or past habits, it marks a profound step towards evolutionary living. Stepping into the inner domain is intriguing and daunting at the same time; in one sense, if we knew what was before us, we might quickly turn around and run as if being chased by a wild boar, yet in another sense, as one begins to experience that inward movement as an ever-expanding love, they will never look back. In some cases, one may feel socially rebellious because they have begun to record new grooves over the societal brain's record. Here exists the very question we, as a global community, are beginning to ask ourselves about religious dogma, governmental dependence, and the hope of someone or something that will ultimately change us or save us. Hamlet's[60] famous soliloquy, *"To be, or not to be–that is the question,"* is in renaissance today. It is a question that prods us to think differently and find the courage to embrace our own distinctiveness, "and perchance to dream: aye there's the rub." The central focal point of turning inwards is the connection to a higher power, God, and the realization that life is the grandest school in which to learn of the brotherhood and sisterhood of mankind.

The science of yoga is the strongest advocate of meditation. Countless texts explain a multitude of techniques in which to both understand the mind and unravel it. The actual result of the practice of yoga is one in which the mind-body and indwelling spirit become fully unified, merged into a broader field of consciousness that is not limited by time and space. This merging is what the term yoga means. What is meditation? Prayer and meditation are often intercorrelated as the same thing when they are actually two different practices. Mantras are also a closely related practice of meditation although it also differs from meditation. The commercialized asana (postural yoga) of the last century has been characterized as a type of meditation, moving from one posture to the next while linking the inhaling and exhaling breaths; however, this is not meditation and does not define what meditation truly is. Postural yoga is mostly being used as a form of exercise that improves concentration, a precursor to meditation.

To properly define and understand the practice of meditation requires some exploration of the Vedic-Hindu traditions, which have emphasized the importance of meditation as an integral theme of its spiritual heritage. Epic scriptures

---

60   A monologue from Act 3, Scene 1 in the play Hamlet, by William Shakespeare.

such as the Ramayana, Bhagavad Gita, Mahabharata, and Yoga Darshana of Patanjali all make strong references to awakening the meditative power of the mind for overcoming the challenges of life on earth. In fact, the teachings of such great texts help us to simplify the management of the mind through meditation and remind us that the practices should not be over-thought so that the mind does not indulge itself in the process of thinking. These wise and practical teachings are concise and profound, leaving the individual to explore any specific lesson (verse) with the intention of adapting its message into one's own life. The mystical meanings of these scriptures should be studied by the guru of the lineage, who helps to personalize the meditation practices and expand them toward the unlimited potentials of the human mind. This is referred to as **svatantra**. Initially, the ardent student is captured by a certain verse because it largely pertains to their current state of evolution; and at the same time, the guru deepens the meaning of the scripture's teaching. The student learns how to develop a methodology that works properly, expanding the meditative mind so that meditation becomes integrated into every aspect of his or her life.

Vedantic meditation teaches us that the mind is more powerful than the body and it is through the mind that we can heal the body and go beyond the container of individualized consciousness. Any disorder or problem experienced in the body is correlated with the mind except in those incidents related to an accident or the misfortune imposed by the outer environment or other persons; but even then, such circumstances are rooted in chronic karma (prarabdha). This means that it cannot be avoid or changed, but instead must be experienced to fully exhaust it from ever reoccurring. All given circumstances are the result of previous choices and actions originated by the mind. According to Vedanta, the mind and body are vehicles of consciousness, meaning that they function according to how consciousness is permitted to flow through them, and the flow of life force varies from person to person. Through the practice of meditation and development of a meditative mind, one can allow a greater quantity of consciousness to flow into the body, increasing its strength, capacity, and promoting longevity. Meditation is a process of working with consciousness so that it can be discovered in its ultimate grandeur as the source of creation. The highest appeal of life is the discovery of that One energy that upholds the many facets or expressions and the dynamic kaleidoscope of what we call life. The same energy that pervades nature also exists in human life in all ethnicities and cultures. Life becomes much more enjoyable when we can appreciate how Divinity in its singular form is expressed into the diversification of human life.

Measuring Success

If there is one thing that humanity is drawn to, it's the idea of success defined in the form of materialism or money. This is especially the case in urban societies where consumerism is the predominant daily life activity. Why is it that humans have become so convinced that more money will bring them happiness? Why do they believe that the amount of money one acquires defines one's success? It is, in fact, not a natural part of the human dilemma, but is instead a conditioned behavior and learned belief. We do not need to have money or currency to be able to attain something. Before the development of currency, approximately 3,000 years ago, societies in ancient times engaged in a barter system. This practice of exchanging of goods and services for mutual benefit predominated in a world as it was growing connected by cultural groups trading with one another. The barter system established long-lasting relationships which helped small villages to diversify their production, materials, and skills, and develop into larger towns or cities. Eventually, bartering led to the development of currency in the form of coins made of metals like silver, gold, and bronze and in China and Lydia[61] where the use of coins began, they were stamped with images of emperors and kings. In Persia and Rome, coins bore the faces of Gods. The name for Indian currency, the rupee, is derived from the Sanskrit word rupyakam, meaning a silver coin.

The very premise upon which humans make exchanges is based on the principle of reciprocity. Reciprocity means that we ideally attain something when we put forth our effort to give something intended to bring value and harmony to others. What we call currency today is based on the original practice of reciprocity, a flow of energy. Money is merely a symbol of value; however, it has no value in and of itself. Money as a form of currency, from the Latin term *currere*, is symbolic of an exchange between two individuals or entities. In the practical sense anyone should be able to understand the equanimity inherent in this concept. However, humanity has lost the principle of reciprocity, objectifying money itself, making it the focus of attainment, the object of our desire, rather than enjoying the real benefit of the energetic

---

61   Ancient kingdom in Anatolia, modern western Turkish provinces.

exchange that is taking place. As human evolution continues to unfold, it will dissolve centralized forms of finance controlled by governments and institutions that abolished the benefits of reciprocal exchanges between individuals. Decentralized finance supports reciprocity. Reciprocity enhances spiritual development so that wealth can be measured by the level of exchange between individuals rather than by institutions. Most financial institutions are influenced by fear-based motives that enslave societies to live uniformly, destroying the creativity and aspiration of the human spirit engaged in giving and receiving.

Humans have become confused by what is making them feel good during these exchanges. Whether in the exchange of bartered goods, coins, or modern currency, the intention of experiencing mutual benefit has been obscured. It is not the actual attainment of the monetary form that brings joy, but instead the act of reciprocity that promotes positive feelings within us. Success lies in the principle of reciprocity as it promotes detachment from all the names, forms, and delusions of attaining actual money. Humans have become attached to the form of money and lost sight of the actual positive experience that reciprocity brings to our hearts. Reciprocity is a harmonious blend of hand (act), head (thought), and heart (feeling). Our connection to family, people, and community help destroy the illusion that success is an object, that joy can be found in money and the things money can buy. This world is filled with those set on getting money 'by hook or by crook' and they have lost sight of the real gains to be made in generous acts, thoughts, and feelings that is a result of living harmoniously with others. If we truly want the best for the world, then we must have a greater awareness of the types of relationships we are having with all living beings.

Satsanga Leads to Success

The mind is a tricky device that has many limitations. Even though it longs for attachment to what it is Real, the existence of God, it becomes confused and attached to what it wrongly perceives as joy. Yoga teaches us how to use the mind and then detach from it. This is what the God Shiva represents in yoga, the destruction of Raga, the attraction to names and forms (namarupa). When the mind is not filled with love and devotion it waxes and wanes like the moon, influencing the element of air (Vata). Unharnessed thoughts disturb the mind's capacity to recognize what lies within the heart, and the mind attaches instead to illusory reality, desires, and aversions. When our attachments bring pain to the ego, the mind pushes them away (dwesha). The pattern of attracting and then averting occurs because the ego is particular; it develops likes and dislikes according to the relative world. Anytime a person, place or thing is pushed away, it is a result of the conditioned experience. This becomes the repeated pattern of the mind. There is the desire to attain something with the idea that it will bring happiness and success, and then for one reason or another, because of memory, we no longer want the object and push it away because our mind has become identified with what it represents or reminds us of. If detachment is the solution to this seemingly perpetual problem of the mind, then how does one attain Real success?

Satsanga or spiritual community is considered the single most important factor in helping a person discover the universal spirit. When one says, Namaste, the common greeting of India and yoga, they are recognizing that the spirit within is the same in another. Namaste is not a recognition of a person's body or their name, it is the gesture of recognizing that the universal spirit dwells within all. Shankaracharya, one of the greatest Vedantic gurus or teachers said that satsanga leads one to liberation.[62] The basic point to understand is that your environment is more powerful than you are, so if one wants to change, one must start by changing where they spend the most time. Satsanga is derived from two Sanskrit roots, *sat* meaning truth, and *anga* meaning limb or joining together; thus, satsanga is interpreted as people joining together in truth.

Swami Jyotirmayananda makes an important point about detachment in saying, "The concept of detachment is poorly understood by most people. To most people, the word implies becoming cold, indifferent. Nothing could be more incorrect. Philosophical detachment is quite the opposite. Through satsanga you break the chains of psychological dependence on people and objects and gain an internal sense of freedom[63]." As a result of the positive collective consciousness of satsanga, one's personal awareness is uplifted away from the delusive objects and people that the mind and senses have naturally been attracted to. It is important to understand the detachment that arises through regular satsanga is philosophical and does not mean you cannot enjoy

---

62 "*Satsangatwe nihasangatwam, nihasangatwe nirmohatwam, nirmohatwe nishchaltatwam, nischaltatwe jivanmuktih.*" "Satsanga leads you to detachment, detachment destroys moha or delusion, you become rooted in God within you, unaffected by the world. The state leads you to jivanmukti or liberation." Yoga Research Foundation, Miami, Florida, Swami Jyotirmayananda, The Art of Positive Feeling.
63 Yoga Research Foundation, Miami, FL, Swami Jyotirmayananda, The Art of Positive Feeling.

the company of family, friends, and nice material things. Satsanga helps one to enjoy life while not becoming vulnerable to the objective world.

It is a common case when counseling a person on overcoming certain habits or health issues that I recommend they get support. After clearly recognizing that a person's health record is not supportive of overcoming whatever issues the client wants to resolve, I explain to them the importance of satsanga. Few can do it alone unless they have developed a strong will power over their mind-body relationship. Satsanga is very important for children today who, in the complexities of the modern world, are looking for their own sense of safety to discover themselves just like we all strive to do. Through satsanga, children learn the art of reflection and contemplation and continue to empower their higher-intuitive mind while it is still much less conditioned. Adults have internalized their conditioning, beliefs, and habits so repeatedly for years and years making it much more difficult to change. We hear it in the language of adults with such statements as, "It's easy for you because you are into yoga," or, "At my age it's not worth it, I want to enjoy the things I like," and, "After the kids go to college, I will have plenty of time, so I'll start then." All of these are excuses of the ego or conditioned mind and reflect a mind devasted by the delusion of time and space consciousness. While the golden age of India is long gone, its traditions remain alive and well in renaissance and fortunately through countless centuries of small private satsangas held in homes and small villages, the wisdom of the higher ages has been preserved. Let us continue to practice with one another.

Chapter FOUR

Mind Over Matter

I've always been a supporter of mind over matter.
If you don't mind, it doesn't matter.

Sri Sivaya Subramuniyaswami

Distinguishing Between the Mind and Brain

Although the brain and mind are generally lumped together and identified as one entity, there are profound differences between the two. Modern science and Western medical practitioners are fascinated with observing the brain, while yogis for thousands of years have explored the various realms of the mind and consciousness. The brain, like all the organs of the body, is influenced and programmed by the mind. The brain stores impressions through an action that occurs at the synapse, the point of communication between two neurons or between nerve cells, communicating to muscles, glands, etc. These exchanges occur among three different parts of the triune[64] brain: the

---

64   The triune brain was a term coined by American physician and neuroscientist Paul D. MacLean in the 1960s. Although MacLean taught a linear evolutionary view of brain development, the author contends that each part of the brain becomes more active according to the influence of the cycles of human consciousness (yugas) or collective consciousness. During the descending dark ages, the reptilian brain is more active as was reflected in territorial disputes and wars. During ascending

forebrain, midbrain, and hindbrain depending on what a person is thinking or intending. From a broader perspective, the human brain reflects the cosmology of earth, moon, and sun. These three aspects of the brain influence different aspects of our life as influenced by the quality of the mind's consciousness. The sun is signified by the cerebral cortex (forebrain), the moon by the hypothalamus and limbic system which includes the amygdala (midbrain), and the earth is signified by the cerebellum and brainstem, parts of what we refer to as our reptilian brain (hindbrain). The earth, moon, and solar brains are part of the mind-body complex which is a miniature replica of the universe.

- **Earth Brain**

From the perspective of integral yoga, each part of the brain is supported by consciousness and the quality of light that is dispersed through the wheels (chakras) of light managed by the mind. Therefore, the earth brain (hindbrain) manages how we live in relationship to the earth and our direct environment. In the earth brain, a person's direct experience with their surroundings is of primary importance, providing a focus on basic needs like thirst, hunger, material possessions, sexuality, and the information received by the five senses. This part of the brain manages a variety of conditions and conditioning impressed upon the mind over many lifetimes. The earth brain functions can be compared to the instincts of an animal. This part of the brain controls the basic orientation a person has to their body just as one has a relationship with the structure of the earth.

From the perspective of the Tantra-Hatha yoga system, the earth brain dwells mainly in the first and second chakras which are influenced by earth and water elements. The quality of the consciousness in this area can be referred to as tribal, territorial, protective, and limited to one particular area of expertise. For example, a person who has a certain level of intelligence regarding computer technology has a difficult time applying the intelligence to another area such as language or interpersonal communication. An earth brain dominant person does not prefer to travel or move around much, otherwise they feel disoriented. In general, the earth brain energy is predominantly a downward force that has complete dominion over the senses, and in Sanskrit the energy is referred to as **tamas.** The simplest way to understand the earth brain is by viewing life from the perspective of the body and all its limitations.

---

cycles, the limbic (moon) brain becomes more developed. When the collective consciousness reaches the higher ages of truth, the intuitive neocortex (sun) region of the brain becomes activated.

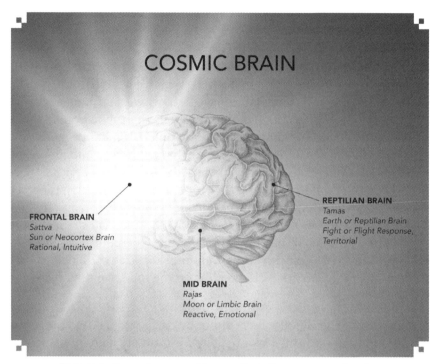

COSMIC BRAIN

FRONTAL BRAIN
Sattva
Sun or Neocortex Brain
Rational, Intuitive

REPTILIAN BRAIN
Tamas
Earth or Reptilian Brain
Fight or Flight Response,
Territorial

MID BRAIN
Rajas
Moon or Limbic Brain
Reactive, Emotional

Trinity Brain, its consciousness and its connection to the sun, moon, and earth.

If a person is negligent of their health ignoring basic health principles, avoiding exercise and reasonable bedtimes this will lead to major health issues and reflect in their dependency on something outside of them to heal them. How a person treats their own body is reflected in the relationship they have with nature. Such an earth-brain dominant person will depend on doctors, medications, and a healthcare system to save them, and may maintain the attitude that they are not responsible for their health, perhaps blame genetics, society, and the government for their health issues. As the world's collective consciousness continues to evolve into the higher ages, an emergence of consciousness for personal responsibility, health, and spiritual evolution will naturally clash with a majority of humanity looking for the outer world to save them. Ayurveda and yoga boldly proclaim, "You are the answer! You are the solution!" This is because only you can change your ways and evolve toward health and happiness.

- **Moon Brain**

The moon brain basically controls the aspect of the mind that creates thoughts and emotions in three forms as related to the elements air (vata), fire (pitta) and water (kapha). Vata-type emotions are mainly fear and anxiety and an overall feeling of uncertainty. Pitta-type emotions are anger and aggression that lead to violence in extreme circumstances. Kapha-type emotions are depression and sadness. The amygdala is the epicenter of emotions, storing past experiences that are awaiting the next thought to be placed into motion. An important question related to moon brain activity is, What happens if these stored emotions lay dormant for a long time without ever being triggered? For example, an apparently healthy person on the outside who may not have any symptoms or show deficiencies in diagnostic tests may still be holding deep-seated emotions in the amygdala. That stored emotion is suppressed negative energy that slowly leaks out over time to weaken certain organs that are most susceptible to attack, depending on the type of emotion, element or dosha.

For this reason, chronic diseases cannot be categorized based on genetic disposition alone, and this explains why a seemingly healthy person can suddenly discover a chronic disease such as cancer thriving in their body. Modern diagnostic tools are very useful; however, they cannot measure karma or samskaras (deep seated mental impressions) that have a major influence on the health of the entire body. These mental scars are likened to wounds that influence repeated projections within the mind field at unconscious and subconscious levels. Overtime, the impressions ripen and mature into manifested experiences, or, alternatively, physical ailments. These impressions also influence the production of thought patterns on the conscious level that trigger emotions or reactions. Thus, the mind plays a primary role in the body's health in addition to how it disseminates a person's past karma. The mind is like a synapse of the brain; it is a tool or point of contact between our inner and outer world. This is why yoga aims at slowing the mind. A wise mind reduces the upheavals of mental conditioning that make us vulnerable to associations with names and forms, creating confusion with who we are. Understanding and working to reduce mental patterning (samskaras) can alleviate much of our human suffering. We can gain knowledge of what is Real and negate impressions of what is unreal: the body, mind, ego, emotions, thoughts, and the entire world process.

According to ayurveda, diseases do not suddenly appear, they must have a basis in the body-mind complex. The good news is that this is where love and devotion as Bhakti yoga come into play and are vital healing aspects for any sentient being's life. Bhakti yoga helps to heal the moon brain and convert suppressed and very commonly hidden emotions in the amygdala into positive feelings. In future chapters, we will explore the topic of transforming the energy stored in the emotional body towards something very positive and useful in the world.

The moon brain causes a person to wax and wane like the moon, creating moments of indecisiveness and reactions they may often regret. The moon brain is rajasic, with energy moving outwards, sometimes directed (pitta) and other times dispersed (vata). Fortunately, ayurvedic wisdom can rely on Vedantic philosophy and its practical principles to help those that are moon dominant in their personalities to manage their thoughts and emotions in a constructive manner.

Transcending the moon brain can be a lifelong task because it is where our attachments are formed. The moon brain attaches a person's consciousness to tangible things in the form of people, places, and things. As the moon brain aligns mostly with the principle of rajas, it functions through the second and third chakras. A healing breakthrough of the moon brain moving into the heart center typically appears as either one dramatic event that cracks open the mind or as a series of events. A healing breakthrough indicates that a person is proceeding in the direction where they can find their way to truth (dharma).

The secret to balancing this emotional part of the brain was discovered by yogis in ancient times through the practice of Hatha yoga, the system of balancing the sun and moon energies done anatomically by distributing equal amounts of energy to the left and right sides of the brain. Pranayama, the yogic techniques of breathing are regarded as the most powerful forms of self-reformation, because how we breathe is directly correlated to how we think. Yogis recognized the mind as a fickle device that struggles with managing the perpetual thoughts that invade it repeatedly, thereby increasing the risk for emotional dysregulation, the byproduct of excessive thinking. A restless mind leads to irrational behavior that can compromise a person's wellness. The yogic breathing technique referred to as alternate nostril breathing (nadi shodhana) is a remarkable practice for managing the left and right sides of the brain, bringing the moon brain into balance. What alternate nostril breathing does is slow the mind, reducing the number of thoughts, thereby reducing the risk of triggering past conditions, the negative patterns of thought that lead to poor use of one's intellect. A. Parthasarathy supports this point, "The human mind can become ruinous if the intellect is not developed enough to govern it."[65] Developing intellect is another way of emphasizing purification so that mindfulness can exist. There is much freedom that comes from emptiness of the mind. The more one thinks, the greater risk for emotion because emotions are triggered by thoughts; and as emotions fill the mind, the organs of the body take on their vibration. Alternate nostril breathing is particularly important in unraveling the subconscious mind that stays active through our dreams, making sleep poor and less restorative.

As the evening is characterized as the time of the moon, bringing darkness, coolness, and mystical quality to the night, it is an important time for strengthening the immune system. Alternate nostril breathing can be done just before meditation or sleep to calm the mind. Science claims that people are oriented toward dominance on either one side of the brain or the other. The left brain is where analytical and scientific functions are carried out, and the right brain is where we carry out artistic and creative endeavors. The left brain is characterized as intellectual and the right brain as sensitive and intuitive. The methods of yoga work with the mind to optimize the functions of the brain, whether it be breath-work, mantra, or meditation they all manage the mind. Managing the mind heals the brain so that it functions to create healthy lifestyle patterns. Meditation is very helpful for releasing the excess mental impressions that have impacted the amygdala, hiding away in the midbrain.

- **Solar Brain**

Awakening of the solar brain leads to an evolutionary lifestyle and requires continuity of practice and effort. When this part of the brain is awakened, the mind is no longer fractured from the world and recognizes the light of consciousness behind all existence. In yoga, the concept of the spiritual eye originates in the solar brain. The sun is the soul and everything humans are looking for; it is the light of truth and reflects harmonious living with nature. We practice focusing our attention on the spiritual eye in yoga meditation when the two physical eyes, symbolic of duality, are turned upwards to the one point between the eyebrows (the tip of the triangle). This is done as a

---

65   The Fall of The Human Intellect. Mumbai: A. Parthasarathy, 2007.

practice of transcending the limitations of the downward and outward forces of the earth brain and moon brain functions which can be understood through the concepts of as rajas (outward) and tamas (downward) quality of consciousness.

If meditation works so well and scientific research proves its efficacy, why aren't more people doing it? The fact is that more people are meditating than ever before. It is a trend that keeps on growing as a remedy for heightened levels of stress in our modern lifestyles that are not very balanced, especially if we factor in toxic diets, alcohol, and prescription medications. The Harvard Medical School research[66] findings regarding the impact that meditation has on reducing stress come from functional magnetic resonance imaging (fMRI), a scan that records the brain's activity. The fMRI technology has allowed scientists to witness the positive influence meditation has on the brain, and specifically highlights the amygdala's levels of activation when participants were viewing emotionally charged images before and after being trained in meditation. Results show that after only two months of practicing regular meditation, participants had significantly lower levels of activation of their amygdalae.

The Different Aspects of the Mind

The mind, according to yoga, has two major aspects: inner and outer, and they perform the subtle functions of consciousness. The outer aspect of the mind depends on the senses to collect information, make decisions, and develop likes and dislikes. The inner aspect relies on positive feeling or intuition to cultivate pure knowledge unconditioned by the ego. There are interactions between these two aspects, however the outer mind (manas) is responsible for disease of the body and results in behavior that usually compromises evolution. One of the basic prerequisites to living an evolutionary life is to learn to turn off the outer mind.

One afternoon my friend Swami Chidananda[67] and I were speaking about

---

66   Harvard Medical School (HMS) research on meditation was inspired by Herbert Benson's, *The Relaxation Response*, during the 1970s riding on the popularity of transcendental meditation (TM). Research at HMS has continued today with Gaëlle Desbordes, Professor of Radiology and Professor of Psychiatry Benjamin Shapero who began conducting research in 2012 using functional magnetic resonance imaging (fMRI).
67   Integral Yoga Institute, New York City, founded by Sri Swami Satchidanandaji Maharaj (Sri

meditation and wondering why so many make it so difficult when it is simply about "sitting down and shutting up." This discipline, alone, is so fundamental to developing a meditation practice. One must have a willingness to explore and find respite from the chaotic nature of the world. There is an ongoing battle within the mind. Our outer mind goes out into the world looking for satisfaction, and our inner mindful awareness develops a hint of knowledge, something much more profound and satisfying within. "Meditation is the means, knowledge is the end, meditation is the process, knowledge is the culmination."[68]

The practice of meditation is mostly a struggle, its designed to shift the mind from its outer aspect (manas) and bring it inward towards its higher intuitive aspect. However, one cannot come to meditation to resolve an agitated mind, meditation may create more agitation because there is too much contrast. If one is positive, contented, and comes to meditation with an attitude of surrender, then meditation will transcend the outer mind and allow us to focus on the mind's inner higher domain. Most of the work of preparing the mind lies in a proper lifestyle, one that is simple, slow, introspective, quiet, disciplined, and pleasurable. The outer mind (manas) is purified with lifestyle, while the inner mind (buddhi) is groomed with meditation. As long as one continues to impress the outer mind through the senses with dull and restless energy, its capacity for transcending towards its higher nature will be very difficult. This is precisely why the Raja yoga eight-fold path presented by sage Patanjali begins with non-violence (ahimsa). Whether it be in action, words or even dietarily, violence to any living thing dulls the mind, tarnishing it, removing its delightful essence, and thereby confusing and delaying its evolution with short term attractions that perpetuate the ongoing story of the ego. The mind, through the ego and the five senses, projects itself outward; this creates one's daily living reality or cinema show. The buddhi nature of the mind is the power to discriminate between what is real and unreal, and this discrimination is sustained through practicing meditation.

The outer mind thrives on the power of our intellect as it acquires information and builds intelligence. But as we have learned, the information of today is the garbage of tomorrow, in that it has no real value beyond a cluster or thoughts, ideas, opinions and figures. For example, take a moment to read the cover

Gurudev), 1914–2002.
68   Sri Swami Sivananda, Dhyana Yoga, A Divine Life Society Publication.

of a newspaper dating back before your age. The information seems lifeless, dull and does little to engage your attention besides a passing fascination with what was happening long ago. This is the nature of the outer mind; it is best satisfied with a story it can engage with as it builds ongoing and relevant mental illusions. Vedantic philosophy enumerates several types of illusions that the outer mind encounters, which all must be overcome so that the higher mind can prevail.

1. Illusions of difference (Bheda Bhranti) – because of the nature of the world, the mind develops the attitude, "I am different," creating a feeling of separateness from all living things. As an aspirant develops their sensitivities, a natural compassion or feeling develops in the mind that brings one closer to all living things.

2. I am the performer (Karta Bhotapan Bhranti) – through repeated activities, the mind becomes associated with actions and the idea that "I" am doing these things rather than realizing that Braham (God) is what is moving through you, that the actions of the body are merely being borrowed as instruments of the Divine.

3. Illusion of contact (Sanga Bhranti) – contact of any type is false because it is being experienced by the senses. This sensory information creates the illusion that one is touching, smelling, or seeing something. Again, this divides one's inner consciousness from the all-pervading pure consciousness. One can overcome this by experiencing the world like a stage show and recognizing who is really watching the show.

4. Illusion of modification (Vikara Bhranti) – if the world is perceived as changeable or as part of a process, like even the concept of evolution, it is an illusion. From the perspective of pure consciousness, evolution does not exist, there is nothing to change, how can we change God, the supreme absolute source of all existence?

5. Illusion of the reality of the world (Jaga Satyata Bhranti) – from our perspectives gained using the ego, senses, and nervous system, the world seems so real. Vedantic meditation practices such as, ***becoming the witness***, ***formless meditation***, and ***mantra*** are all powerful swords for conquering the illusion of the world. Remove the "I" from idea and you are left with the root word for ***dead***.

A revolution occurs within your personality when one aspires to overcome the illusions of the mind. Integral yoga and its higher forms, mantra, meditation and satsanga, collectively aid in this process. Initially, what appears as a mechanical sadhana (practice) becomes an integrated shift in one's mental attitude when observed from a broader perspective. At first, if the aspirant feels overwhelmed with the barrage of mental illusions, then satsanga is required to settle the mind through the power of collective consciousness. Once the mind begins to settle and a calmer state is established, then mantra japa (recitation of Divine name) curves the mind inward creating greater detachment from the disturbances of the world and calms the mind even further as the mind becomes more interiorized.

After this interior state of mind is more established, then meditation awakens into expanded consciousness beyond thought, emotions and subtler mental modifications (vrittis). For Divine intelligence (God) to enter, the mind must be calm, this is the purpose of meditation, to train the mind. Do not look for results or inspirations in meditation because it is a process. Enjoy the rewards of the higher mind as awakened by meditation through calmness, peace, and happiness. Buddhi brings cheerfulness and sincerity in every circumstance. Judgement of others is a barricade placed there by your ego, so learn to move such thoughts aside and substitute them with positive ones so that the process of evolution may continue. ***Never settle for the laxity of the world; instead, shake it up with your creative and limitless will power.*** Albert Einstein recognized this in his own life and in the lives of many revolutionary souls when he said, "Great spirits have always encountered violent opposition from mediocre minds," and this comes from one of the greatest scientists of our times.

The royal system of yoga (Raja) refers to the vastness of the mind as *chitta*. This word, in a limited sense, refers to the mind's unconscious and subconscious aspects. When the mind operates through its lower aspect as manas, the outer mind, it uses the senses to gather impressions that can lead to the development of the ego (ahamkara), a false sense of who we are. Manas is simply an aspect or function of chitta. However, when the mind uses intuition, or a reasoning capacity normally developed through meditation and devotion, this higher mind aspect is referred to as buddhi. This is our higher intellect, not to be confused with intellectual knowledge gained through memorization or repeated association. The term buddhi is referring to intellect that has been purified by discrimination (viveka), detachment from the fluctuations of the world (vairagya), spiritual listening (shravana) that extracts what is pure and inspiring from the mundane experiences of the world. Spiritual listening is listening to spiritual discourses (satsanga), a practice that cultivates a reflective mind (manana). Of highest importance is to know that these practices must be sustained with the primary desire to aspire to attain liberation (mumukshuttwa) as reflected in evolutionary living. In the general sense, Vedanta uses the concept of chitta to describe whatever the mind has collected, so we work with our chitta wherever we may be on the path of evolutionary living.

Ayurveda and Yoga Heal the Brain

While yoga aims to heal the mind, awakening to its many illusions, any practice intended to heal the organs of the body does aligns with the intentions of ayurveda, as this approach emphasizes bringing one's life into harmony with nature's cycles. Ayurveda focuses on establishing balance (homeostasis) of the five elements through the system of tri-dosha (vata-air, pitta-fire & kapha-water). Since each of these elements (doshas) is aligned with all the organs of the body, including the brain, ayurvedic remedies have the principle aim of establishing a new relationship, one that is shared between the mind and the brain. The mind is the instrument of consciousness while the brain is the organ that receives, records, and stores all the impressions. Ayurveda heals us, not merely by fixing a faulty organ or an isolated part of the body, but in its profound goal of promoting one's relationship with natural laws, thereby changing one's relationship with pure consciousness. This process will make a person's brain much more receptive to positive impressions such as healthy food, good associations, and the famed daily and seasonal routines blossoming within ayurveda's branch of medicine called Svasthavritta.

We are all familiar with the idea that the brain can be changed. In allopathic medicine, we use the concept of neuroplasticity to describe this. In other words, a person is not stuck with the brain they were born with. Research and science have concluded that what you impress the mind with repeatedly will ultimately impact the brain for better or for worse. Well, this makes perfect sense to most of us, but people continue to do many things they evidently know are not good for them. Or perhaps they don't, and that's why they continue to do such things. Unless a person has had the blessing (because of past karmas) to awaken from the mental illusions that perpetuate a time and space mentality, they will continue to partake in the most mundane things, like watching violent forms of television and media, drinking alcohol, and eating unhealthy foods, just to name a few "normal" things they think they should be entitled to enjoy. Establishing health through ayurveda is a matter of working through layers of illusion about pleasure, joy, and health.

A quite serious factor for many, one that creates a compounded layer of illusion is addictions. Addictions to substances incumber the mind further, fragmenting it from the body as a result of chemical dependencies, creating neurological disturbances that no longer allow the brain to operate coherently with the nervous system. From the Vedantic viewpoint, it is the ego that becomes addicted to feeling a this superficial high. To the ego, this feeling of being stimulated by the addiction is sensationalized as high but the reality is that any type of addiction or dependence on anything externally is derived from the lowest forms of consciousness. So, getting high on anything outside of us, whether it be a substance, person, place, or thing, is perpetuating a low level of awareness that places the brain into a deep slumber, far from the healing awareness that promotes well-being. One must first heal the relationship the mind has with the body by feeding the brain healthy foods, and this is consistent with the fundamental branch of biology called physiology. When the mind-body relationship is sound, one has a stable platform from which to begin living an evolutionary life.

Evolution and Technology

The internet has become a world-wide-web for distributing information and has increased human productivity; however, it has also led to many complexities in mental health and stress and has impacted the quality of lifestyle. Technology, unless used properly, entangles us emotionally and mentally because most people interpret data from their own perspective and according to their needs and desires. Today, large media companies compile and store the personal data of their users and record patterns in which you utilize the internet, control the types of advertising you are exposed to, and also remind you who they would prefer you to communicate with. Media is one of the most complex technologies of our time, and if not used properly, can further perpetuate the human mental crisis. This is because the media outlets focus on persuading humans to follow a "One-way" mentality as is the case in the ideals of socialism and communism. It aims to sell the "stories" that keep people engaged in something that is dramatic, sensational, and most of all unreal.

Any type of grand scheme to create a centralized institution or product that provides all the solutions for humanity is a part of the illusionary force referred to in Vedanta as maya. The ego develops and adapts accordingly to the society it is exposed to and is shaped by culture and history. The illusory world process is maintained by conformity, leading to the demise of the free will all humans are endowed with to explore and discover the mystery. Technology can be a very utilitarian tool, but it can also limit our exploration of the soft powers that lie within us. All humans are endowed with a special technology that can far exceed the capacity we rely on in computers. The human mind is the most powerful instrument anyone could imagine; a concentrated mind can penetrate the atoms and molecules of any living thing and understand its make up. The mind can attract the most glorious moments in one's life with a mere thought. The mind can open our hearts to experiencing love for all living beings, but it can also close the heart into living callously.

Before India was conquered by foreign invaders, during its golden age, the soft power culture thrived with Yoga, Ayurveda, and the entire platform of Vedic wisdom traditions that are mostly founded on the principle of non-violence (ahimsa). Sadly, ahimsa was misunderstood to mean that all are welcome on your land regardless of the violent intentions certain groups have to undermine its peoples while not protecting their wisdom traditions. For this reason, the varna, or caste system, was in place in Vedic culture to demonstrate that certain individuals have innate skills of a powerful warrior while another person has a tremendous capacity as a skilled laborer. Overtime the caste system was not aligning individuals with their specific abilities and interests but restricted a person to live under a specific category according to their birth status. This was another major factor in the demise of the Vedic culture and led narcissistic values to penetrate the family unit. Anyone who aspires to evolutionary living must embrace the concept of individuality and personal responsibility, otherwise, we will be left with humans all acting the same way externally, following the rules, so to speak; while at the same time, internally, their consciousness is rotting away with neglect, attachment, anger, fear, and suffering for the soul that yearns for freedom from bondage to the body.

As we interact with one another peacefully, good communication is of vital importance. Much misinterpretation occurs when we communicate using technology as a medium. This compounds the already existing issues and complexities of interpersonal communication. Interpersonal communication through technological gadgets removes our direct experience with the feelings of others and the subtle nuances that people generally rely on to connect and clearly communicate. First-hand, normally paced physical communication is being undermined by the fast pace of machines. Another modern problem that has developed for the brain and human evolution is an area of technology called artificial intelligence (AI), which refers to intelligence that is derived from a machine or any type of programmed gadget. What this branch of computer science aims to do is to replicate human intelligence in machines. This is concerning to begin with because if humans were so intelligent, why would they need to create a machine to replicate their actions? The 'intelligence' being referred to in artificial intelligence is merely patterns and ideas of a brain that has been exposed to a series of mental conditions. We need to understand what real intelligence actually is and where it comes from.

Pure intelligence (mahat) cannot be replicated because it is derived from the very source of pure or Divine consciousness. We cannot label the functions of the human mind, characterize what it is creating using modern names and forms of science and technology, and then label it as intelligent. Over many lifetimes and a multitude of fear-based actions, the human mind has become so conditioned that it has become far from intelligent. Vedanta recognizes one intelligence that pervades all living things, and we can see one aspect of Divine consciousness in our living world by recognizing the intelligence within the instinctual behavior performed by animals. We also see pure intelligence in humans when instincts are developed through intuition. Few today have access to real intelligence that is unobstructed by the ego, senses, and the emotional brain. Thus, human intelligence is artificial unless a person has learned to live according to the natural laws of this universe and has discovered the ancient yogic secret of **bhavana**, "a Sanskrit term which implies feeling blended with attitude, a quality of the heart. Bhavana is the most important factor leading to spiritual evolution[69]." In simplest terms bhavana can be defined by the saying, It's not what you do, but how you do it! The importance lies in the attitude that a person carries when performing their actions.

Take for example a person who has a job they do not enjoy, while they spend their days working away performing all the necessary physical actions, their mind is somewhere else. Each week they collect their paycheck and receive their material benefit for their actions; however, all week long the person is harboring very negative thoughts about several co-workers and their boss.

---

69   Swami Jyotirmayananda, The Art of Positive Feeling, Yoga Research Foundation.

All this stress is piling up into negative karma as a result of the judgements and critical thinking of others. While this goes on for some time, the person may have acquired a monetary gain, but unfortunately has regressed on the evolutionary path. This same scenario is found in marriages and often leads to very destructive outcomes. A positive attitude must support all of our actions so as to produce that wonderful feeling that God is growing nearer to us than ever before. Otherwise, what a miserable life it would be to live with the idea that the next job, person, place, or thing will reward us with everlasting happiness. The highest ideal of integral yoga is to teach us to renounce the idea that the objective world will bring us everlasting happiness. The process of disentanglement occurs in stages of evolution, as one paints their picture on the canvas of life with the colors of their consciousness (gunas).

As we approach the end of each year, we are reminded of how quickly time passes. The world is now faster and busier than ever, so much so that people don't return calls, texts, emails, etc., and if they do, it may be days or weeks later. Even though we have a variety of communication gadgets to connect us, we still cannot find the time to connect and communicate with others. The question is whether or not technology is actually improving our level of communication and intimacy. Is it bringing people to connect on a deeper level beyond weather talk and relationships gossip and helping us to move Godward? People still strive to attain one thing, and it's the same things regardless of where one lives, happiness. Even people who are very spiritual and surround themselves with good people, still might find themselves asking, Is there something more? Is what I am doing going to reward me in some way beyond what I am experiencing at this moment or perhaps in the future?

For example, one way to approach using the internet is for education or promotion of positive news and research. Additionally, we must limit our use of digital communication because the stimulation from videos and negative information speeds up the mind. The user's mind becomes desensitized, wherein the mind becoming more and more detached from the heart. The more our societies become disconnected from feeling and living a heart-centered existence, the more problems we will see in the world. Feeling, combined with positive attitude, is what shifts our spiritual or practical activities from being mechanical into actions that transform our consciousness.

This is precisely why, after a few years, people fall away from practicing physical yoga; they become bored of the repetitiveness, just as anything that is reduced to mechanics limits its return of reward. However, when we add meaning to the ritual of asana, when we integrate bhavana, the right attitude, then any action becomes transformed into karma yoga and can lead one closer towards liberation. When people do not balance their responsibilities between the head and the heart, emotional instability can result, and they may make decisions and choices that hurt themselves and negatively affect those around them. The hand is the action, the head represents having the right attitude, and the heart blends in feelings of love, gratitude, and compassion.

Chapter FIVE

Healing the Body Promotes the Evolution of the Mind

Knowing that I am different from the body, I need not neglect the body. It is a vehicle that I use to transact with the world. It is the temple which houses the Pure Self within.

Sri Adi Shankara

Diet in the Modern World

When one begins to care for their body, it indicates that he or she has established a certain degree of discipline over their body. Exercising the body is important for many obvious reasons and the health benefits of exercise have been scientifically validated. Self-care is one of the cornerstones of ayurveda because healing can begin when one recognizes the body as a temple, as a sacred place to expand in awareness and consciousness. Unlike highly misinterpreted religious practices that have fallen to dogmatism and worshipping the Divine as something external, ayurveda and yoga bridge the relationship between spirit and nature and provide an integrated model for evolution that begins with the body as a replica of nature. How one regards their own body is reflected in their relationship with nature.

The ego's cleverness traps one into thinking that if one changes their body, the mind will change and cope better with the world. But this is not true. Similarly, changing the world or people is not a solution. Change must begin with one's own mental attitude, and then the entire world adapts to this as a projection of one's consciousness. Healing the body largely begins with diet, and ayurveda and yoga teach us that eating can be a sacred time for healing and introspection. Sadly, American culture has denigrated food to the level of sustenance only, and we live with the fast-food phenomenon that swept this country and many others. Many people around the world believe that partaking in fast food equals more time for everything else, everything that is more important than food.

The topic of diet in today's age is a very interesting one, especially if you live in the United States or any large major city in the world. The amount of variety found in most major cities is daunting, especially if you analyze the diet of most people. Most diets are comprised of a small handful of the same food types such as grains, fruits, dairy products, vegetables, and large amounts animal products. From these categories, most people tend to eat the same things every single week repetitively, probably by choice, because it feels natural to do so. The three main points I try to get across when speaking to either a private counseling client or to a large audience at a conference are listed below.

1) Diet is the single most important factor that can influence positive evolution both individually and collectively, and one's dietary choices will naturally influence our global ecology.

2) Fixed formula-based diet programs do not work for all. They may work for some, while for others fixed diets can bring many complications. In some instances, the diet may work for a few weeks or months until various symptoms like skin issues or low energy begin to arise, to name just a few symptoms. The mind-body complex (prakriti) must be in reciprocity with nature, and we look at the diet to see whether foods are heating or cooling. This basically means that you are eating the foods that are in season and available respective to where you live. Ayurveda, as the science of life, teaches us that the body benefits from the habituation of foods, meaning that eating the same foods regularly is good for the body as it adapts to creating a relationship with those foods. Habituation, meaning not only habituation with the nutrients derives from foods, but more importantly, the energetic relationship

the food harbors with the five elements[70]. Let us remember that from the perspective of ayurveda's core philosophy, the human body is a miniature replica of this universe, therefore, there are billions of little universes living on earth and each one must find synchronicity with nature depending on their current longitude and latitude.

3) A plant-based diet promotes health of the body and influences mental wellness. The term "plant-based" is modern replacement for the age-old term "vegetarianism" which originally included eating dairy products such as milk, butter, and cheese. This shift from the word vegetarian to the word plant-based is an attempt to disassociate oneself from the inhuman and corrupt factory farming of animals, particularly over the last 50 years. The term "vegetarian" has begun to trigger an association to this industry because being a vegetarian most likely includes dairy products largely derived from farms where cows are treated unethically. After years of being commodities for the dairy industry, they are sent to slaughterhouses for the beef industry and their skin is sold for the still enormous leather industry. Thus, following a plant-based diet provides a stigma free identification for those who do not eat meat but may consume some dairy products in moderation. The term "plant-based" is considered, by many people, to be a more conscious diet because it may include making responsible choices with regards to dairy products. To clarify and distinguish a plant-based diet from veganism is simple because a vegan diet does not include any food-product that is derived from any type of animal, while following a plant-based diet may include some dairy products. Obviously, the term "plant-based" is broader in scope and is also an easier place to begin, especially considering most individuals who are beginning to embrace such diets come from a severe background of eating animal foods.

---

70   The five elements are earth, water, fire, air and ether and according to the esoteric yoga traditions represents the building blocks of every human being spiritual anatomy that lies within the astral or light body called chakras. The plant and animal kingdoms also contain these five elements, although what distinguishes mankind from them is the capacity to reason or intuit. Biology and instincts are structured and programmed while in humans it is learned or conditioned. The latter has free will while the former follows DNA.

The Role of Asian Dietary Ethics in Western Cultures

In Asian cultures, it is common to eat many foods with your hands for prac-tical purposes and as a way to connect with the food, its aroma and texture. Eating with the hands also allows one to enjoy eating more slowly and take in food in smaller quantities which is very good for digestion and for managing body weight. In India, it is also a very common practice to pray before eating as food is considered a sacred aspect of our lives, recognizing food itself as Divine. Food is not only sacred but is medicine. Many ancient medical systems focus on diet, like ayurveda, Unani, Siddha, Japanese, Traditional Chinese Medicine (TCM), and the Greek medical practices were largely inherited from the Babylonians and the Egyptians. The early roots of Western medi-cine began in Greece and much credit is given to Hippocrates, Aristotle and Herophilus. Greek medicine focused on three primary factors: diet, drugs, and surgery. Diet was analyzed based on geographical factors which were of primary importance when seeking to reduce the symptoms of diseases and prevent them from further spreading. Greek medicine was actually holistic and designed to treat the individual… sound familiar? Yes, it is probable that this Greek, and even Roman concept were influenced by ayurveda. However, unfortunately, many of these preventative practices were eventually ignored and even forgotten, replaced by practices such as drugs and surgery. Coun-seling and education are the most important factors missing from modern medicine today, and the dependency on drugs and surgery has destroyed the health of entire cultures throughout the world.

 Sharing a meal is certainly one of the most intimate aspects of interperson-al communication and promotes positivity and intimacy in the mind. The common practice in India, and Asia in general, is to eat on the earth (floor) seated in front of one's food in a cross-legged position. From the ayurvedic perspective, this is very calming, as one is grounded by the vibration and proximity to the earth. This is especially the case when eating outside and sitting on the soil and being surrounded by plants. Also, the opening of the hips, as the knees are pointing away from each other, is another factor that has a very positive effect on digestion. This is because as the hips are more relaxed, the nerve plexuses, that bundle in the lower gastrointestinal tract, hips, and buttocks, are stretched, creating a sedative effect on the nerves. The quality of the environment, with respect to noise and other elements related to modern lifestyle like cars, trains, tv's and music can counteract the sedative effect that sitting has on the nerves. Sitting on the sidewalk in the middle of a city will bring little benefit in this regard. Mealtimes in Asian culture always include warm fluids, such as soups or hot teas, both of which support healthy metabolism. Also, it is common to include positive atmospheric elements like flute music, candlelight, or a water fountain in order to create a soothing and sacred environment for digesting the medicine of food. All these practices can easily be integrated into our lives today, affording us great benefits towards health and creating more sanctity around food.

Family-Seated-Eating together on the ground connected to the earth.

Evolution of Diet

For the majority of life on earth, humans have lived as farmers, hunters, fishermen, and gatherers who have collected all types of food directly from the earth. Eating from the land, fishing from the seas or rivers, and growing simple grains like corn, wheat, and rice, depending on the geography, was a core part of life. Humankind traveled and populations developed based on their capacity for cultivating food. The scientific concept of the first Agricultural Revolution is dated at beginning between 8000-10,000 BC, probably occurring at similar times in different parts of the world. This timing places it within the Golden Age (Satya Yuga) of Vedic culture.

Scholars of history and science view the Agricultural Revolution as a time when a new relationship between humans and the natural world made significant positive differences in the lives of many people. However, Vedic India was highly evolved. Why do scholars ignore this? Instead, looking at other regions of the world, they measure evolutionary advancements with regard to material aspects of agriculture like domestication of animals and farming, and present a linear progression from low to high cultural features and increasing cognitive complexity. In contrast, the evolutionary patterns in Vedic India at this time during the Golden Age show features of a high culture marked by an expansion of knowledge that was scientific, complex, and advanced. The texts, teachings, and dietary practices are evidence of an expansive understanding of the dimensions of consciousness, cosmology, and sacred forms of worship with the living earth. The elements of the earth were never considered separate, but rather were revered as extensions of human life.

Western scholars characterize the cultural changes taking place during the Agricultural Revolution as developmental, where societies became more advanced and complex, depending upon what animals they domesticated, what they were learning from the land, and what crops they were harvesting. These material changes eventually led to the creation of a lifestyle that was more efficient, hygienic, and more socially pleasurable. Changes in agriculture and dietary practices were happening across the globe in many cultures, and specific climate, geographical and ecological circumstances affected the evolutionary trajectory of a specific society. This theory uses a materialistic framework to consider dietary evolution.

However, India has a history that has been largely ignored by Western scholars because it does not align with this materialist linear progression. Vedic India presents evidence of an advanced culture that integrated ecology, technology, spirituality, and diet as part of a cyclical evolutionary pattern[71] called yugas. Herein lies a paradox between the linear perspective of Western scholars and the evidence of a society that was already evolved. The highly evolved beings in the Golden Age of Vedic culture were rishis and seers who disseminated a wisdom tradition that we are now rediscovering.

The Golden Vedic era spanned thousands of years of oral wisdom traditions,

---

71   The cyclical view of evolution finds its origins in chapter one of Manu Samhita (Manava Dharmasastra) (Manu's Law Codes), Manu was a rishi of the Vedic Golden Age (Satya Yuga).

noble kingdoms, prosperity, plant-based communities and, most importantly, demonstrated the Aryans[72] lived in harmony with nature and attained the highest levels of consciousness. The Industrial (scientific) Revolution, that developed during the European Renaissance and lasted into the eighteenth century, is marked by advancements in medicine, economics, technology, and much more. However, this period did not build on the wisdom available if people had interpreted scriptures, art, artifacts, and other cultural expressions left behind by ancient wisdom traditions.

Take for example the Pashupati Seal[73] of the Harappan Age in northern India, or the cave drawings of Lascaux in Chauvet, France, both of which have been characterized by archaeologists in a literal and simplistic manner as art produced by primitive cultures instead of as indicative of cognitively advanced people. Here we see that science presents a viewpoint of primitive hunter gatherers whose dietary habits changed along with our cognitive abilities over time. The associations made between

Pashupati Seal is one of the earliest depictions of the God Shiva, Pashupati means Lord of the animals, found at the Mohenjo-daro site and dated roughly 2700-2100 BC. The posture depicted is Mahamulabandasana or the great seal pose.

---

72   Aryans was a term that defined the original and indigenous people of northern India. The Sanskrit term simply means noble. Consequently, when India began its long decline in dharma (principles and values) the term Aryan started to became misused repeatedly and was associated with a false narrative called the Aryan Invasion Theory concocted by the British to justify their occupation of the Indian subcontinent.

73   Lord Shiva is called Pashupati, the one who removes the pashas (8 fetters) from one's personality. Vedic scriptures refer to the quandary of human life as that of animals (pashus). God as Pashupati is the lord of animals. The seal symbolizes an understanding of mind and the importance of turning to the high life (sattva) that supports clarity of lifestyle, diet, and consciousness. Thus, Pashupati symbolizes the important relationship shared between humans and animals.

humans and the instinctual nature of animals indicate that humans would follow a carnivorous diet. Science today acknowledges that a carnivorous diet is barbaric and basically unhealthy. If diets were used as a measure of our evolution, then we could see that humans have certainly not changed very much, in fact some would agree that modern diet has shifted backward in contrast to the recent scientific evolution. Early human's brains are associated closely with the consciousness of apes. The human brain evolved more as we became sedentary, began using language, and made other advancements during the Agricultural Revolution, the religious eras, and the Industrial Revolution.

This perspective asserts that we are now reaching a zenith, an Information Age, with science leading the way for humans who depend on advances in technology for their evolution. This modern viewpoint quite possibly is accurate when describing humans living in many cultures across the world; however, there is one clear exception. The ancient Vedic culture developed a long period of the Golden Era when humans had a remarkably different relationship with nature, animals, the physical body, and their diet. These relationships indicate a highly evolved culture.

Because, initially, the wisdom was not persevered as a written tradition, it is difficult for any person without proper training to interpret what was left behind correctly without using intuition and allegory. The higher ages reveal that Nature was not something to take from but rather viewed as an extension of human existence. This instilled a respect for all life which made India a mostly a vegetarian culture, traces of which are still in practice today, particularly in the yoga lineages and Brahmin caste. Regardless of how advanced a society is, there is always diversification of consciousness, meaning that all types of people still exist as depicted in the original caste system of India.

I refer to the caste as an alignment system that presents four distinct categories that help people recognize their true qualities or talents as influenced by a person's karma over many lifetimes. The caste system, where a person's occupation and standing in society is determined as result of their birth into a particular family is one that most people criticize for being discriminatory. This was not the original function or intention of the system that was developed by the sages of Vedic India. The aim of the Varna system, incorrectly defined as caste, was originally designed to recognize a person's natural disposition and to align the person with their innate talents and qualities. The fourfold categories can also be correlated to the four branches of yoga.[74] Just as the caste system was misunderstood and used by many foreign invaders to undermine India, the same was done with the dietary principles that upheld to the nation's values. The pre-invaded India predominantly followed a vegetarian diet, and introduction of meat was mainly a result of Moghul (Islamic) rule and European invaders such as the Portuguese and British.

In brief, we don't want to ignore the obvious influence science has had on many areas of modern culture, everything from medicine, psychology, genetics, to the entire modernization of our transportation systems; however, these external developments may not necessarily be indicative of evolution of consciousness. In fact, the relationship one has with nature is more indicative of a person's evolution than the intellect used to develop and operate modern instruments. As Mahatma Gandhi said, "The greatness of a nation and its moral progress can be judged by the way its animals are treated." The nineteenth and twentieth centuries mark the infancy of the evolution revolution as reflected in changes towards a plant-based diet, concerns for the ecology, and the freedom to be spiritual without having to adhere to the dogmatic practices of the major religions. Diet during the higher ages in Vedic India most likely differed from that of other civilizations of the time, as it would have demonstrated the uniqueness of the land of yogis. If such agricultural societies thrived from living off the land for millenniums, it is a testament to the fact that a local diet is the best diet. Humans living harmoniously with their surroundings is the most evolved way of living and eating.

Today's concept of superfoods or ***somaras*** was likely born in Vedic India as there was a sacred regard and use for these foods. Such foods include the following: powdered herbal tonics with brahmi, ashwagandha, and amalaki; the use of ghee (clarified butter) combined with herbs called gritha; oozing asphalts or shilajit; black salt; and the very famous preparation called chyvanprash, a medicinal fruit jam named after a great a yogi that combines fifty-two herbs and spices, honey and ghee. There is no more superb a food that exists today that can compare to this ancient jam recipe for increasing immunity and longevity.

A Puranic story tells of chyvanprash. This special paste was created by the

---

74   Sudra are skilled laborers (Bhakti yoga), Vaishya are businessmen-merchants (Jnana yoga), Kshatriya are warrior-fighter (Karma yoga), and Brahmin are teachers and spiritualists (Raja yoga).

Ashwini Kumars, the twin physicians, the sons of the Sun God, Surya. This paste was given to Sage Chyvan because the Ashwini twins were very impressed by the devotion offered to the sage by his wife Sukanya, a princess who was much younger than Sage Chyvan. He had lost his vision because of an accidental prank by Sukanya when they first met. The celestial healers, being enthralled by the attractive princess and knowing that the Sage was much older than his wife, enticed her by offering to restore the youth of her husband. Although it was a mischievous proposal, it required that Sage Chyvan bathe in the river with the Ashwini twins. Sage Chyvan agreed, since the offer was being presented by the physicians of the Gods, he felt he had nothing to lose.

Before dipping into the river with the twins, Sage Chyvan was given a spoonful of this medicinal jam, and the three of them dipped into the river together. As they suddenly rose out of the water, they appeared identical to each other, which forced Sukanya to choose her real husband from among the three of them. Fortunately, her prayers to the Divine in the form of Bhagwati Jagadamba had developed her feeling capacity of discernment (viveka) and she was able to choose her real husband. He now had a youthful body because of the blessings from the Aswini twins and from taking the special paste (prash) which restores one's youth. The paste was named chyvanprash as a result of this serendipitous occasion.

Each person evolves according to their own consciousness and other factors as indicated in their astrological chart. As diet is something that everyone must do, it becomes the single most important factor influencing one's spiritual evolution and equally has the capacity to benefit ecological health as well as the longevity of humanity. The evolution of one's dietary practices begins with non-violence. While many may find it natural to practice eating vegetables, grains and fruits, others will struggle with it, and of course this depends on one's culture, karma, and other factors.

Vegetarianism is the most crucial factor for the evolution of humanity as diet is something that directly impacts every human being on the planet. Two primary factors exist, one is the direct impact diet has on the human body and its physiology, and the second is the impact diet has on the environment and the particular concern related to greenhouse gases[75]. It's obvious that the

---

75   It's a global problem with livestock responsible for 14.5 percent of global greenhouse gases. Cattle are the number one agricultural source of greenhouse gases worldwide. Each year, a single

importance of plant-based diets is being recognized in major cities across the world and most particularly in the USA with the multitude of veggie restaurants and "natural grocery" stores. Isn't it odd that we must label a grocery as "natural" to distinguish it from conventional stores? In addition to the natural groceries is the diversity of non-animal protein options and alternative dairy products. The other new development is the sustainable or "clean" meat movement, that creates animal meat without factory farming and without ever having to kill a cow.

Factory farming is far different from the practices of hunters and gatherers who procured meat from smaller game or through scavenging, and it is also much different than eating meat that was prescribed according to ayurveda for the purposes of healing the physical body.

Most of the meat produced today is a result of factory farming, and whether it be cattle, poultry or the many other types of animals farmed in our own and other countries like China, South America and even many parts of Asia and the Middle East, this treatment of animals presents the greatest obstacle to human evolution. Never, in the history of humanity, has the treatment of animals been so atrocious. How can any sentient being, that by the grace of God was given the capacity to reason, find justification for hurting any creature that was also born from the womb of Divine Mother (prakriti)?

For evolution to occur on a global scale, our spiritual communities must continue to embrace the importance of non-violence as a means for propagating peace on earth. Meat is primarily consumed in industrialized countries. India, the second most populated country in the world, has the lowest consumption of meat products. The ancient sages of India understood the importance of diet as it is a direct reflection of one's quality or level of consciousness, and this is evidently still the case today. As a person's relationship to nature expands in sensitivity, naturally one grows in compassion for all living things. Sensitivity is not to be confused with being emotionally triggered, as is the common stereotype. Spiritual sensitivity increases when transcendence occurs between the sensory aspect of the mind (manas) and the higher intuitive aspect of the mind (buddhi) as determined by consistent spiritual practices (sadhana), good associations (sangha) and performing good deeds for others (seva).

---

cow will belch about 220 pounds of methane, which is shorter lived than carbon dioxide, but 28 times more potent in warming the atmosphere. Frank Mitloehner, a professor at UC Davis and air quality specialist in the Department of Animal Science.

Dietary Quality Versus Quantity

In ayurveda, the topic of food quality refers to how foods are combined and prepared, as this is a major factor in how diseases are created. *Viruddha Ahara*, incompatible foods (diet), play a major factor in overall health and longevity. A person can eat a fresh organic piece of fruit but if it's combined with yogurt or milk its quality of nutrients will not be absorbed into the body. This relates to how one combines food. Similarly, food preparation matters. Nutrients and energy within food dwindles over time, so it is best to eat food that has just been harvested.

Let's say that a person decides they want to eat some broccoli for dinner and heads to the local market to pick a fresh and organic sun-soaked bunch, then great! However, if, while strolling around the market, his eyes are captured by the succulent images of a delicious spread of foods on a magazine cover and decides, "I'm going to have that instead," his dinner menu may change. He still decides to purchase the broccoli, and when he arrives home, he puts the broccoli into a bag and tosses it into the freezer. Weeks later, or perhaps even months later, he is rummaging through his stored food and stumbles across the bag of broccoli and decides to eat the broccoli. This simple story illustrates one common example of viruddha ahara because the broccoli has, after kept in the freezer for so long, been made deficient in lifeforce and potency (prana, virya,and kala). Even though some crafty cooking may make the broccoli taste enjoyable, a freezer cannot preserve what the body needs most, the light of the sun, carrying lifeforce and the potency of vitamins minerals. A can, box, or package does the same thing to any food. Such packaging damages zinc, an important antioxidant, as well as vitamins A, C, and E. When these nutrients are compromised in our foods, we can correlate this loss to oxidative stress and inflammation. For this reason, local and fresh foods are the best forms of food to build immunity and prevent health issues. Fresh local foods, and the ways in which they are prepared and combined, have an impact on fertility.[76]

The way in which foods are prepared and combined with other foods provides also influences metabolism, the primary system of the body. The importance

---

76   "It has been estimated that nearly 50% of infertility cases are due to genetic defects. Clinically, it is a highly heterogeneous pathology with a complex etiology that includes environmental and genetic factors." Zorrilla and Yatsenk, Manuscript titled "The Genetics of Infertility" 2013.

of food combinations was brilliantly recognized by Herbert M. Shelton[77] in the 1950s who also influenced vegetarianism and the expansion of the modern health movement of today. Shelton recognized fruits as special foods that should be eaten alone, and this is consistent with ayurveda. While much of the information provided in his book was groundbreaking and encouraging for the dawning American health culture, it differs in several ways from ayurveda, and aligns with Western nutritionists. Shelton categorized foods in the typical manner with proteins, starches, fats, fruits (acid and sub-acid) and non-starchy and green vegetables. The basic premise behind Shelton's food combining science is how the properties of foods directly influence the catalyzing of enzymes as chemical reactions of cell metabolism.

Ayurveda recognized this concept thousands of years ago, broadly referring to it as the digestive fire (agni). The concept of fire or Agni is a sacred concept of both ayurveda and yoga. Ayurveda particularly recognized that this fire (enzymes) is responsible for performing important functions like building muscles and the seven major tissues (dhatus), destroying toxins, and assisting in breaking down food particles during digestion. One truth about metabolism, aside from the wisdom of food combining, is that digestion begins in the mouth, with both salivation and chewing preparing foods with a greater capacity for their assimilation inside the gastrointestinal tract. For this reason alone, eating slowing is important so that foods are well chewed before descending to the stomach. Ayurvedic dietetics is distinguished from Shelton's food combining model and all major diet fads with the concept of the six tastes (shat rasa). All food can be categorized within these six categories: sweet, salty, sour, pungent, bitter, and astringent. The tastes are all based on their correlation to the five elements (earth, water, fire, air, and ether) and how they influence the three doshas:

- Vata (ether-air) is balanced with salty, sweet, and sour tasting foods.

- Pitta (fire) is balanced with sweet, bitter, and astringent tasting foods.

- Kapha (water-earth) is balanced with pungent, bitter, and astringent tasting foods.

---

77   Food Combining Made Easy, originally published in 1951 by Dr. Shelton's Health School, San Antonio, TX.

Food compatibility is probably the single most important factor in evolutionary dietetics, second to a following a plant-based diet. Incorrect food combining, preparation, and misalignment of the six tastes according to the seasons and doshas are the major factors responsible for the main forms of chronic diseases, inflammatory conditions, and immunity. Below I have provided some of the main principles in food combining and evolutionary dietetics.

Eating Laws of Nature:

- Leave each meal slightly hungry and with the feeling that you could eat more.

- Eat fresh (seasonal) and organic.

- Eat slowly, calmly, and in a quiet and natural place if possible.

- Avoid eating when emotional (anxious, angry, or depressed).

- Avoid cold fluids with meals.

- Avoid excessive fluid of any type with meals.

- Avoid drinking something cold after having hot tea.

- Avoid overly spiced, salted, or oily foods.

- Avoid eating honey that has been baked or heated.

- When eating dairy products, be mindful of the source of these products, and consider the living conditions of the animals and how they are being treated.

- Follow a mostly plant-based or vegetarian diet unless a necessary doshic or medical imbalance calls for the benefit of meats.

- A balanced meal contains all six tastes.

Food Combining:

- Fruits should be eaten separately – Variations can exist depending on one's digestive fire (agni), the season, and age of the body.

- Fruits should always be eaten alone, including fruit juices, which should be taken separately.

- Fruits are best taken in the morning time, before 12 noon.

- Honey and ghee in equal proportion should be avoided.

- Avoid incompatible spices, herbs, and oil according to the seasons (for example, avoid pungent spices in the summer and cold sweet foods in winter).

- Avoid over heating or re-heating oils and dairy products.

- Fish and milk should be avoided.

Dairy Products:

- Purchasing dairy products from local farms whenever possible is a way to develop a direct relationship with those individuals in contact with the cows.

- Avoid dairy products that are pasteurized or homogenized.

- Raw cow milk is the most medicinal, especially when taken warm and with spices like cardamom, turmeric, ginger, nutmeg and saffron.

- Goat's milk is good for kapha types and not recommended for pitta types or those with hyper acidic conditions.

- Cream is heavy and should be avoided as it is more likely to block important channels and create congestion. If your tongue has a white coating, it's a good indicator to avoid it.

- Sour cream is the most acidic and can aggravate pitta related conditions such as reflux, heart burn, ulcers, aggravated skin conditions and fevers.

- Yogurt is nourishing and important for weakness and debility. Best eaten at lunch, not in the morning or evening. It combines well with cucumber as in the Indian raita, yogurt salad served at most Indian meals. It also combines well with cilantro, cumin, coriander or even a pinch of cayenne. Sour yogurts can aggravate pitta or acidic related conditions so yogurt that is sweet is best for vata and can also be enjoyed by pitta types.

- Cheese is gluey, produces stagnation, and is not easy to digest. It should be avoided by kapha types, except in slight moderation in summer. Try to eat cheese that does not contain rennet (cows intestinal lining), has little or no salt, and is not strongly fermented. Most commercial cheese contains rennet. Radish, cumin, cayenne, black pepper, and mustard (seeds) are good things to combine with cheese to make it easier to digest.

- Cream cheese and cottage cheese are light and easier to digest, as well as paneer (farmers' cheese used in Indian cuisine).

- Butter is a major commercial product and should be avoided because it is usually made from pasteurized milk and includes high amounts of salt and coloring agents. Ghee or clarified butter is an ayurvedic super food. It is made from raw butter and considered tri-doshic (good for all mind-body types), although in moderation for kapha types. It increases strength, boosts immunity, improves vision, skin luster, increases metabolism and is an excellent food for memory, meditation, and overall mental clarity.

Grading the Potency of Food

Science and modern medicine often measure the value of a diet, food, and nutritional markers in terms of longevity, but overlook the impact of diet on the quality of daily life and ignore the energy or lifeforce within food. In ayurveda, priority is given to the life force (prana) foods carry. While you may be able to freeze foods and some of their vitamins and minerals, you cannot preserve prana. For this reason alone, food should be eaten fresh, and this presents one of the greatest issues surrounding health and immunology. Foods today are boxed, canned, frozen and sit in warehouses and in delivery trucks for countless hours, days, and even weeks or months before it arrives to your mouth. This includes herbs and spices which, in many homes, spend years inside kitchen drawers and cabinets where they stay, barely used and losing prana over time. After several days, any food becomes energetically deficient, and after months, dried herbs and spices lose much of their potency and vitality even though the taste remains. Progressive healthcare will include these basic principles and will begin to teach the importance of one's direct access to foods from local farms.

One of the first places I start consultations with my clients is by advising them to buy their foods daily and from local markets that stock foods from local farmers. Avoid freezing foods or reheating leftovers unless they were cooked on the same day, and even then, heating should be moderate. Every time food is reheated it loses its vital force (prana). One ideal way to warm any food that has been refrigerated is to place it in sunlight either on a plate or in a pot for 10-30 minutes (depending on the time of year), followed by warming it on a stove top oven for a few minutes on low heat.

The faster any food is heated the more damaging it is to the life force. Microwaves basically shock the food with electromagnetic radiation waves at a very fast pace. It's interesting to point out that microwaves are far more popular in American culture because eating is all about speed. Over 90% of households in America have microwaves, however, only 10% of households in Asian use them, where the pace of life is slower in general. Cooking is given more value in Asia than it is in the west (even though American kitchens are three-to-four times the size of any other country).

Freezers should be used minimally, and only for a few items that require freezing, like non-dairy ice-cream desserts. Eating vegetables that are slightly cooked, keeping them somewhat crisp, is a good health habit, as they provide a scraping action on the gastro-intestinal tract. As per the ayurvedic view, this is important because excess gut microbiomes (bacteria, archaea, and fungi) build up over time. When the intestines are negatively influenced by the doshas of air, fire, and/or water, the excesses are a build-up of toxic waste, known as *Ama*. Vegetable roughage prevents this build up from occurring. Moderately cooking vegetables preserves the prana (life force) that is so vital to health and longevity.

The importance of making the body-mind complex healthy enough to be worthy of sustaining consciousness or immunity, this evolution we are all capable of, has sadly, been completely removed from the modern lifestyle, especially with regards to diet. Ayurveda does provide this conceptual frame for us with its concept of immunity as ojas. Ojas reflects the importance of the body's durability, strength, and capacity to endure the outer factors of modern lifestyles such as stress, poor sleep, viruses, infections, and circulatory issues that stagnate the blood. Good ojas, a functional immune system also provides the capacity to feel inspired, positive, and delightful. Ojas gives us the capacity to endure the trials of life and the tests of karma.

Diet and the Doshas

The term *dosha* is commonly used to describe a person's mind-body type; however, since the term has a negative connotation and means that which is faulty, spoiled, or dark, it is really not the ideal manner in which to describe a person. Instead, a proper term is *prakriti* which is correlated to creation, Divine Mother, and the power of nature. Ideally, one would prefer to be aligned with such attributes rather than to be classified in a category of a dark (dosha) being. The main point to understand is that **there are neither good nor bad constitutions, all humans are made up of an orchestration of natural elements (forces) that have both positive and negative attributes.** It is karma, a sum total of a person's choices-actions, that determines whether the elements will function in a negative (dosha) or positive (prana) manner.

Prana is the essential quality of all food, water, and air (oxygen) and thus these attributes, combined with karma, and the will of God, determines the nature of one's life. While many in ayurvedic circles emphasize the negative factors of the doshas, I would like to highlight the positive mental attributes of each. The doshas perform functions and influence the body's metabolism. One's constitution, one's prakriti defines the nature of one's existence in mind and body, it is an assessment of how the elements will influence one's health. The doshas appear in varying degrees in every human body and the balance or imbalance depends on several different factors like culture, genetics, karma, and lifestyle. These are the three doshas and their main attributes:

> **Vata** – creative, spontaneous, adaptable, quick, delightful, inspired, witty, imaginative, expressive, communicative, festive, sensitive, and sincere.

> **Pitta** – focused, strong-willed, driven, moderate, motivated, confident, balanced, and colorful.

Kapha – stable, consistent, reliable, loyal, friendly, sensual, patient, supportive, slow, and strong.

Establishing a sound understanding of these qualities will allow one to approach diet and lifestyle with wisdom. The basic idea behind an ayurvedic diet is this: what is good for one is not necessarily good for another. Each person should adapt their nutrition according to their unique mental disposition. Metabolism reflects the nature of the mind. When a person is highly focused, their metabolism will be strong, but when the mind is fast, it creates irregularities. When the mind is slow and stable, the bowels are usually regular. Adapting to the right diet can be difficult to achieve, especially for families with many members, or when cooking for a group with many different constitutions. However, there are simple ways to adjust to this way of eating. One way is to plan food preparations for all according to the seasons, but then making specific spice blends or sauces that can be added to an individual's portion, thereby allowing them to make their own dish sweeter or spicier. This includes the manner of preparation, i.e., grilling, boiling, sauteing etc., and also the herbs and spices that are used. The tri-dosha system of vata (air), pitta (fire) and kapha (water), is universal and can be adapted to any culture, climate or individual. The tri-dosha system divides our dietary needs into three categories according to a person's mind-body type and addresses specific short-term imbalances that one may be experiencing, like hyperacidity or excess gas.

The biggest misconception about ayurvedic dietetics is that it requires adhering to a fixed or rigid formula of foods. Quite the opposite, ayurveda teaches us to enjoy all types of foods depending on the season or geography. Unlike modern diet fads, an ayurvedic diet aligns with nature's laws and maintains the philosophical perspective that the mind-body complex is a miniature version of the universe. So, this means that wherever you go, you should aim to stay in harmony with nature and the elements that surround you, as they influence you more than anything else, even more than good company.

Consider this simple observation I have made as I have traveled much between very dry and humid regions in both India and USA. I observed that people who live in very dry areas like those of the western United States have very dry skin, and as they get older, their facial skin is substantially wrinkled. Especially when compared to someone living in the southeastern part of the United States, where the climate is humid because of the tropical-rainy weather the living areas developed around many lakes and canals. The same case exists between northwestern India, that is mostly desert, and southern India which is much more humid. The differences are stark, and the skin of the human body reflects the terrain in which one lives or spends the most time. The human body mirrors the area and environment one is most often exposed to.

This truth applies both externally and internally. Humans cannot live without water, and it is not natural to live in areas that dry us out, even though modern engineering has devised a way to pump water into vast geographical areas. However, humankind cannot overcome the power of nature, for it is upheld by the supreme consciousness of the creator (Brahman). The most important factor with regards to diet is wisely adapting to the climate and the culture one is in. For example, if you are in a tropical region like southern Mexico, then you should eat foods that are sweet and bitter as these will cool the body and balance pitta dosha (fire element). If you live in an area like London, England, where it is cold and damp one should eat spicier foods that are pungent in taste as this will heat the body and balance kapha dosha (water element). If someone lives in California or Nevada, one should eat salty and sour tastes as these will reduce the physical dryness and help to balance vata dosha (air element). There are of course many other factors to consider, but this is an example of how to apply the practical wisdom of ayurveda. I cannot begin to tell you of the number of ayurvedic counseling cases I have seen where people who live out of accordance with the basic principles of the six tastes (sweet, salty, sour, pungent, bitter, and astringent) and thereby create substantial health issues for themselves.

Three Pillars for a Healthy Life

If diet was recognized as important by the sages of ayurveda thousands of years ago, at a very different time in the world with only a minute fraction of today's population, then imagine the impact a natural diet can have on our health today? Today we are burdened with the residual toxicity of prescription medications, alcohol abuse, foods sprayed with pesticides, and the fast pace of modern lifestyle. Ayurveda recognizes three primary factors central to health, mental wellness and longevity called **upasthambas**. They are diet, sleep, and sex, including exercise. Each of these three pillars focus on invigorating the most important system supporting health and longevity, the immune system (ojas). The basic fact that the soul is encased in the human body and blessed with the gift of life indicates the person has another opportunity to eradicate karma in its various forms, such as negative mental impressions, dismal activities that have no purpose, and poor associations, all of which require much energy at the expense of the body, the vehicle of life. A perfect example of this is seen in the scores of people who do not enjoy what they do for work which produces tamasic mental energy.

In focusing on the upasthambas, an evolutionary life is available. One of the challenges with the modern lifestyle and its focus on accumulating material wealth is the lack of physical exertion required to perform many actions that long ago required physical effort and were an integral part of everyday life. Keep in mind that until the recent technological revolution (dwapara yuga) most people played an active role in cooking, maintaining and even building their home, washing their clothes and either riding a horse or walking long distances every day to get where they needed to go. This daily exercise has many benefits for the body for health, mental wellness, and longevity. One of which is circulating the blood, as hemoglobin plays a key factor in blood function and allows the heart to function properly. Circulation promotes life and stagnation leads to death. When the energy in your body is moving, the energy in your life will also move. All things must flow, and a lack of blood flow can lead to a multitude of health problems as reflected today with diabetes, heart disease, obesity, cancer, and inflammatory conditions, all of which are influenced by the quality of blood maintained in the body. Ayurveda recognizes the importance of walking as it is gentle and natural function of the human experience.

Sexuality also promotes healthy circulation of blood and vital reproductive fluids (shukra). One key factor with regards to sexuality is its corrective influence on immunity (ojas), fertility, vaginal dryness, chronic fatigue, and lack of aspiration for life. Additionally, from the perspective of yoga, sexual energy should be preserved and transmuted towards spiritual disciplines like mantra and meditation, as these are aids for quieting the mental disturbances (vrittis). Tantric and Taoist[78] systems have taught the importance of preserving the sacred energy of ojas (immunity) through compression of a secret pressure point at the base of the scrotum moments before ejaculation. This allows for preservation of the semen while still experiencing the sensual pleasures of sexual intimacy. Sexual intercourse should be reduced during the

---

78   *Tao Of Sex*, by Stephen Thomas Chang.

summer when the sun is strong and exhausting and can be increased during the cooler seasons. Sexual intercourse should be avoided during menses as this also requires much energy and can dry the vagina, although intimacy through affection and compassionate gestures are soothing to the nervous system. Ayurveda regards the natural downward eliminatory function of the body as vital health and anything that obstructs those functions should be avoided as this could aggravate the doshas and create other health related complications. Downward functions (apana vayu) include ejaculation, urine, feces, menstruation and maintaining a healthy sleep schedule.

- Sleep is one of the most crucial factors in promoting health and well-being. The body needs regular consistent rest, but in today's lifestyle there are many obstacles to restful sleep. Good sleep habits can be achieved by following these recommendations:

- Reduce stress by simplifying your lifestyle. Make choices that are realistic, practical, and efficient. This can be done by supporting your local farms and community stores for foods and other necessities.

- Create a home space that is quiet, far from city noise, traffic, or loud music. The sounds of nature are the most ideal, in the form of water, light wind, birds, crickets, etc.

- Create a technology buffer of about 60-90 minutes before sleep. Avoid computer work, do not watch television, and remove any electrical devices, like those for wifi from the bedroom.

- Take a warm bath with 1-2 tablespoons of sesame oil in the evening; this is very calming to the nervous system and an important aid to sleep.

- Nasal oil drops are helpful in resting the eyes and calming the mind. Sesame oil is typically the base oil for most formulas. Ghee can also be used.

- Massaging ghee around the eyes and even ghee drops into the eyes are calming and help to sedate the optic nerves.

- Practice alternate nostril breathing exercise (pranayama) for about 5 minutes while sitting up in bed just prior to sleep.

- Sandalwood oil added to the third eye (bindi) is cooling and relaxing. Simply dab some essential oil on the spiritual eye, then press gently to the area apply some pressure while mentally chanting Aum (cosmic sound).

- Meditation is also very helpful, as the mind becomes very calm, making it easier to enter the deep sleep state. Turning the eyes upward to the point between the eyebrows (ajna chakra) awakens the intuitive mind and helps the mind detach from lower mental conditions.

- Mantra or recitation of positive affirmations are very helpful for clearing negative impressions from the mind.

- A good way to transition into sleep is to read sacred texts or any book filled with knowledge and insightful messages that encourages one to reflect and grow.

The goal of these practices is to calm the mind's instable nature (chitta) and enhance its capacity to enter the deep sleep state. Dreaming does not support good mind-body synergy or rest; thus, one must aim to unravel the subconscious mind where one's shadow nature lies. The period just before sleep and just upon rising are very important for overcoming mental conditioning, negative patterns, and habits. It is common practice for people to shower and cleanse their body before sleeping, as one cannot imagine getting restful sleep if the body is filthy and odorous; however, little is done, on the part of most people, to clean the mind so that it becomes clear for deep sleep to occur. A drugged, fatigued, or alcohol induced sleep is mindless and perpetuates ego consciousness that leads to nowhere. As my Vedanta teacher often says, "Take care of the body, but do a little more to take care of the mind."

Our culture is infatuated with care for the physical body, while the mind is left behind to decay. Upon rising, it is important to make God your first thought or visualize the image of a preferred guru or saint, as these are powerful images to latch the mind to as it comes out of the sleep. Such imagery helps to transcend one's consciousness, leaving the heaviness of the body and putting aside the concerns of worldly life. This is also an important time to begin reciting your personal or *ishta* mantra as an exercise for developing control of the mind. Positive affirmations can also be used if one has not been initiated into using Sanskrit mantras. Mastery over the mind allows for the capacity to concentrate it. Yogic concentration (dharana) is the most essential quality of the mind for spiritual evolution and success in daily life. The power of one's attention is reflected in the quality of one's life. Diet, sexuality, and sleep are considered such vital principles because ultimately, they affect the quality and power of one's attention.

The Tasty Medicine of Herbs and Spices

Herbs and spices are an extended aspect of ayurvedic dietetics because they provide ways to energize foods and create a desired influence on the doshas. Herbs and spices have not only played a major role in treating chronic diseases and acute dysfunctions in the medicinal tradition of ayurveda, but have also shaped Indic culture, many Asian cultures, and have especially played a major role in traditional Chinese culture. The use of herbs and spices provides a bridge between philosophical understandings, scientific knowledge, and spirit. Even though research has provided empirical evidence of the efficacy of herbs and spices, still there remains a mystical value that cannot be measured.

These magical and colorful plants influence our physiology while creating a sensual connection with nature. Humankind and nature have maintained a relationship through the integration of these components in dietetics. Plants carry the wisdom of consciousness and help to connect us to the Divine through them. By no coincidence, the color green is attractive to humans for its capacity to calm and expand the mind, purify the senses, and increase our understanding of life. Spices are regarded for the colors and flavors they add to foods; however, spices have remarkable medicinal qualities that promote healthy digestion and improve circulatory function. It is hard to imagine that major wars[79] were fought over spices that were prevalent in Asian cultures, and most particularly India. Let's look at the major differences between these two aspects of nature's bounty:

Spices – a spice is a concentrated form of its original state found in nature, and can include tree bark, a plant's roots, stems, flowers, seeds, or fruit. All spices

___
79   Dutch-Portuguese War (1602- 1663) was nicknamed the Spice War and was one of many battles that took place over spice commodities. Pedro Álvares Cabral is documented as leading the first expedition that brought spices from India to Europe which eventually influenced the demand for spices throughout Europe. The Arabs had maintained control of spice routes from Asia to Europe for centuries and thus created a need for Europeans to find new routes to the Far East. Many other European countries with colonial aspirations also discovered spices accidentally on their voyages abroad. India has reigned as the top spice producing country in the world for millenniums.

are edible, usually colorful, and have a strong taste, even in small amounts. Spices are used mainly for cooking and enhancing the flavor of foods. Indian cuisine is recognized for its diverse use of spices in every meal and even in many types of drinks like the famed chai.

Herbs – these are substances derived from trees, plants, roots, leaves, and bark and are taken for specific medical purposes. In some cases, herbs like tulsi (Indian basil) or cocoa is used to cook or prepare certain dishes. In ayurveda, herbs are classified as either heating or cooling and are recognized based on the elements predominant in them (earth, water, fire, air) in order to address excesses of the doshas. While spices are used for cooking, herbs are taken in the form of powders (churna), tablets, wines, oils (applied to the skin), skin pastes (lepanas) and many other forms.

Both herbs and spices have medicinal qualities and have been used for preventative and curative purposes for thousands of years. Modern Western cultures have become so ignorant and uneducated about the value of herbalism and cooking with spices that it does not occur to most persons to use them when they are sick. It is not coincidental that the main spices used in the most common Indian culinary dishes are some of the most medicinal. Even though most spices have a heating quality, one should not assume that using spices for cooking will make dishes spicy. When spices are used in such a manner that results in food tasting hot, creating a burning sensation in the throat, this is a poor and disproportionate use that will adversely affect most people, especially vata (air) and pitta (fire) types. Spices should be used to flavor foods, not to make them hot and spicy.

The Motor of Metabolism

The foundation of the ayurvedic concept of health is a balance of the elements (doshas) within the body. We begin in the digestive tract, trying to ensure that the primary organs of the gastrointestinal tract (colon, small intestine, stomach) are functioning properly and not being overburdened with digesting foods. Western anatomy and physiology consider only two kinds of metabolism (constructive and destructive). Ayurveda recognizes six total stages of digestion which are divided further into three phases as influenced by the doshas.

The Six Stages of Digestion as per the Six Tastes and Elements

- Sweet (water and earth) – 1st stage begins in the mouth with saliva and chewing so that prana can move the food down to the stomach. It is for this reason that ayurveda recommends eating something sweet before eating a meal in order to prepare for healthy digestion.

- Sour (fire and earth) – 2nd stage takes place in the stomach with the secretion of hydrochloric acid. The acid aids in breaking down foods and supports the extraction of nutrients.

- Salty (water and fire) – 3rd stage takes place at the pyloric valve which helps food pass from the stomach to the duodenum.

- Pungent (air and fire) – 4th stage is a function of the jejunum and involves strong secretion of intestinal enzymes.

- Bitter (air and ether) – 5th stage is influenced by air as the force of circulation that moves food waste to the ileum, the last part of the small intestine.

- Astringent (Air and earth) – 6th stage forms the feces and forms peristalsis.

The Three Phases of Digestion as per the Doshas

- Digestion: Kapha – 1st phase takes about 1-2 hours and involves fluids and enzymes flowing into the stomach. The feeling of being grounded, satisfied, and at times heavy is a result of kapha. The saliva in the mouth is characterized as a form of kapha (water) called bodhaka. In the mouth, spices catalyze enzymes to fire up.

- Assimilation: Pitta – 2nd phase takes about 2 hours, and more energy is being used to further breakdown the food as it moves from the stomach into the small intestine. Enzymes catalyze secretions in the stomach that take account of what has arrived, and that begin the process of assimilation. This process produces heat that is felt in the upper body and which rises to the head. If spices create perspiration in the scalp or even across the forehead, it is an obvious indication the food is too heating for the constitution. This second stage is mostly characterized by the amla, the sour stage, and is correlated to pancreatic secretions, called pachaka pitta.

- Elimination: Vata – 3rd phase takes another 2 hours and is essentially the final process that depends on good circulation (apana vayu) in order to prepare the food waste for elimination. In this third, katu, the pungent stage, the air and ether elements are activated in order to eliminate waste by moving them to the colon for release of earth back into the earth.

The cycle of birth and death takes place in the digestive system every day. Foods without spices are bland, so they do not have the spark of flavor and fire so necessary for the body to eliminate thoroughly. This is especially important as the body ages because metabolism slows down substantially as the body approaches fifty. Cumin, coriander, and fennel are three remarkable spices that work effectively to kindle the digestive fire (fire) without aggravating it.

The most important factor in using spices in the diet lies in their preparation. Using cumin, coriander, and fennel in their original seed form is best especially when fresh. All spices in their seed forms should be sauteed in ghee, clarified butter, until the seeds pop, as this releases the energy or volatile oils within the seeds that hold their medicinal value. The two most famous roots of Indian ayurvedic cuisines are ginger and turmeric; both are somewhat similar in appearance, but markedly different in tastes. Both ginger and turmeric are heating because of their unique qualities and tastes, and they are both useful spices for maintaining a strong agni. One of the things I have enjoyed most about my decades of travel throughout India and Asia is the use of spices in some of the greatest culinary dishes that have garnered international recognition, like curries, dals (Indian lentil soups), masalas (spice blends) and chutneys (spicy condiment). Spices enliven the body, make the blood flow, increase the skin's luster, and improve mental clarity. Below is a list of some of the most common spices and their medicinal benefits.

Spices to Promote Healthy Digestion

Allspice – this Jamaican spice is antiviral, antibacterial, analgesic, anesthetic, is good for alleviating colds, is helpful for regulating the menstrual cycle, and is an overall digestive enhancer.

Black Pepper – kindles the digestive fire, inhibits the growth of cancer cells (lung and breast), counteracts constipation, arthritis, lung congestion and respiratory issues, prevents Alzheimer's, and reduces fat.

Cardamom – aids in digestion (agni), is soothing to the stomach, reduces bad breath, reduces the risk of blood clotting, calms the stomach nerves, clears sinus infections, and is good for calming asthmatic responses. Cardamom is good for vata types with sensitive digestion as it soothes the nervous system and awakens the function of the spleen. It goes well in milk to reduce milk's mucous forming effects and promotes overall balance to the digestive system.

Celery Seed – mainly used for treating gout, reduces menstrual cramping, heals ulcers, and kills Helicobacter pylori bacteria. It can lower blood pressure, reduce excess water (diuretic), and is effective for colds and flus. Celery seed has been used to treat cancer and inflammatory conditions. Celery seed is very high in manganese, a lesser-known mineral which is important in activating enzymes that produce proteins effective for increasing bone density. It also contains magnesium and phosphorus, both of which support bone strength.

Chile – as one of the hottest spices, chiles are good for all types of pain including arthritis, is an effective fat burner, increases digestive fire (agni), combats headaches, lowers LDL "bad" cholesterol, reduces blood clotting, and regulates heart rate and circulatory functions.

Cinnamon – is antibacterial, heals wounds, increases agni (since it is heating), assists in controlling blood sugar levels, diabetes (type-2), and polycystic ovary syndrome (PCOS), and helps prevent cancer. As a pungent spice, it has a stimulative effect on the circulatory system.

Cloves – are great for preventing bacterial infections such as H. pylori, has mild anesthetic properties, counteracts the effects of herpes and hepatitis C. Cloves are very beneficial for many issues related to asthma, cough, and even laryngitis. Cloves are good for kapha and vata but increase pitta.

Cocoa – as a bitter, it is great for inflammatory conditions related to pitta, cholesterol (reducing LDL), improves arterial function, lowers blood pressure, improves the overall function of the cardiovascular and circulatory systems, strengthens heart function, regulates diabetes, softens skin and reduces wrinkles, and improves mental clarity.

Coriander – one of the best spices for pitta because of its bitter energy, it reduces hyperacidity, counteracts inflammations such as bladder, urinary tract, and vaginal yeast infections, calms symptoms of irritable bowel syndrome (IBS), reduces constipation and diarrhea, lowers LDL cholesterol, skin conditions such as eczema, psoriasis, and rosacea, and helps to regulate kidney and liver disfunction.

Cumin – is high in antioxidants, is an anti-carcinogen, supports joint strength and density because it is high in phytoestrogens, and is good for regulating diabetes and epilepsy imbalances. Cumin is an important spice for vata types as it goes well with basmati rice and many vegetable dishes. Cumin, as a cooling carminative spice, aids in digestion and calms the nervous system without drying the body.

Curry Leaf – this leaf is most commonly used in dishes from India, Sri Lanka, Burma, Malaysia and Singapore. Curry leaves balance high blood sugar (diabetes), and is a remarkable antioxidant containing beta-carotene and vitamin C. It is an anti-carcinogen, lowers cholesterol, and restores memory loss. The curry tree leaf is not the same as curry powder, and various recipes include the leaves. Curry powder is a popular blend that usually contains many different spices such as ground chili peppers, turmeric, cumin, cardamon, curry leaf, mustard, cinnamon, nutmeg, and cloves.

Fennel – is grounding and good for soothing the stomach since it is in the licorice family. Fennel aids in relieving menstrual discomfort as it is a good anti-inflammatory. It is a remedy for colic (excessive infant crying), and can be beneficial for persons suffering from arthritis, cancer, heart disease, and even glaucoma.

Fenugreek – promotes digestion, serves as a nerve tonic, increases hair growth, and supports symptoms related to influenza, allergies, and even toothaches.

Ginger – this super root is a super medicine that is commonly used to reduce high fevers and improve digestion, to calm nausea, and relive arthritis and asthma. It also reduces LDL- cholesterol. Ginger supports all the tissues and is great for addressing abdominal pain, discomfort, and headaches. Ginger is good for the respiratory system as it reduces coughing.

Licorice – the combination of sweet and bitter tastes of licorice makes it very soothing for digestive issues like hyperacidity and general abdominal pain. It is good for many common cold issues, coughs, respiration, and bronchitis because it is an expectorant. Licorice mainly benefits vata as a mild laxative, and pitta for its soothing qualities.

Lemongrass – is known as the calming spice that is good for vata, anxiety, and insomnia. Lemongrass improves circulation, reduces LDL cholesterol, and helps to prevent cancer, oral candida, and yeast infections. It is often called citronella, and it is the main ingredient of a well-known tea in Brazil called *abafado*.

Mint – is one of the few spices that are cooling and is good for reducing anxiety, indigestion, irritable bowel syndrome, allergies, cough, chronic obstructive pulmonary disease (COPD), and polycystic ovarian syndrome (PCOS).

Mustard – these tiny little seeds spike up the fire of digestion, dry up excess water in the body which makes mustard seed good for kapha types. Effective in treating chronic obstructive pulmonary disease (COPD), high cholesterol, heart disease, insulin resistance (pre-diabetes), and diabetes. Mustard seeds are derived from the plant (Brassica alba cruciferae), which is similar to broccoli, kale, and Brussels sprouts in its cancer-fighting properties.

Nutmeg – contains myristicin, a volatile oil found in celery, parsley, cumin, and many other spices. It is good for vata related conditions like anxiety, and has been used to treat epilepsy, cancer, depression, LDL cholesterol, and even reduces wrinkles.

Oregano – is a heating Italian spice most well-known for fighting intestinal infections, staph, and vaginal yeast infections. It is effective in treating parasites, cancer, heart disease, high blood pressure, and liver diseases like hepatitis.

Parsley – As one of the few commonly used spices that have medicinal properties, parsley is medicine for the heart, diabetes, ulcers, reduces constipation, and is good for those with bad breath. Those with high pitta should avoid it. Parsley promotes good menstruation and is good for treating kidney or gall stones. Overall, it is very nutritious, as it is high in vitamins and minerals like iron. Parsley aids in building the body's tissues, muscles, blood, and plasma, and supports the female reproductive system.

Rosemary – works to prevent liver disease and blood clots, reduces anxiety and stress, and effectively treats arthritis and memory loss. It is heating and recommended for pitta types in moderation. Rosemary is considered a stimulant and, as a carminative, it increases absorption of nutrients and minerals, reducing gas and distention.

Saffron – is one of the best spices for the blood, and is good for pitta types, but effective for all doshas. Saffron is a super medicine for cancer, erectile dysfunction, infertility, hypertension, memory loss, and Parkinson's disease. It is an effective medicine for reducing menstrual cramps and PMS and, when added to a warm cup of milk at night, can treat insomnia.

Sesame Seed – produces a highly regarded oil (til) and is used in ayurvedic medicine as the base for most of the body oils. Sesame seeds are good for treating Alzheimer's disease, orthopedic conditions, cancer, LDL cholesterol, hypertension and heart disease, and works to calm the nervous system.

Star Anise – is used to treat cancer, cold sores, hepatitis B, influenza, and tooth and enamel decay. It fights off foot fungus and bacteria overgrowth, is rich in antioxidants, and can help to regulate blood sugar. Star anise can be used effectively for all types of infections such as ear or urinary tract infections. Studies have shown that it can reduce plaque build-up in the arteries and has anti-inflammatory properties.

Thyme – this spice is most commonly used in Italian cooking and is an incredible antimicrobial. It can be considered good for overall antiaging, and to treat influenza, cold sores, coughs, colitis, and ulcers.

Turmeric – like ginger, turmeric is a superfood that combats intense diseases like cancer. It enhances digestive strength, and improves blood health; in fact, it is considered a blood cleanser. Turmeric is great for all types of skin conditions like psoriasis, eczema, and gum issues. It reduces hypertension and helps to regulate blood pressure. It is used to treat cystic fibrosis and diseases related to the gallbladder and kidneys, such as gout. Which is influenced by poor kidney function. Turmeric, like most spices, is very much associated with Indian cuisine, although turmeric has found its way around the world through the famous golden milk recipe in which turmeric, in powder form, is combined with cinnamon and black pepper and added to a glass of frothy warm milk.

Spices are remarkable supplements to a diet of natural foods; however, spices cannot change the energy of foods that have been damaged by freezers, pesticides, boxes, and cans. The entire process for healing the body must be integral and requires awareness of what foods we are choosing to purchase. Cooking with spices is one of the great preventative measures endorsed in ayurvedic medicine although spices need to be adapted to the constitution (Prakriti) and the environment one is living in. Simply sprinkling spices on everything we eat shows a lack of awareness and may work to a certain degree. Spices should be applied specifically with one's own body in mind.

There are many ways to integrate spices into one's daily diet to support immunity and digestion. The famous chai (tea) is a perfect example, used to kindle the digestive fire and keep the gut clean and clear of polyps and undigested food waste (ama). When the metabolic function is hampered with poor diet and lifestyle habits, then residual waste pieces fester and become toxic waste in the gastrointestinal tract. What begins then is disorder (dosha), and various symptoms come with it.

The Interesting Story of Chai

When most people hear the word 'spices' they usually think of the flavors and foods of Asian culture and most particularly India. The original name for India is Mahabharata, meaning Great India, and reflected in its name was its vast and diverse geography encompassing an area that was much larger than the India of today. Of the close to six thousand herbs and spices that are known in medicinal pharmacology, at least 4,500 can be found on the Indian continent. This mainly has to do with the Himalayas as the largest mountain region in the world, and the fertile land along the river systems on the lower plains in the northern part of the country. In fact, during the Vedic era (at least 1000 B.C.) the region was referred to as the land of the seven rivers.

Chai is a blend of spices, and the term chai simply means tea. It is known to the world as a blend (or masala) of spices to drink in the morning or during an afternoon break. The practice of drinking spices in milk or combined with water is common in India. Chai includes spices such as ginger, cardamom, peppercorns, cinnamon, and various others depending on the region. Three different regions in India offer distinct variations of chai: Gujarat, Maharashtra, and Bengal. These variations developed over time according to the region's history. Additionally, many of the invaders of India influenced it in some way or another. It seems probable that it was the Portuguese who are responsible for spreading knowledge of chai outside of the Indian continent into Europe and then eventually to the Americas. It was the British who added black tea to chai and encouraged companies and laborers to enjoy afternoon tea (high tea) which was a longtime ritual in England before the colonizing of India. However, this was more than continuing a ritual, it was a ploy to encourage tea drinking in order to increase sales of tea in both domestic daily use and in the business of exporting tea to Europe.

Chai was Hijacked by the British

Chai as a spiced drink is best to have in early in the morning as these spices have a particular benefit to the digestive system, and they are effective when managing kapha dosha (phlegm). They also offset the increase of body fat by creating a strong metabolism. Balanced digestion is one of the cornerstones of ayurvedic medicine because digestion is the mother of all systems. The health of the digestive system determines the body's ability or lack of ability to sustain health and wellness. Each ingredient in chai contains a multitude of benefits for digestion, complexion, improved immunity, and circulation; it is essentially a cup of tasty medicine. I like to add a special mineral pitch to my chai called shilajit. Shilajit is a superfood of the ancient yogis and connected to Mahadeva (Shiva) himself. Adding a small pinch of this powdered black oozing asphalt, loaded with minerals, gives a great boost to your immune system. Shilajit gives chai a unique smoky, earthy flavor. It is magnificent for reducing toxins and cleansing the colon.

When the British added black tea to chai it changed it substantially for the worse, as black tea leaves contain a high amount of caffeine. When consumed daily, as is commonly the case, it can tax the adrenal glands and lead to chronic fatigue syndrome. Caffeine is not recommended in the least for Vata (air) types or anyone struggling from poor sleep, nervousness, or poor concentration. Chai is best without the black tea, the way it was originally intended to be according to ayurveda's practical wisdom.

Originally, chai was prepared with cow's milk, but over the last century, it has become a common practice to combine it with water and milk in a 50/50 ratio. Today, fewer and fewer people in Western culture are drinking cow's milk as a result of the increased consciousness of the inhumane treatment of cows, and the health risks associated with bovine growth hormone (BGH), which is often injected into factory farmed cows to increase productivity. Not only is such treatment of cows, or any animal for that matter, unethical, the impact of these hormones on the human body is linked to many chronic health issues, including cancer and early onset menses in young (pre-teen-age) girls. The use of this hormone is not permitted in the European Union, Canada, and many other countries.

In my ayurvedic counseling practice, I spend much time encouraging my clients to reduce the amount of dairy and caffeine they consume, with varying emphasis, depending on their constitution. The other issue with drinking chai is with regards to how it is sweetened. Many franchises aim to sell more drinks, so they sweeten chai with high amounts of sugar. High amounts of sugar in the modern diet have been linked to diabetes, obesity, inflammatory conditions, and psychological addiction to food and beverages. The main issues with the chai sold in commercial places is the poor quality of spices, the processing of the spice blend, and the type of milk and sugar being used.

Commercially processed white sugar is made by first extracting sugar juice from sugar beet or the sugar cane plant, however, problems begin when adding chemicals and preservatives while processing after this initial extraction. There are many alternatives to this processed sugar. Traditionally, in ayurveda, honey is used as a conduit for taking herbal medicines as it is a super and medicinal food. Honey is considered highly purifying for the mind, it improves vision, and increases the synergistic quality of herbs and spices when taken together. Jaggery is a form of sugar mostly produced in Maharashtra, India, and its use dates back thousands of years as mentioned in ayurvedic texts. Chai is much more effective and soothing when it is sweetened with honey or jaggery and does not take away from the savory tastes of the spices. Powerful energizing jams, like the classic chyvanaprash are also sometimes sweetened with jaggery. Coconut sugar is another type of sugar that is soft and soothing in taste and has a lower glycemic index, which means it is easier to metabolize and reduces the risk of diabetes.

Ideally, the best form of chai is derived from organic fresh spices that are brewed with some type of organic nut milk of your choice, however it is not comparable to the restorative properties of healthy cow's milk. Such a blend brings great enhancement to the digestive, circulatory, and immune systems. It works best when integrated into a lifestyle regimen and enjoyed in the morning when kapha dosha is predominant between 6-10 am. Drinking chai will promote bowel regularity and keep you connected to using spices in your diet for health and wellness and not just using spices for special occasions. Using spices daily is essential to good health. Mother Nature has given the world such remarkable food medicines in the form of spices, and the world owes much to the wisdom of ayurveda that has made its way around the world in the form of a sweet little cup of tea. Jai Chai! (Victory to spiced tea!).

Chapter SIX

Nature is the New Religion

In nature's economy the currency is not money, it is life.

Vandana Shiva

Redesigning Religion

Many people are questioning what the term "spiritual" means because its meaning has digressed away from its original meaning in the esoteric traditions. For many in the modern era who have grown apathetic and turn away from the dogma of major religions, living a natural lifestyle has become the new spiritual. In many ways, natural lifestyle is replacing traditional religious practices. One aspect of this lifestyle is meditation. Meditation has many forms and the power it has for connecting us to our true nature is being recognized by all types of people.

The practice of meditation has been associated with the Eastern mystical traditions for countless millenniums. Meditation practice is probably the most iconic of the ancient practices of the mystics. Let's be clear, meditation is not a religion, and in fact, rather than bind us to dogmas, meditation leads to freedom from desires, pain, and suffering. When these mental conditions are overcome, bliss is revealed as the source of our existence. A great sage[80] once

---

80   Sri Bhagavan Ramana Maharshi.

said, "When there are thoughts, it is distraction: when there are no thoughts, it is meditation." There is light in the senses, there is light behind the mind and intellect, there is light operating the cosmic mind (Hiranyagarbha), and then finally, there is the light of Brahman (God), pure consciousness. Meditation illumines these functions of our life and purifies each of these so that our individual consciousness comes to unite with the supreme source of light that is behind all existence. This is what the myriad techniques of yoga aim to do. Whether it be the ego, mind or the senses all are sustained by the light of pure consciousness.

Religion that is not defined by a person's daily conduct is based on blind faith and does not foster the essence of what it means to be spiritual. In Vedanta, the process of self-inquiry (vichara) into the nature of one's existence, is one of the primary practices for evolution. Religion has nothing to do with spirituality if it creates division amongst humankind and perpetuates violence. When a person is described as "religious" it usually means that they follow certain practices and beliefs according to a particular system that aims at eradicating pain and suffering while promoting bliss. Yet many of these religious practices appear conflict with the way that many now consider a spiritual lifestyle. If the purpose of religion is to promote bliss and remove pain from human life, would it not endorse a universal truth? In doing so, religion would embrace the diversity as a part of the magic, that people evolve according to their own self-awareness. This would promote the appreciation of life and the consciousness that upholds this world.

Cultivating Consciousness through Culture

Integrating ayurveda's principles into one's lifestyle is more about cultivating a consciousness culture rather than just following a set of principles. Ayurveda is a profound system that was practiced millenniums ago and yet it is highly relevant today, mainly with regards to its ideals of harmonizing one's relationship with nature. Many recognize that humanity has lost its regard for nature, so integrating ayurveda into our lives is a way to find it again. The concept of living in harmony with nature has two profound implications. One is its practical side whereby we apply the principles for greater balance of the mind-body relationship, which, without doubt, is needed today on a very fundamental level. The second implication of living in harmony with nature is in gaining at least some understanding of "the world" as merely a projection of the mind; this is from the perspective of Vedanta.

Ayurvedic routines without Vedantic philosophy can perpetuate attachment to the body and increase a person's sensitivity to the world. Without the underlying foundation of Vedanta, ayurveda becomes similar to a project like the "save the world" or "save the oceans" movements. One becomes focused on saving the body as if that is what dictates one's quality of life. Ayurveda is meant to be part of the evolutionary pathway and is a spiritual endeavor. When one does not care for the body, spiritual evolution does not take place. God has a physical body and it's called earth. Even though God cannot be destroyed, when humans damage the relationship they have with nature, in the many ways we have witnessed over the last several centuries, we endanger humanity. This is because our pathway to spiritual freedom is eroding.

The practice of selfcare (svasttavritta) and harmonizing one's relationship with nature promote balance and longevity so that ego's attention to the body or one's identification with the body is gradually minimized. The selfcare practices of ayurveda are well balanced with the sacred rituals of yoga and the mental attitude taught in Vedanta. Cultivating consciousness through culture depends on a balanced relationship between outer and inner awareness. Consciousness expands as one builds the capacity to listen and learn from the world. The entire Vedic traditions of the golden ages (satya yuga) were based on these ideals of listening and learning. This cultural focus on balancing inner and outer awareness spawned a devotion for God that remains today; and it was accelerated in 19th and 20th centuries by an entourage of sages like the Bhakti Bengalis[81] that applied these ideals to overcome the British empire.

The relationship that one has with "the world" should be examined with the microscope of nightly introspection to eradicate the mental conditions that bind us to anything that the mind, intellect, ego, and senses fall prey to. The practice of introspecting "nightly" does not only mean to find a quiet and calm place to sit and reflect on one's day, although this is a good practice. The mystical and more profound meaning of nightly introspection[82] as mentioned in the Bhagavad Gita is based on interiorizing the mind through a methodical and scientific process. The aspirant begins to remove the shadows (hence

---

81   *Sun, Moon and Earth, The Sacred Relationship of Yoga and Ayurveda*, Chapter Six, "The Rise of Bengali Yoga." by Mas Vidal (Lotus Press, 2017).

82   **Verse 1, Chapter 1,** "*On the holy plain of Kurukshetra (Dharmakshetra) when my offspring and the sons of Pandu had gathered together, eager for battle, what did they, O Sanjaya?*" From *God Talks with Arjuna: The Bhagavad Gita*, by Paramahansa Yogananda (Self-Realization Fellowship, Los Angeles).

use of the term nightly) that cloud over the mind. These shadows are simply referring to conditioned consciousness, and we strive to prevent such conditioning from manifesting where they create a robotic personality.

The average person lives in the world based on their subconscious or unconscious mind. This directly influences their capacity to live in a conscious manner. The only way to change the consciousness of a culture is to change the subconscious mind. Everyone has to be trained in exercising the conscious mind. This is what yogic techniques are for: to release the power of super consciousness and become a jivanmukta, a liberated soul, while still living in the physical body. This is precisely why asana, the third limb of Patanjali's eight-limbed system is so foundational to higher consciousness; the aspirant must exercise discipline over the body, the spine, and create physical stillness so that one can enter and transcend the subtler domains of subconscious mind. This is the magic of Integral (Sampurna) Yoga or Kriya (Raja) Yoga as taught by the great lineages of India, like those of Swami Sivananda, Paramahansa Yogananda and many others. Yoga provides the teaching and the techniques for transcending the major states of consciousness.[83]

The Role of Sleep in Advancing Culture

How we sleep plays a major a role in advancing our own consciousness and the consciousness of our culture. Sadly, our modern culture requires drugs, alcohol, smoking cannabis, television and even sexuality to fall asleep, some of which are forms of toxicity for the subconscious mind and further weakens the conscious mind. Mental activity during sleep in the form of dreams is not desirable from the ayurvedic perspective because this mental activity (frequency of brainwaves) expends energy that depletes immunity (adrenal function). This mental activity is directly borrowed from our immune system's source of energy called ojas. Ojas is not only immune strength on the physical

---

83   Four basic states of consciousness are unconscious, subconscious, conscious and super-conscious. The Sanskrit wisdom literature defines the mind as Antahkarana Chatushtaya (four aspects): Chitta (unconscious and subconscious), Buddhi (enquiry-sakshi, discernment-viveka), Ahamkara (ego playing the role of egoism) and Manas (sense mind used for experiencing the practical reality – Karmendriyas and Jnanendriyas). The Unconscious mind stores the Samskaras (seed tendencies, reflected in the robotic nature of most people). The Subconscious mind contains the Vasanas that are the source of one's sentiments and feelings referred to in Sanskrit as Shubha . The Mind or Chitta is a term that is considered as all inclusive. Based on the Jyotirmayananda (Yoga Research Foundation, Miami, FL).

level, but also the higher momentum of aspiring to Realize one's true nature. Every human being is imbued with the desire to know God; however, this desire is so buried by negative impressions that the subconscious mind disables one's capacity to be conscious (aware). The negative impressions cause us to become like robots, programmed by the past and the wrong environments.

When the subconscious mind displays mind movies, such activity as seen through dreams, often a person arises with a feeling of lethargy or feels disorientated upon rising. In order to live an evolutionary life, the subconscious mind needs to be nourished with positive dialogue that does not engage in gossip and needs to be interacting with groups and places impressed with high vibrations. If a person cannot easily access such positive places, then nature is the place to go, where Mother Nature will help purify the mind, bringing out inner calmness and peace. Again, using the mind to discipline the body is important, but using the mind to discipline itself is more important and this is what the spiritual path is about.

In Vedic thought, the moon is symbolic of the mind and all its fluctuating aspects. As the moon appears in the sky, it reflects a shadowy and ever-changing nature. Awakening the sun as proposed through yoga (Hatha and Tantra branches) involves awakening subtle yet powerful energies dormant in the spinal chakras. These energies carry the positive light of awareness. Awakening the sun as the fire of devotion is most important because this leads to purification of the heart.

In many aspirants, it was expansion of the heart that helped them transform beyond the negative attributes of the lower chakras. When these lower centers (chakras) are illumined with the light of awareness, understanding, or devotion as heightened feeling in the heart, the moon is allowed to shine. The shadows that color the mind are removed. The shadows of the mind are ego and intellect, so clearing the mind in the evening before sleep is a powerful ritual for increasing one's consciousness. Clearing the mind helps one detach from names and forms and the constant barrage of, "I want this…" and "I need that…", etc.

The sadhana (discipline) of using deep sleep as a period for the exploration of one's pure (inner) consciousness and learning[84] was explored by yogis as

---

84 Sleep learning is a term mentioned by Paramahansa Yogananda in 1940 at a talk given at

an effective way to grow closer to the unified field, the realm of pure consciousness. What matters most is what you do during the moments before entering the subconscious domain (pre-sleep) and the moments before you exit (post-sleep). In other words, this means it is important to be aware of what is being practiced repeatedly during these important junction points. These two periods are timely tools for removing the blemishes of the unconscious and subconscious mind to awaken the cosmic mind or super consciousness. *The consciousness of a culture is reflected in its nightly activities as this time is valuable for unraveling the impressions of the daily battlefield.* So, as I mentioned earlier, it is good to bathe the body before bedtime, but it is even better to do a little more to cleanse the mind of the mental pollutants of modern lifestyle and the past impressions that are carried from one life after the other.

Techniques and Practices for Training the Conscious Mind

A. Keep High Society – mingle with individuals who live an evolutionary life, eat healthy, and exercise self-discipline (tapasya). Every human being is a product of their environment because collective consciousness is more powerful than one individual; therefore, choose your groups and societies carefully.

B. Positive Speech – speaking positively and using affirmations helps to keep the mind fresh and uplifted and keeps the lifeforce (prana) in the higher centers.

C. Grooming the Subconscious Mind – affirming positive thoughts before sleep and commanding the mind to awaken at a certain time helps to condition the mind. Scheduling certain tasks upon rising, like making the first thought of each day be God, Guru, a favorite saint, or a thought of sincere gratitude.

D. Avoid Making Excuses – take responsibility for every experience, listen to what the world is telling you, learn from it, give love, and let it go!

Self-Realization Fellowship, Golden Lotus Temple, Encinitas, Ca. Adaption of an article titled, "Training the Conscious and Subconscious Minds for Success" was published by Self-Realization Magazine, Spring 2015.

E. Positive Affirmations – the original yogic form of this is called japa or *ishta* mantra.[85] Japa is the practice of reciting a specific mantra given to you by your guru that aligns with your unique disposition. It is most important that one feels an affinity for divinity through the mantra. Positive affirmations in your native language are also effective in this regard. Find a short verse or poem that really resonates with you and repeat it daily, or when you notice a negative thought enter your mind, replace it with your affirmation. Classical Raja Yoga refers to this as *praktipaksha bhavana* and has three forms suppression (recognizing the negative thought and moving it aside), substitution (replacing it with the mantra, affirmation, or positive thought) and sublimation (diverting the energy to a higher place). **Negative thoughts are a form of energy that can trigger emotions; however, through praktipaksha bhavana such negative forms of energy can be converted into powerful forces to overcome adversity and promote self-transformation.**

F. Contemplate and Think Deeply - exercise will power toward becoming still in the seat (asana) of meditation. Along with silence and solitude, will power will support deep contemplation. Develop the capacity to think creatively and discover new ways of doing things. Transform your vocation (artha) into a higher service (dharma) for humanity. Ask yourself if the work or task you are performing aligns with the law of reciprocity: if your work benefits you, it should equally benefits others.

Techniques and Practices for Training the Subconscious Mind

A. Create a Sacred Space – your bedroom should be appealing, feeling relaxed and calm. Darken the room, turning off unnatural lighting, and light an aromatic candle by your bedside moments before sleeping. Freshen up and splash water on your face, fluff the bed, massage an ayurvedic body oil on the head, ears, and feet and play some relaxing music or chants as you prepare for bed.

---

85   Japa mantra has two basic forms, firstly is the basic recitation of the mantra with consideration of its meaning and using proper pronunciation to the best of your ability. Secondly, and more importantly, the advancement in mantra practice is reflected in one's mental attitude (Bhavana). As the aspirant (sadhaka) continues their mantra practice with devotion, even with defects in pronunciation, one eventually experiences liberation.

B.   Make a Commitment – to yourself that you will practice these techniques every day. Write down your commitment, remind yourself with notes on your desk, nightstand, and bathroom, and plan your evening accordingly so that you have the time to do this. Making a commitment means you are setting aside energy to practice this just before falling asleep, and are not just going to plunge into the cavern of sleep. It's important to make this mental note for yourself.

C.   Practice Concentration – while practicing your positive affirmations, avoid any external music, sounds (if possible) or anyone speaking to you. The practice should be fluid and uninterrupted in order to properly penetrate the subconscious mind.

D.   During the Pre-Sleep Moments – begin to repeat the positive affirmations for whatever it is you are trying to accomplish. Begin this process in a soft whisper and then transition into a mental whisper.

E.   Negation of Mental Disturbances - do not allow negative thoughts to enter while you are affirming or reciting your mantra. If a negative or contradictory thought appears, continue recitation until the negative thought is obliterated. Continue this practice even when you notice yourself falling asleep. This practice is regrooving the brain (activating neuroplasticity) and purifying the subconscious mind.

F.   Practice Consistency - continue this practice for weeks, months, or even years until success appears in the conscious mind and the desired result manifests in your life. That is success.

The Real Meaning of Finding the Guru

The word "guru" is probably the most recognized Sanskrit term of the yoga tradition, second probably to the word "mantra", both of which have been bastardized by the media. In India, many sincere teachers are connected to the country's vast spiritual heritage through lineage (parampara) in an unbroken transfer of knowledge extracted from states of supreme consciousness. These individuals become part of a monastic order (sampradaya) and take vows as a renunciate (sanyasi). They renounce materialism and dedicate their life in service of the teachings of their lineage.

All types of people are recognized as gurus; however, while some are focused on promoting spiritual evolution, others are appreciated on a more academic level. Some gurus are highly regarded for their lofty levels of consciousness and their knowledge with respect to the practical reality. One such person was Sri Aurobindo Ghosh, a powerhouse of consciousness credited for initiating the modern renaissance of Vedic culture while also leading an inspiring social movement. This movement encouraged the youth of India to reclaim the soft powers of yoga, martial arts, and other great Vedic arts to overcome colonialism. Another such a person was Rabindranath Tagore[86] who was an author, poet, and educator.

Traditionally, a guru can either be married and regarded as part of the Brahminical caste, or a guru can be regarded as a sanyasi who renounces any material belongings, practices chastity, and lives a more secluded life in a monastery or ashram. Those who follow the monastic path can eventually become a Swami, one who has been initiated into the Swami Order of India that is linked to the Shankaracharya, the spiritual figure head. Dashanami Sannyāsins, ten-subdivisions, are associated mainly with the four maṭhas, sacred temples, established in four corners of India by Adi Shankara who reorganized an old heritage going back many millenniums. There are several stages of the monastic life before one finally becomes a sanyasi, one that has renounced attachment to the material world. This type of renunciation is also a metaphor that any aspirant can embrace by renouncing the idea that anything from the relative world will bring inner contentment or happiness. Generally speaking, the teacher-guru student relationship is the most sacred of the Vedic-Indic culture. Their relationship sustains the extensive and sacred Sanskrit literature of Vedanta and the other five main philosophical expressions, (shad darsanas) as well as all the many subbranches (Upa-Vedas) of the Vedas, keeping them intact, for thousands of years, until today.

As a result of the law of karma and rebirth, one's biological mother is considered the first guru and reflects the deepest human bond which exists between mother and child. For many obvious and obscure reasons, it is a relationship

---

86   This prominent and pivotal figure left an indelible mark on modern history of India. His educational principles are still being practiced today and his poems became the national anthems for both India and Bangladesh. He was the Noble Peace prize winner for literature in 1913. The father of yoga in the west, Paramahansa Yogananda dedicated a chapter in his famous *Autobiography of a Yogi* to Tagore, entitled, "Rabindranath Tagore and I Compare Schools."

that influences most people for their entire lives. Just as the moon is closest of all the major planets to the earth, so it is between the human mother and her child. However, the mother-child relationship is not always rosy and can sometimes reflect a difficult relationship between two souls in previous lives. For example, a husband who treats his wife poorly in one life, through either personal neglect or disloyalty to his so-called beloved, may in the next life be born as the son of a mother who abandons him. Through this and various circumstances, he creates a distant relationship with the mother. The way a relationship begins is not as important as what the relationship becomes; of highest karmic importance is where they end.

The sun, as the largest planet, is the most distant from earth, although all life depends on it. In the same way, the inherent nature of every human being propels a search for truth and happiness that may be distant, far from one's current location on the evolutionary pathway. Happiness and fulfillment in life depends on the sun (soul connection) as the indwelling soul; this inner sun is often referred to as the Self or *sva*. The search for a guru has more to do with an inner process of awakening to higher consciousness by connecting to the soul, rather than with actually finding a person who will teach us everything we need to know about getting enlightened.

Certainly, a guru can transmit great wisdom to their student-devotees as well as provide specialized methods from the vast yoga tradition that one can resonate deeply with. However, and more importantly, the guru, whomever this person may be, is facilitating a process that has already been put into motion by the aspirant's own search for truth. A well-known saying resonates with this point, "When the student is ready, the teacher appears."

It is the guru–shishya (disciple) tradition, or parampara, that has preserved the profound body of yogic knowledge the world has come to know. In a complex world with many different priorities, it's important to understand that becoming a sanyasi (monastic) and striving towards attaining samadhi (enlightenment) are two very separate things. Taking vows of renunciation does not guarantee one enlightenment, regardless of the courage required to choose such a life, the sanyasi still must work for liberation just as does the householder (grihastha), although the vows and the lifestyle between a householder and a monk will differ substantially. Anyone can live an evolutionary life if it includes a balanced blend of adhering to practical selfcare practices, family and social responsibilities, work, and career and equally integrates spiritual disciplines. The spiritual path is equated with one's inner relationship with God and requires commitment, concentration, and consistency. In other words, one can follow the path as taught by a guru and their lineage while living in the ashram or living in the world. Regardless of the path one chooses, the world is the living guru, and this will provide countless opportunities listen to and learn. This is why the guru is highly celebrated in India. Honoring and respecting teachers and elders is a highly regarded custom in Asian cultures because knowledge has always been embraced with reverence as an essential part of moving towards enlightenment.

India each year honors the Guru with one of its many important festivals on the full moon day in the month of Ashadha, correlated to the early monsoon period and around the summer solstice. Originally, the Guru Purnima day was marked to honor Veda Vyasa, author of the Mahabharata, son of Sage Parashara, however, the event now honors all gurus. Sage Parashara was raised by his grandfather Vasishtha (Guru of Rama of Ayodhya). Sage Parashara authored one of the most comprehensive texts on Jyotish (Vedic Astrology) called Brihat Parasara Hora Shastra. One of the main guru mantras, *Sri Gurave Namaha*, is a homage to the guru. The term *Sri* is a prefix used to purify the name of any person and is connected to the Goddess Lakshmi. *Gu* refers to darkness or the cave of the heart, *ru* means to remove with light, *Na* is negation, and *Ma*, is me or mine. This mantra offers reverence to the guru and explains that negativity is overcome with the light of pure consciousness.

The opening of the heart center (chakra) signifies the initial glimmer of light that invokes the dormant (unconscious) person as they begin the gradual movement towards conscious living. This energetic movement awakens one's power of inquiry (vichar) into the nature of one's existence. It is considered a blessing when anyone experiences this as it represents a break from the regressive patterns of conditioned consciousness towards a new evolutionary life. These inner experiences are sacred and should be kept private or shared only directly with the guru or spiritual counselor otherwise they lose their upward momentum. Inner experiences can take many years and even lifetimes before they manifest and for this reason one must continue to strive consistently in their meditations and spiritual practices, otherwise the momentum is lost.

I often refer to these experiences as "spiritual candies," gifts presented to us by Goddess Lakshmi to encourage us to keep ascending our consciousness through increasing devotion and knowledge for the Divine in all living things.

One never knows when these spiritual primers will occur and it does not guarantee the discovery of a Sat-Guru immediately, the presence of the supreme Guru who takes responsibility for the soul. The guru initiation may not take place until the aspirant has attained some harmony with nature, with their own body, and with other lifestyle principles as taught in ayurveda. The guru comes when the aspirant is ready to become a disciple, one who is devoted to their spiritual evolution, when the end of the path to liberation is near. The guru alone is not enough; the guru relies on the disciple to eventually develop the understanding that the entire world is part of their evolutionary process, that it is a projection of one's own mind and reflects one's current state of consciousness.

One's silent inner prayers transform from pleas into a powerful grace that beckons. These inner prayers become a kind of surrender and a call for inner change. That supreme guru is within, guiding the devotee's consciousness through intuitive glimpses of truth as the witness (sakshi), enlivening the inner guru into all the moments of life. It is also true that such awareness can be aided by cultivating a relationship with an outer guru (in physical form or not) and nurtured through attunement to the guru in the present moment. As Vedanta proclaims, nothing else exists but the present moment and the more conscious one can become, the greater the supreme Reality alone will exist as pure consciousness. The entire world process is thus dismantled to reveal the One supreme Reality behind all matter and all living things. Violence to any aspect of the world does not hurt the world as much as it hurts you. "One who possesses this Art of Living is a Rishi, all the world harmonizes with them, they are met with no obstacles, because they keep themselves in accord with the One."[87]

---

87   Swami Rama Tirtha, *In the Woods of God Realization, Notebook VII* (Swami Rama Tirtha Pratisthan, Lucknow, India).

Chapter SEVEN

Transforming Your Life with Integral Yoga

*The real spiritual progress of the aspirant is measured by the
extent to which he achieves inner tranquility.*

Sri Swami Sivananda

Deconstructing Integral Yoga

Integral Yoga (Sampurna) provides keys to evolutionary living derived from the vast and ancient tradition of the Vedas. Across the globe, yoga has gained increased awareness in the last century, and its many forms leave people asking the same questions, What type of yoga should I begin with? or What type of yoga should I personally practice? Often, I ponder how to answer such questions in the simplest but yet profound way. As many dedicated practitioners of yoga understand, it's important that, as this ancient tradition continues to grow into the hearts of many, yoga be applied as an integral system that can be woven into our daily lives as an evolutionary lifestyle.

Most people today learn about yoga by going to a public postural (hatha) class, perhaps at a local fitness or yoga center. However, bringing a deeper understanding of integral yoga into our lives is another measure of devotion to practice that we discover is much more difficult. Many in the postural yoga scene are often reminded of the importance of the eight limbs of ashtanga, also called Raja Yoga. One such practice is that of embracing nonviolence (ahimsa). Another is truthfulness (satya). Postural yoga classes do not really teach how to integrate such yogic principles into one's lifestyle or apply them to circumstances that confront many of us in daily life.

The aim of hatha yoga is to focus on physical purification as a means of preparation for meditation. However, if yoga is not promoting spiritual evolution through greater endurance and fortitude within the daily trials of our life, then it's not working the way that it should. If yoga is not providing solutions for your common day-to-day problems, then what is it doing? If one is not learning to see the good in the world and feel a growing love for all living things, seeing the light in all souls, then as Sivaya Subramuniyaswami says, "Then something is wrong with you; do something about it."

From the perspective of the integral yoga teachings, every human being has four distinct aspects to their personality. Each person will demonstrate greater strength or weakness within these aspects depending on factors like karma, culture, constitution, and one's level of evolution. The four qualities, or latent powers are: 1) practical, Karma Yoga; 2) intellectual, Jnana Yoga; 3) emotional, Bhakti Yoga; and 4) spiritual, Raja Yoga. As the aspirant maintains continuity of effort (abhyasa) in their yoga practice (sadhana), they will be more successful in developing these powers which are, in essence, the supreme energies of the soul.

Yoga not only means union but implies reunion, a reawakening of powers that define our true nature and lie in the soul of every human being. It is always a sad story to hear when anyone misuses these powers for greed or material gain, as is the common case in the world today. People are literally killing themselves, abusing their health, and taking much for granted, all for the sake of monetary gain or position. The powers of the soul can be developed through the integral yoga system as it aims to bring about the highest ideal for humanity: illumination.

- ### Karma Yoga

There is a practical side to our lives that we all enjoy. We work, create projects, take care of our homes, take up hobbies, find places to visit, and endeavor to entertain ourselves. This type of activity is predominantly what we see in the world: activity that is solely centered around a person's life, their responsibilities, and the needs of their immediate family and friends. However, such use of our energy in this manner becomes redundant and is simply only one superficial aspect of being active.

The practical nature of each person in yoga should be guided and evolve into serving humanity. This is referred to as Karma Yoga. Karma Yoga can be simply defined as selfless service. As a person becomes more selfless, they grow in their morality. The selfish force of greed must be overcome by spending more time thinking of ways in which one can help others. There are many examples of this, such as supporting a friend by listening to their challenges or doing some work for an organization that promotes the welfare of humanity, animals, or the environment. Whatever it is, let your actions be dedicated to the benefit of others. In this way, we transform our thinking from "me" to "we." We are all children of this universe sharing this beautiful planet together.

Each of the four aspects of integral yoga can be viewed as having two predominant layers. The primary form of each of the four branches reflects a more superficial aspect of the quality and the secondary form is more subtle and related to the finer, more hidden, virtues of each person. There is good in everyone. whether it is evident or not. All humans want to do good in the world, and some more than others. People are encouraged to do good mostly because it is what everyone else is doing, but it also feels good when one helps another; that is the power of reciprocity. This approach to helping others is still somewhat selfish; it is prompted by external influences, and it has much to do with the fact that most humans make choices driven by the ego, layered with expectations influenced by the emotions.

Regardless of the motive, every act of doing good brings a greater reward than the act itself. It opens something inside of us that we don't seem to understand; it is like a bounty of joy that never ends. This inner reward demonstrates the connection we share with all things. Spiritual laws teach us that everything we do influences the whole, unlike the scientific view that views life as separate from the cosmos. The uniqueness of the spiritual view of life is that it increases the power of relationships and acknowledges that all actions function in a nonlinear fashion; they circulate to teach us to perceive the meaning behind our experiences. So, as I mentioned early in the book, much truth lies in Sivananda's statement "Do good, Be good." Goodness is a natural quality of the soul and reflects the spiritual nature of our lives.

- ## Jnana Yoga

The intellectual side of our life is evident, in that we enjoy understanding the nature of things; and is particularly evident with recent developments in technology. This age of technological advancement[88] is part of an ascending age of consciousness that increases our rate of communication, however, it also increases the speed of the mind.

The internet has become a network for the distribution of information that continues to hypnotize people into spending countless hours per day on their computers, often very mindlessly. While the practical aspect of life can be correlated to our feet and hands, the intellectual side is opposite, in that it involves the brain and mind. The intellectual aspect of the person in yoga is referred to as *jnana*; however, this is not merely the lower side of intellect that is developed through memory, jnana refers to a higher capacity every person has to acquire knowledge through the mind's power of intuition. This is not merely a gathering of facts and figures like a historian, but should be understood as a refined form of intellect known as **buddhi**, the discerning power of the mind. Yogic wisdom contends that a lack of discernment leads to pain and suffering through repeated incarnations into the material world of time and space. This is also known as 'the feel it and believe it to be the real' world of the senses. Yoga aims to expand this part of our consciousness as awareness through knowledge. The ideal of Jnana Yoga is the cultivation of understanding that our happiness does not come from the world; instead, it is found within the Divine Self as one develops a growing understanding of the Real source of all pleasure: pure consciousness. Nothing can replace it.

- ## Bhakti Yoga

All human beings experience life through their senses, so naturally, all of humanity enjoys touch, affection, sexuality, time with their family, and the camaraderie of friends. There is an aspect of us that wants to be cared for and healed through touch. Equally so, this behavior can be seen in animals. Humans enjoy the sensual, as in sensory, quality of nature, trees, cooking food, and eating, and in many respects, these encounters are very intimate

---

88   Dwapara Yuga began in 1700 A.D. and continues for a total of 2400 years. The Kali-yuga of darkness, disease and territorial conquests prevailed for 1200 years before the dwapara cycle (of the ascending arc). More detailed explanation on the yugas cycles can be found in my book, *Sun, Moon and Earth: The Sacred Relationship of Yoga & Ayurveda*.

parts of our lives. The sensual aspects of our personality are connected to the sentient nature innate in all humans; however, Bhakti Yoga is a much deeper and more profound state of mind that is united with the heart.

Humans cultivate intimate relationships because they enjoy how it makes them feel on a sensory and emotional level. At times, relationships even invoke deep experiences that bring out aspects of oneself previously unknown, particularly within intimate relationships.

Our emotional or affectionate traits can be broadly referred to as ***bhakti***. This particular path teaches us how to convert the reactive nature of emotions into devotion for God through the repeated effort of disciplinary practices like meditation and a detached mental attitude (vairagya) from objects or sensory experiences. The primary form of our sentient life exists primarily on a sensual level, and often is blemished by selfish motives. The secondary level of this quality exists as devotion, and bhakti represents the transcendence of our feelings and emotions to a more refined level in the heart as love for the Divine. In other words, it awakens the power of giving love without having any expectations of ever receiving it back, in any form.

If you observe the lives of most people, they live trusting that things will work out; they have a somewhat blind faith approach to life. Humans take risks with their lives by constantly doing things that at times may not be good for their health, especially with their diets or abusing intoxicants, taking financial risks, or even enjoying adventurous thrills while placing their lives at risk. People living on the material plane of consciousness live under the assumption that whenever they perform a task, there is an expectation of some reward. The speed of society today is dangerous, because it is intensifying the focus on an instant gratification mentality. This is dangerous, because if a person is not "satisfied" by another person, place, or thing, they discard what they were attached to and seek to replace their attachment with another person, place, or thing in an instant. Such behavior perpetuates a vicious and destructive cycle that promotes involution. Like a dog who has been conditioned to receive a treat when he performs a good deed, thus salivating even before receiving the treat, humans perform actions with attachment to the fruits of their actions.

- **Raja Yoga**

The primary level of this human trait of devotion reflects a willingness to experience a sense of freedom, an unbound courageous feeling. It may move through us only for a fleeting moment because underneath it, there is the guise of security because we think, if this experience of freedom does not work out, it can be replaced. The use of this unbound sense of behavior in this outward direction is merely a superficial act of courage. However, the deeper side of this has much more profound implications that can lead an aspirant to the inner power of surrender. Surrender is the cornerstone of the highest yogic path known as *Raja*. The yogic act of surrender involves performing all actions with love and compassion, remaining detached from the outcome. Letting go of fear awakens the power of surrender because we become anchored in something that is neither tangible nor replaceable. We become anchored in something that is always there, the real Self, the very essence of our existence.

Once, a great yogi encouraged me to see the Divine hand behind the events in my life that I could not understand. In other words, he was encouraging me to perform all my activities and practices with a trusting faith; the Divine intelligence has me covered regardless of a positive or negative experience. Plans are never permanent, and as a result, life is what happens when we are looking the other way. In many ways, life is often what we never expected it to be, and leads us to understand there is a greater force influencing our life from beginning to end.

Yoga as a Psychological System

These four principles (practical, intellectual, emotional, and spiritual) are part of what makes up the entire human being and they align with the four main paths of yoga. Yoga, like many other great teachings, has come to be expressed in very literal interpretations without much understanding of the metaphor and allegory embedded within Vedic teachings. This has happened during the expansion of scientific viewpoints. Insight into any ancient spiritual tradition, and most particularly yoga, requires the intuition as developed through meditation, mantra and sadhana and natural living. Unless one has reached the heights of liberation, interpretation of a teaching will be limited to the same capacity one has for the transformation of the self. Therefore, lineage (parampara) is so important; knowledge that is transferred through liberated teachers carries shakti, the power of transformation.

It's important to understand that sadhana is not limited to the spiritual practices that one adheres to in a concentrated period of effort or in a structured group yoga class. I was once having lunch with my first astrology teacher Chakrapani, and he asked me, "So, how are you?" I answered, "Good, been doing much sadhana!" and he quickly interjected before going on further by asking, "What is sadhana?" I silently reflected for a moment and then replied, "Discipline!" He said, "Yes! Exactly." and so sadhana is the discipline of your life, a mental discipline over everything that you do! From the integral yoga perspective, yoga sadhana is everything that you do, it's how you live on earth.

The aim of yoga is in the reformation of the entire human mind-body complex so as to attain freedom from bondage to the physical body, the senses, the mind, emotions, and the entire world process. The simplest way to put this is, Your happiness is not dependent on certain external conditions. With consistent practicing of integral yoga, the mind begins to reflect a level of equanimity regardless of the outer circumstances. This is because yoga is about reuniting with the life-force that pervades all living things. However, the common negative stereotype is that yoga requires one to live carefree of responsibility and to selfishly immerse oneself in the world of practice. It is, instead, a practice of learning to live in the world while remaining beyond the illusory reality of the world. Through this union with the life-force, we can ascend beyond the world process to the supreme state of freedom as promised in the Vedas. Prana can either move us deeper into the world of entanglements or it can move us to ascend to the heights of liberation. Keep in mind that prana goes wherever the mind goes, and so the essence of integral yoga is in managing how we use the mind, how the mind is being integrated into the world.

Vedanta and Yoga

Vedanta is truth, the basis for all existence. The ideal of the Vedanta philosophy is that one all-pervading consciousness supports life. Vedanta is the basic philosophy behind the entirety of the Hindu religion. Vedantic teachings are derived from India's Vedic heritage where great texts like the Ramayana, Bhagavad Gita, and Yoga Vasishta tell stories through dialogue between the Guru and disciple. These dialogues present various ideals and aims for humanity so that they can apply the teachings and live an evolutionary lifestyle. The spiritual knowledge that is derived from the Upanishads is Vedanta. Probably the most famous Vedantic text is the Bhagavad Gita, and what Krishna propounds to Arjuna (his disciple) is essentially knowledge of the Upanishads.

The system of Yoga provides the methodology for experiencing the truth, or singular experience, of unified consciousness. Another way of understanding the relationship between the two is that Yoga teaches you how to behave and Vedanta teaches you how to think. In contrast to these wisdom traditions, any other school of thought that teaches you what to think is developing the conditioned mind and endorsing the fabrication of the ego. However, Yoga and Vedanta both have the same intention, but provide different methodologies for attaining this inner state of happiness. Yoga looks to ayurveda for its principles on lifestyle and self-care, and Vedanta teaches how to cultivate the proper attitude.

In Vedanta, the most important experience is that of the present moment. Vedanta does not focus on attaining something or arriving at any particular place. In other words, there is nothing to attain in terms of enlightenment, instead, what is important is that one moves from ignorance to awakening or expansion of the realization that you are that, the immortal Self. It is the foremost affirmation that You are spirit or *Tat Tvam Asi.*[89] In Shakespearean English: *Thou Art That*. Then by the grace of your guru-guided consciousness, one shifts into the supreme Realization, "I am Brahman", *Aham Brahmāsmi,* I am one. Whether it be Vedanta or Yoga, the result is the same. Vedanta flows towards liberation (moksha) via the process of inward inquiry (vichar) and integral yoga unfolds the mind through its four forms as Karma, Bhakti, Jnana and Raja.

In this current age, more people are searching for God in one form or another, whether it be via a natural or abstract form of God (Brahman) as the personal guru, or as an actual personality that walked the earth. Regardless of the path, form-based or abstract, perhaps such images become a key to open the door to evolutionary living. Great spiritual figures such as Sri Ramakrishna taught his followers, 'To seek God first and then comes the world.' Great teachers will

---

89   The Mahavakyas are referred to as the Great Utterances of the scriptures called the Upanishads: 1) **Prajnanam Brahma** – pure unconditioned consciousness is Brahman; 2) **Tat Twam Asi** – Thou art That – explains that the innermost self is no different than the Absolute Reality, the consciousness that sustains all life and the entire universe; 3) **Aham Brahma Asmi** – affirms 'I am Brahman,' the Realization that one is not the mind, ego, intellect or senses, but instead, the inner being is the Absolute Brahman; and 4) **Ayam Atma Brahma** – the Self is Brahman (God).

never tell you to follow them, but instead, to follow the teaching. The teaching, or the process of awakening the higher faculty of intuition, is the guru. The guru is inside of you! This is what any guru is trying to do: to awaken the power of consciousness that lies within.

In general, from the perspective of Raja Yoga (Patanjali's Yoga Sutras) the focal point, the reason for the internalization of the mind, is to develop the capacity to concentrate the mind and develop the attention that leads to the experience of samadhi (enlightenment). Once the mind has been internalized, then other higher techniques can be applied, such as self-inquiry (vichara), discernment (viveka) and establishing the mind in a witnessing (sakshi) state. All of these are powers of the mind that develop through practice of integral yoga and become movements towards spiritual freedom.

One of the central themes in applying Vedanta lies in seeing the good in all experiences. When one dwells in negativity, this gives energy to shadows of the mind. Ayurveda, the science itself, recognizes the mind has a channel called **manovaha**, related to the importance of cultivating positive impressions (samskaras). By focusing on what is positive, the mind can learn to channel the light of any experience as a source of inspiration. This does not mean one should turn a blind eye to dangerous people or circumstances, but rather, one should observe the world in its illusory transparency, knowing that a grander force is behind it. Practical Vedanta is about differentiating between the clouds and the sky. The clouds are about moving and shifting circumstances, and the sky is always there, blue, clear, and eternal. The same goes for the mind, its ego, and the emotions, which are like the clouds always moving and changing, however, beyond these we are free and limitless in our potential.

During my formative years on the path of yoga, a dear counselor of mine shared with me a very practical way to overcome the obstacles of life. It was a like an exercise I could apply to life's circumstances. During those years, I was questioning the nature of my existence, my purpose in the world, and wanting to attain a clear sense of direction: should I go the way of the world, or should I follow my heart, the deeper calling of my soul? I kept resisting the world and was challenged by the conditioning from family, society, and the world around me.

Was I to follow the pack, so to speak, and do the right thing according to what society deemed successful and proper, or should I listen to my inner calling? For years, my resistance to follow the way of the material world was so strong that I considered the monastic life. Evidentially, I was experiencing an identity crisis, in that my entire life was centered on being the person my parents wanted me to be, and all that I observed in the external world. My parents became great teachers in this respect, and I was able to separate their loving intentions from their conditioned habits of culture and modern lifestyle. Like most people, I became a product of my environment, chasing the illusion of external wealth and outer fulfillment. I kept discovering that everything that I thought I wanted to become or attain never brought me happiness and would only fill me with temporary contentment that led to greater depression and emptiness.

The world kept turning me to look in another direction, toward a different type of fulfillment, and gradually this began to shape my dharma, my spiritual direction. I realized that my vocational work (artha) was beginning to align with the inner calling of my spiritual life. This episode continued for many years. The most difficult part about it was in gaining awareness of the movements of my conditioned mind (ego) that were drawing me towards materialism and superficial recognition. I was also yearning for self-realization, so these two energies were pulling me in separate directions. Subsequently, I learned that this paradoxical mindset is common during the formative years of the soul's reawakening toward spiritual evolution. I learned not to resist the outer movements of my life, but, more importantly, remain consistently committed to my spiritual practice. I cultivated a slowing down that would change the direction of my mind.

Sadhana is essentially a disciplinary structure that allows one to harness greater control over the mind and prana, the life force that influences all aspects of our life. Over time, my postural yoga practice began to change from one of physical intensity into learning to approach each pose as gestures of devotion and surrender. Additionally, my diet became simple and I began to apply ayurvedic principles with greater understanding. Thus, my relationship with nature and all living things grew stronger as I began to understand nature and her forces as integral human potentials located within myself.

During this period in my life, as my awareness of my soul blossomed, the four powers of the soul became my process for unraveling the grips of my conditioned mind that was shackled to the illusions of the material world. I learned that, through yoga, my soul's light could begin to shine. As I developed greater discipline over the mind, I became more aware of the guidance I was receiving by listening to the experiences of my life and by learning from the people, places, and things I encountered. I began to grow in love and thus surrender to the Divine process with greater ease, fully trusting that I was exactly where I was supposed to be.

These soul qualities are within everyone and can be developed by anyone who sincerely wants to heal from the bad habits and karmas of many births that have conditioned the mind to repeat these patterns again and again. All beings are inherently born with these inner potentials; however, they must be developed through regular practice (sadhana), good associations (satsanga), and selfless service to humanity (seva).

Observe the world around you and much of what you will find is what has been repeated over and over again. Youth, school, work, marriage, kids, old age, and retirement, and in the end, we leave alone, realizing once again that we are not alone, but instead, we are all one. So many individuals have been blinded by lifetimes of ignorance (avidya) and many are coming into a discovery of the fact that the only way to freedom is in recognizing the impermanence of the world; this is a signature theme of Gautama Buddha's teachings. Attaining this knowledge requires self-study, or what Raja Yoga teachings refer to as **svadhya**. We should embrace the idea that each of us is wholeheartedly responsible for the quality of our life. As Swami Jyotirmayananda says, "You are the architect of your destiny."

In the coming chapters of this book, I share a perspective on the four forms of yoga. They are the means to spiritual evolution. I provide an application of the integral yoga model as the bedrock of the postural yoga system I highlighted in my book, **Sun, Moon and Earth**, and lastly, I point out some of the underlying themes contained in the timeless Vedantic scriptures.

Another one of my intentions is to demonstrate that a yogi does not look any particular way, a true aspirant can be materially wealthy or poor, work for a company or as a gardener, be married or single, live as a baker, a poet, or play the role of mother. Regardless of the outer life path, the aspirant (sadhaka) can learn how to integrate yoga as an inner living methodology in order to aid the soul in ascending to the heights of spiritual freedom.

While America has mastered the craft of outer efficiency through technology and innovation, India has mastered the science of inner success and continues to produce saints like a high-speed manufacturing plant. Integral yoga prods us to reform our attitude, to shape our thoughts, to open our hearts, and to dedicate our actions to the one supreme consciousness that pervades all existence. When we serve the world with these ideals, the world becomes our guru, a living teacher who is always with us to guide us back to the supreme Divine love that we all are seeking.

Important Themes of Epic Vedanta Texts

Unlike the modern religious movements of the last two millenniums, the Vedic wisdom traditions, traditionally referred to as Sanatana Dharma (the eternal tradition), have neither a beginning nor an end. Vedic wisdom is cyclical and continuous, without limitation, and always in existence. The knowledge of the Vedic traditions has been disseminated through countless lineages that transfer the teachings orally through profound psychic metering, a manner of codifying knowledge to provide humanity with a key to the mysteries of creation.

Eventually, during the impending subsequent dark ages, yogic sages such as Valmiki, Vyasa and Vasishta, Parashara, Patanjali, and many others, began preserving and codifying the teachings in writing to provide human souls with a roadmap to higher consciousness living. Several epic texts (scriptures) such as the **Mahabharata**, **Ramayana**, **Yoga Vasishta**, the three main texts of Patanjali, and other texts, shaped the entire Indic culture that is now in renaissance. These teachings have also significantly influenced Asian and European culture and have provided awakening souls an auspicious path towards spiritual liberation. During the dark ages, the basic range of human consciousness was limited to very gross levels of physicality, sustenance, and conquests over territory in order to enhance power. The finer levels of energy awareness only recently began to reemerge in the eighteenth and nineteenth centuries.

Veda Vyasa, author of the Mahabharata which contains the Bhagavad Gita.

The basic premise of these scriptures is based on the guru (teacher) and disciple (student) relationship, recently discussed here, which presents an allegory. Every aspirant should not only seek the guidance of a realized or illumined master, but also rouse the awakening of one's capacity to access intuition as constant feeling within one's own heart. Through allegory, these timeless stories help remove the dark cloud of illusion (maya) that is perpetuated through the mind, ego, senses, and emotions. The central tenet of Vedanta is that only one truth exists; however, it is the responsibility of every individual to find their own unique path that leads to that realization. As our lives change and evolve, so do our interests, and whatever is necessary for our evolution will manifest through the individual's mental projector.

The material world (bhu lokha) is filled with countless wars, death, disease, deadly viruses, political conquests, material inequalities, and constant attractions and aversions. The Vedic texts present the universal plight of human life and how we can overcome challenges. The most successful way to do so is to convert the outer challenges into inner transformations that spur us to awaken our consciousness beyond the limitations of names and forms (namarupa). Our modern age desperately needs a tradition, teachings that people can align with in order to bring humanity back into accordance with natural laws. The earth doesn't need humanity, but humanity is in desperate need of living in a world (guru) that teaches humans how to live. Humanity cannot continue to kill animals and destroy nature and blindly expect to maintain a beautiful and peaceful world.

The Ramayana is a remarkable text and is the earliest detailed work of Yoga-Vedanta, as it is dated to approximately 500 B.C. The Ramayana presents spiritual counsel given by Sage Vasishta to Prince Rama in the Bala-Kanda section of the *Ramayana*. The counsel is considered a first step to the more advanced lessons of the *Yoga Vasishta*. The *Ramayana* was written to promote devotion in the human mind. Devotion, portrayed by the monkey-God Hanuman, symbolizes converting the emotional aspect of the mind into love and devotion in the heart. The *Yoga Vasishta* itself presents some important themes that address many of the human problems we face today.

What I've learned from the *Yoga Vasishta* is very applicable to deconstructing the mind's attachment to all things associated with the world process. The text itself is formatted as stories within stories, and it presents the world as a long dream of the soul from which it must wake up. These interconnected stories within stories are layers of a plot designed to reflect the complexity between the material (maya) world and the mind. The **Yoga Vasishta** begins with Sri Rama becoming aware of the transient nature of life and the many worldly aims he has. Then he experiences great dispassion (vairagya) for life and the things of the world. This evolving mood eventually transitions itself into a yearning for spiritual liberation (Mumukshuttwa). As with Sri Rama, so too this yearning is within us. If we reflect on our own awakening, it began with a distaste for the ways of the world, everything from clothing, diet, personality, and most of all, in the relationship we share with living things. In awakening, the distaste transitions to something very different in the ways we choose to connect and serve. What begins. as an inner revolution turns into an outer one.

Like the **Bhagavad Gita**, the Yoga Vasishta presents the path of liberation in a two-fold approach through either the path of knowledge (jnana) or the one of action (karma). This two-fold approach is a model for living an evolutionary life that encourages us to learn and cultivate the intentions behind our actions; both always go together. Anytime we have to clean up the mess made from our mistakes, we realize that lack of awareness or understanding is at the root of every error. All of our life-long unconscious experiences can be seen as layers of an ever-lengthening story created by the ego that entangles us into a complex web, making the world appear more permanent than it really is.

In the **Ramayana**, eventually Rama is rewarded when he reaches complete liberation as granted to him by his guru, Sage Vasishta. The Divine Goddess is central to India's ancient spiritual culture; women played a major role in the teachings and were even worshipped as Goddesses. One example was the wife of Vasishta, Arundhati[90] who was considered a Vedic Sage, a Rishi. There were many other women saints, like Devahuti, a devout aspirant who gave birth to nine daughters and one son, Kapila Vasudeva. He became a highly luminous sage whom his own mother considered to be an incarnation of Lord Vishnu, and so she took him as her guru. Kapila Muni, as he became known, was the author of the Samkhya Philosophy, one of the six main expressions of Vedic thought. Devahuti, his mother, evidently attained liberation (samadhi) and left an indelible mark on the spiritual legacy of India, as a mother, a dedicated

---

90   Stories of her life are found in well-known texts such as the *Siva Purana* and the *Bhagavata Purana* and were featured in Valmiki's *Ramayana*. This makes sense since Vasishta played a major role in this epic. Arundhati was the great-grandmother of Veda Vyasa, the author of the *Mahabharata*. Her cave, Gufa, is near her husbands in Uttarakhand, near Rishikesh, located on the banks of the river Ganga.

wife, and most importantly, for living a spiritually disciplined life that led her to attain the highest goal. Kapila Muni's Samkhya philosophy influenced the development of ayurveda, the Vedic branch of medicine, and also influenced other systems of ancient medicine that were founded on the principles of the five elements. Samkhya philosophy is a universal wisdom expressed through timeless scriptures and disseminated by aspirants who, through their own sadhana, became assigned specific roles as torchbearers of Divine knowledge. They have supported humanity's quest for purposeful living which all begins with what appears to be simple lifestyle exercises. However, they can have a profound effect, that of preparing us on the path towards spiritual evolution.

Below are several exercises influenced by epic wisdom scriptures that one can apply in order to cultivate the great power of jnana (knowledge) in which vairagya (dispassion) becomes a therapeutic tool for healing our consciousness. I will expand on these exercises a bit more in upcoming chapters.

Exercises for Cultivating Greater Knowledge

1. Reflect each day on the stories of your life, the stories within stories. Introspect on how each story is made up of a layer of ideas, thoughts, and belief systems that support a grander story.

2. Become aware of your narrative. Who is telling the story in your head that is manifesting outside of your mind in your life? If you can change your narrative, you can change your life.

3. Realize the short-term pleasure that material objects bring and shift your attention toward the experience of the present moment. This will help you see what you are attracting (raga) and how it eventually becomes an aversion (dvesha).

4. Embrace the Raja Yoga principle of aparigraha (non-possessiveness) and cultivate an attitude where you act in accordance with the belief that your happiness is not dependent on anything outside of you.

5. Increase the practice of inner yogic modalities such as breathwork (pranayama), chanting and affirmations (mantras), and meditation (dhyana), and moderate your physical practices. Focus on the promotion of good circulation, improved digestion, and relaxing the

body. Addiction to exercise or postural yoga can breed association to the body, and this is negative since it strengthens the ego and dulls intuition.

Thus, through knowledge, dispassion, and continuity of effort (abhyasa), the mind begins to develop devotion to God. This path of devotion is called Bhakti Yoga. The understanding of greater knowledge that you have acquired for the Divine should be directed to your preferred image that you feel an inner affinity towards. This will help make your love energy flow more efficiently until it becomes like a river channel that eventually reaches the ocean and expands into subtler feeling and compassion for all living things.

The *Yoga Sutras of Patanjali* present the inward path to discovering the soul in the stillness of meditation. The text presents the obstacles of the mind as afflictions (kleshas)[91] that one must overcome to reach samadhi. Patanjali contends that building the path toward liberation is founded on three primary principles: 1) self-study (Svadhya) as the art of gaining knowledge that helps us to 2) communicate (speech) with others; and have the 3) physical discipline (Tapasya) of surrendering to the Divine (Ishwara Pranidhana), also known as mental austerity. Many interpret surrender to the Divine as having to give something up, perhaps something we may need or enjoy; however, Yogananda defines this vital principle of surrender as devotion to God.

The greatness of the *Yoga Sutras* lies in how it simplifies core themes of establishing the mind in soul consciousness. The text largely presents the internalization (pratyahara) of the senses, a similar point made in the teachings of Krishna within the *Bhagavad Gita*. In the second of four padas, sections, Patanjali explains the science of Kriya Yoga and the power that lies in mastery of the breath and pranic energies. The word kriya stems from two words, *kri* which means action to purify, and *ya* is the bija sound for the heart. Thus, Kriya Yoga aims to purify the heart, removing mental impurities, allowing one to dwell in the pure existence of the heart. The *Yoga Sutras* present a concise system for managing the mind in order to establish mastery over prana and to cultivate dharana, the power of attention. The more focused the mind becomes, the greater the stillness. Thus, samadhi is essentially the

---

91   The five kleshas are the afflictions of the mind as presented in the *Raja Yoga Sutras* of Patanjali. They are Avidya (Ignorance), Asmita (Egoism), Raga (Attachment), Dwesha (Aversion), and Abhinivesha (Clinging to life).

state of sameness, a unification of inner consciousness with the absolute as pranava, the cosmic sound, Aum. Pranava is without end and reflects the eternal joy of the soul.

In the ***Ramayana***, the power of prana is characterized by Hanuman who demonstrates complete mastery of the life force and transmits it into great devotion towards Rama. Thus, in order to have devotion in the mind, one must have control over the mind, and this requires management of prana. Managing prana through lifestyle, practice (sadhana), and devotion to God, is vital, otherwise the material world (the forest Rama was sent to with his wife Sita) will perpetuate the struggles of maya (cosmic illusion). In essence, this story is encouraging us, inspiring us to return to Rama within us. Rama is the love and joy capacity of the Atman, the hidden Self, the Soul hidden in the hearts of all. Devotion to Rama is not limited to outer mechanical action, instead, devotion becomes organic when the inner self is pure and when the mind is free of chitta.[92]

This is the basic framework of human nature, the mind and all of its tools (chitta) curses the Self, not allowing it to express itself fully as happiness and compassion. The tools of the mind, when not properly used, become encumbrances that create afflictions (kleshas). The afflictions deny the Self its capacity to radiate as the light of pure consciousness. In turn, the Self eventually curses the chitta in return when one begins to aspire towards the mystic domain. This is because now the mind must succumb to the power of the light of pure consciousness. This leads to the experience of perpetual bliss (maha bhava) when the inner bliss extends outward into experiencing the Divine essence within all living things.

The transcendental attitude experienced by saints and sages as supreme love is the same power of transcendence that was demonstrated by the gopis, the milk maidens of Krishna's cows. Radha, as the most notable, initially worshipped the living form of Krishna and was often teased by the other milk maids for the adoration she displayed for Krishna. This did not persuade Krishna to

---

92   Chitta is a general term for the mind and its origin that refers to background consciousness, memory, a general term for the mind and its origin. Chitta is basically Mahat, the Cosmic Intelligence. Chitta is one part of a fourfold representation of what is referred to as the Antahkarana or 'internal instrument.' The other three parts are Buddhi, the intuitive-higher mind, manas the lower-sense mind, and ahamkara is the ego.

behave differently, and he continued to play his bansuri flute,[93] dance with the peacocks, and care for his many cows. However, when Krishna departed never to return to Vrindavana, his life began to unfold on a grander scale. It was at this time that Radha and the milk maidens' love transcended into feeling Krishna's presence within all; even though his physical presence no longer existed, they expanded their love beyond name and form into maha bhav. Krishna's life and teachings are symbolic of that pure consciousness or Divine love attained through following the path of integral yoga.

Historical Background on Integral Yoga

The four branches of yoga could be aptly called integral yoga or *Sampurna* as they reflect four aspects of every individual. Basically speaking, the four yogas are the four of you! Each of the four yogas provide a formative path for shaping the whole person, physically, emotionally, mentally, and spiritually. Although the formation of these distinct branches of yoga became more defined when Veda Vyasa wrote the Mahabharata, their existence and practice came from a much earlier Vedic period, and the concept of "integral" is a central tenet of Vedic thought. The four yoga paths are also featured in a more obscure manner within the story of the Ramayana. India's Rishi tradition has been intact for millenniums, transferring the sublime wisdom of the Vedas through mantric metering (vibratory language system), sacred devotional incantations that continue to charm humanity towards harmonious living, architecture (Vaastu), astrology (Jyotish), musicology (Gandharva Veda) and ayurveda (physical healing). The backbone of integral yoga (four yogas) is Vedanta and is the culmination of Vedic knowledge. Veda is a unity and harmony with cosmic consciousness either through the inner path of meditation or the outer path of awareness.

The movement of today's modern yoga practices both in India and the West have their links to the Vedas and the unique culture of India, including the oldest of the books the Rig. Although there are signs of a remarkable intelligence in other ancient civilizations like Mayan, Egyptian, Babylonia and

---

93   This side-blown bamboo flute is symbolic of the Divine love shared between Krishna and Radha and the rasa lila dance. As the story is told in the Bhagavata Purana, one night when Krishna was playing his flute, the milkmaids (gopis) of Vrindavana escaped to dance with Krishna. The dance symbolizes the transformation of love from the limited forms of cupidity (infatuation for one person or group), into an expanded or ecstatic love for all, maha bhava.

others, none demonstrated the comprehensive understanding of every aspect of life like the Indian methodologies for enlightenment. One after the other, ancient civilizations led invasions in the name of political power, religion, or wealth. Can anyone remember even one invasion lead by India? Not one; this is a result of sacred principles and systems of study that have sustained Indic culture.

Presently, not only are these principles still intact thousands of years later, Sanatana Dharma is in renaissance. One hallmark sacred system of practice that stands out is India's regard for the feminine Divine. Worship of the Divine Mother was represented in Vedic hymns and then millennia later in Tantric religious practices with Shakti as the supreme Goddess deity. This Shakta tradition enlivens Shiva, the supreme teacher, or Mahadeva of Yoga, and demonstrates the importance of balancing the sun and moon energies within each person, in conjugal relationships, and, most importantly, between humanity and Shakti's living nature as the Mother of earth.

India is not to blame for the global dominance of patriarchal societies; in my view, this movement was partially propelled, in part, when the Julian calendar was replaced by the Gregorian. Patriarchy arrived in India through a multitude of invasions that gradually deprived society of many sacred rituals, festivals, and traditions, that had recognized feminine power as equally proportionate to the supreme. Consider that the world's major religions each follow the teachings of a single male personality, while Vedic-Hindu religion is not attributed to any one specific male figure. Modern religions also adhere to one book or scripture that is said to be the word of the lord, providing humanity with everything needed for happiness and salvation. Vedic-Hindu traditions have continued to produce thousands of texts through the works of an array of lineages with both male and female leaders. At times, the teachings have been presented by a male figure who reverently regard their female counterpart as superior. This life account of Sri Ramakrishna and his wife Sara Devi explains this point with great fidelity.[94]

---

94   *The Gospel of Sri Ramakrishna: Introduction, Relation with his Wife*, by Swami Nikhilananda.

Totapuri,[95] coming to know of the Master's marriage, had once remarked: "What does it matter? He alone is firmly established in the Knowledge of Brahman who can adhere to his spirit of discrimination and renunciation even while living with his wife. He alone has attained the supreme illumination who can look on man and woman alike as Brahman. A man with the idea of sex may be a good aspirant, but he is still far from the goal."

Sri Ramakrishna and his wife lived together at Dakshineswar, but their minds always soared above the worldly plane. A few months after Sarada Devi's arrival Sri Ramakrishna arranged, on an auspicious day, a special worship of Kali, the Divine Mother. Instead of an image of the Deity, he placed on the seat the living image, Sarada Devi herself. The worshipper and the worshipped went into deep samadhi and in the transcendental plane their souls were united. After several hours Sri Ramakrishna came down again to the relative plane, sang a hymn to the Great Goddess, and surrendered, at the feet of the living image, himself, his rosary, and the fruit of his life-long sadhana. This is known in Tantra as the Shodasi Puja, the "Adoration of Woman".

Sri Ramakrishna realized the significance of the great statement of the Upanishad: "O Lord, Thou art the woman. Thou art the man; Thou art the boy. Thou art the girl; Thou art the old, tottering on their crutches. Thou pervadest the universe in its multiple forms."

By his marriage Sri Ramakrishna admitted the great value of marriage in man's spiritual evolution, and by adhering to his monastic vows he demonstrated the imperative necessity of self-control, purity, and continence, in the realization of God. By this unique spiritual relationship with his wife, he proved that husband and wife can live together as spiritual companions. Thus, his life is a synthesis of the ways of life of the householder and that of a monk."

---

95   A wandering Advaita Vedanta monk, who visited Dakshineswar. Totapuri was born a nondualist and he had no idea of what it meant to worship a Personal God as was the practice that Ramakrishna followed in worshipping Divine Mother in the form of Kali. Totapuri initiated Ramakrishna into Vedanta in which Ramakrishna experienced the complete state of Brahman-Consciousness and evidently stayed in Samadhi for three consecutive days and then continued in this state for six months.

This story displays how Ramakrishna's life was perfectly balanced from the inside and out. He was able to renounce everything as a true monk-sanyasi and make that wholehearted inner connection in samadhi with the Divine. Outwardly, he was able to live as the ideal spiritual partner to his wife by loving and respecting her as a living image of Mother Divine. The guru is within every one of us, and the guru is living with us in the relative world. Integral yoga provides every aspirant a way to make that sacred connection. The wisdom of the higher ages is like the candles of illumination, and the transfer of light intelligence from the guru to the student has its own style and touch. The teacher's light then comingles with the student's light and becomes a vehicle of energy for spiritual discipline (sadhana), for selfless service (seva), and for creating positive associations (sangha).

The great Adi Shankaraya,[96] an eighth century philosopher, reinvigorated the integral yoga movement through the creation of the four mathas (pronounced mutts), monasteries, in order to propagate Advaita Vedanta and promote unity amongst not only the various sects of Hinduism, but also Buddhism, which thrived from 500 B.C. and beyond. Shankara's work shows much similarity to Mahayana Buddhism which endorses the idea that enlightenment can be attained in a single lifetime. Even though Buddhism prevailed long before Shankara's birth, a unifying shift began to take place because of his work. This integral yoga movement repaired the fragmentation in Vedic thought that existed as a result of the descending Bronze and Iron Ages (dwapara and kali yugas). The fragmentation had resulted in a loss of humanity's higher purpose, but Sri Shankara's teachings restored the pathway to evolution and enlightenment. According to views from various orthodox Hindu sects, each of Sri Shankara's monasteries (mathas or mutts) can be energetically linked to each of the four original Vedic books (Rig, Yajur, Sama, and Atharva), each of which have their own lineages.

---

96   Shankara wrote five verses or hymns called, *Pancharathnam Stotras*, one for each of the groups that were following different images or paths toward God. The main deities were Ganesh (earth), Vishnu (water), Surya (fire), Shiva (air) and Shakti (Ether) and are direct links to the five elements. Much of his teachings expanded on the wisdom of the *Upanishads*. His teachings are largely based on extraordinary commentaries of which his masterwork was the *Brahmasutrabhasya* (commentary of the Brahma Sutra). Other commentaries of Shankarcharya include selections of *Upanishads*, the *Bhagavad Gita, Vivekachudamani* (Crest Jewel of Discrimination) and the Saundarya Lahari, probably the greatest work on Tantrism, and considered a textbook of its tantric rituals. He accomplished all of this and much more by the age of 32 when he exited his body.

Essentially, the entire integral yoga system is born of the light of the sun and credit is never given to any particular individual or lineage for its dissemination. The term *avatar* appears in the Sanskrit language literature to differentiate an individualized soul that has been commissioned to return to the earth plane to raise mass consciousness. Such figures are also considered to be Jagat gurus, world teachers, who change the course of the collective consciousness. These gurus, as unique individuals, are not self-proclaimed world transformers; instead, they play a humble role in maintaining a balance between the polarities of sun, moon, earth energies and appear when the collective consciousness in the world is experiencing adharma, lack of purpose, as we have seen in the last two millenniums. As Krishna states, "When religion declines and irreligion prevails I incarnate myself in every age to establish religion."[97]

In the current age, it seems that through Mahavatar Babaji,[98] countless yogis are being trained to play a significant role in guiding humanity back toward evolutionary living. These include, but are not limited to, Gorakhnath (founder of the Hatha yoga sect), Adi Shankara (Advaita Vedanta), Patanjai (Raja Yoga), Lahiri Mahasaya (Kriya Yoga), Swami Sivananda Radha (Divine Light Invocation). Many more yogis are moving about the earth unifying the world that has been broken by approximately two millenniums of misconstrued religious dogmas. Babaji is responsible for reintroducing a powerful ancient breathing technique, pranayama, now called Kriya Yoga, that Krishna himself taught to Arjuna (his disciple) over five thousand years ago. Subsequently, Yogananda was commissioned to spread this technique throughout Western world beginning in 1920.

Bhagavan Krishna, as the central figure of the epic scripture the Bhagavad Gita, extols great insights into how the four yogas can be used as formal paths to liberating the embodied spirit. Krishna goes on to simplify yoga into a two-fold approach of either knowledge (jnana) or practice (karma). The knowledge approach is for those of an intellectual bent, and the practice approach is for the active and practical person. Both are sincere and direct means towards spiritual freedom.

---

97   *Bhagavad Gita* Chapter 4, verse 7-8.
98   Babaji is a maha muni (master of the eight siddhis) and is also known by many names such as Shiva Baba, Tryambaknath and Mahavatar Babaji, a titled given to him by Paramahansa Yogananda as introduced to the world through his famous Autobiography of a Yogi in chapter 33, "Babaji, Yogi-Christ of Modern India.

Yoga has evolved much over many millenniums beginning in the early Vedic Yoga period that was largely based on mantra, pranayama, and meditation, and sacred fire rituals, such as homa's (havan) or agnihotra's (yagya), that date back well over 8,000 years. These techniques and rituals can be considered higher forms of the broader yoga system, as they deal with finer forms of energy with the aim of destroying obscure impressions and subtle desires (vasanas) lodged within in the unconscious and subconscious mind. In essence, the practices merge the mind into the heart, and unify soul with the eternal.

One might wonder what kind of worldly desires would arise from a person living during these times in ancient Vedic India. Desire for material wealth was likely not common, as we correlate the rise of materialism and its corresponding illusions with the industrialization of the Western world that took place much later in human history. However, human strife and illusions in other forms have always existed; the conditions may be labeled differently, but from the perspective of yoga, the cause of suffering is the same: ignorance (avidya) of one's soul nature. From the perspective of Vedanta, it's the force of maya that influences one to believe the world is real.

The fact is, regardless of the historic age, the human mind is afflicted; it is designed to look outward to find superficial pleasure in the world which then leads to attachment and suffering. The entire system of yoga is precisely designed to address the mind and its afflictions. The age in which one is born can have some influence on the nature of the mind because of the cultural norms; however, every individual is responsible for shaping the quality of their consciousness and this is the basis for the law of karma.

Three Historical Periods of Yoga (Early Vedic, Classical and Modern)

- **Early Vedic Period**

During the Vedic era, the majestic landscape of northern India and the Himalayas played a major role in influencing the use of the Sanskrit, a mantra-energy-based language that shaped and defined yoga's practice and expression. Vedic India is considered to have been a distinguished culture, lauded as sacred and vital to the development of yogic rituals and worship of the Gods as forces of nature, not as idols. The Indus valley civilization, as it was later called, existed near a large river in northern India called Saraswati. Saraswati became the name used in the later Hindu religion for the Goddess of intuitive knowledge, education, and creative arts. Allegorically speaking, the flow of the river is symbolic of the knowledge that flows into the mind. The river symbol also signifies the transient or impermanent nature of life.

During this Early Vedic Period, the direct insights of sages and seers, insights received as astral transmissions, synthesized knowledge of cosmologies, the profound forces of the cosmos, with the visible elements in nature. Each of these forces was regarded as a God in the form of wind (vayu), fire (agni) and soma (water), as well as Indra, the cosmic sound, representing the finer electrical forces such as those witnessed in a lightning bolt. The mandalas of the Rig Veda expressed other metaphors such as referring to the region as the land of the seven rivers. This linked the river channels of that time to the seven astral centers of the spine (chakras). [99]

The wisdom of this early Vedic system lacked a detailed explanation of any particular yogic techniques or practices; however, it presented nature's eternal relationship with humans as an auspicious path for "winning the light" in a culture that yearned for self-realization. Some consider this teaching, nature's eternal relationship with humans, to be the original concept of duality. It may have influenced the compilation of the Samkhya philosophy because it points to the dualism between Divine Mother (prakriti) and cosmic consciousness (purusha).

Early Vedic teachings were presented by Rishis who experienced the mantric language as form of energy transmission, or meters, called **chhandas**. There are three main forms of chhandas.

- The Gayatri meter has eight syllables per line and relates to Agni, the God of fire.

- Trishtubh meter has eleven syllables per line and relates to Indra.

- Jagati meter has twelve syllables per line and relates to Surya, Sun God.[100]

99   Point made by David Frawley in his book, *Gods, Sages and Kings*, Part IV, Chapter 1.
100 David Frawley, *Vedic Yoga: The Path of the Rishi*, published by Lotus Press."

Each meter represents different aspects of Divine energy, and the mantras carry the unique energy like a mathematical equation designed to unlock the mind's potential.

- **Classical Period**

Raja or classical yoga is expressed boldly in the works of Maharishi Patanjali. He compiled the vast system of yoga into a more concise system that explains how the mind can be internalized, focused or concentrated, and fully absorbed into a unified state of consciousness. In essence, this Raja yoga is the yoga of meditation, including its methods, powers (siddhis), and states of consciousness. Patanjali's Raja Yoga dispensation is also a treatise dedicated to Kriya Yoga. The second of his four books (padas) is dedicated to explicating the meaning and practice of this ancient breathing technique.

- **Modern Period**

The shift to the third stage in the development of yoga occurred mostly during the medieval period and is attributed to a system called *Tantra*, which simply means teaching or book. Tantra, and more particularly Hatha yoga, deals explicitly with the body, but is not at all limited to it. Hatha yoga has given the term 'yoga' international recognition, and its system has been adapted to form a type of physical exercise for the masses. Tantrism also works closely with the art of tension, or the tensing and releasing of muscles and learning to control them via the mind and prana. The root term of tantra is *tan* and like the English root *ten* in the word tension. Sexual energy can be considered a form of inner tension that induces the release of various hormones such as estrogen and testosterone that create, heat, and cool, various fluid secretions in the reproductive system. This energy is co-creative and promotes creativity, progeny, and if properly directed, can also be utilized for spiritual evolution.

The popular Hatha-postural-breath techniques of tantra yoga, otherwise called Hatha Yoga, can be considered a precursor to the broader tantra system. Hatha Yoga can be a practiced for gaining proper discipline over an enlightening energy, called kundalini, that could otherwise turn life into a cat and mouse chase filled with dazzle and frazzle. In its formulations, Hatha yoga has an integral approach through the postures (asanas), breathing exercises (pranayama), energy locks (bandhas), and unique gestures expressed with the body, hands, and eyes. Hatha yoga also includes a sixfold system for detoxification of the body that aligns with ayurvedic principles for removing toxins from the body. However, tantra is much more than this, and as an integral system, it includes the teachings or books of tantra, mantras (words of power), yantras (geometric energetics), and meditation (dhyana), all of which comprise the inner aspects of tantra.

Inner and Outer Yoga

As we have recently explored in a brief background of the ancient science of yoga it can be surmised that it offers two distinct paths, the inner and outer. Neither one is superior to the other, and it ultimately depends on the aspirant and what is most suitable for their mentality. The outer path begins with cultivating a relationship with the five senses and their functions. For example, some people are very visual and can understand things when they can see them visually; especially when trying to connect to God, they prefer to see a picture to be able to direct their attention. The Samkhya philosophy teaches us that the function of sight through the eyes is connected to the element of fire and through sacred imagery of your guru, saint, deity or even nature, a person can light their fire of devotion. Others, however, may be drawn more to sound or music which is connected to the element of ether. Certain mantras or devotional hymns can invoke a profound feeling in the heart. Even sounds of nature, like a flowing stream or a wave in the ocean, can induce a sense of calm that expands the mind's vision and sensitivity.

Aromas are another sacred method for invoking certain qualities of purity and sensuality, and this is one reason why incense is part of yoga traditions. Different aromas affect each of the ayurvedic doshas differently and are also useful for preparing or clearing the energy of any space. Sandalwood and rose are very sacred to yoga. Sandalwood is remarkable in its effect of calming the mind for meditation, and as an essential oil it can be applied directly to the skin without burning it. Rose is an auspicious symbol of the guru-disciple relationship. The rose symbolizes Divine love, loyalty, and fidelity. Rose aroma therapy can be used to awaken and transcend the mind and move towards the reflective consciousness beyond thoughts and emotions. The senses can be used as a doorway to your spiritual practice.

Other powerful outer practices include pilgrimages to sacred sites such as temples, ashrams, or places where yogis or saints have lived. If one properly enters such spaces in silence and with a receptive mind and heart, the experience of the place can uplift one's consciousness to a feeling of serenity and contentment. Additionally, some physical contact with elements of these spaces can be helpful. The easiest manner is to enter such spaces barefoot in order to connect to the sacred vibration through your feet; or sit quietly in a meditative position on the floor, if possible, even a short period of time can be very helpful. Historically, yogis and saints have been drawn to trees, caves, riverbanks, or mountain tops and so your actual contact with the trees, rocks, or soil in such areas can connect you with their vibrations, held within for millenniums. This power of this experience has been enhanced by the continued visitation of other aspirants feeding the space with devotional intentions.

In India, I have enjoyed visiting caves used by great yogis such as the great Swami Rama Tirtha who meditated in a small cave along the banks of the Ganges River where he attained his enlightenment (Samadhi) in the early 20th century. I had, by then, spent many years studying his books entitled, *In the Woods of God Realization,* and I had learned much from other yogis like Sri Paramahansa Yogananda and Sri Swami Sivananda who were greatly influenced by this young Swami.

A momentous experience I had while visiting Rama's cave encapsulates a very important yogic teaching about not becoming attached to namarupa (names and forms). After having arrived in Rishikesh[101] after a bumpy car ride, I could not stop thinking about Rama Tirtha because I knew he spent much time in the Himalayas when he initially became a sanyasi (renunciate). I decided to visit the Divine Life Society ashram of Sri Swami Sivananda.[102] I was intrigued by Sivananda's background as a medical doctor and his interest in ayurveda; therefore, I enjoyed spending much of the morning there reading his books, visiting his shrine, and speaking to monks. Incidentally, I asked one monk if he knew of Swami Rama, and he shared some simple points on his life. He gave me a general idea of where Rama's cave was located and suddenly my curiosity was afire. Instantly, I decided to head north, and I walked for hours along the banks of the river, meeting many different yogis along the way, and even walking right through a leper colony.[103]

---

101 Rishikesh is a small mountain town on the banks of the river Ganges in the state of Uttarakhand. Rishikesh is considered a gateway of sorts to the Himalayas. Rishikesh abounds with caves, group rituals, and great ashrams like the Divine Life Society.
102 Sivananda is the Sadguru of Swami Jyotirmayananda, a direct disciple, with whom the author has studied Vedanta for many years, and whose teachings have influenced major themes of this book.
103 Leprosy is a contagious disease that mainly affects the skin.

With every stop, I asked about Rama's cave, but most people knew nothing of its whereabouts and didn't speak any of the languages I knew; although one yogi did give me a clear indication that I was nearing the cave (gufa). I learned that general directions don't work very well in India, especially not in mountainous areas along the banks of a mighty river like the Ganga. When I decided to look at my watch, I realized it had been at least five hours of uphill walking through some rugged terrain, yet the cave was not in sight. However, I was determined to find it and bathe in the holy vibrations of Rama's cave.

Finally, I discovered a narrow path that was heavily trod and wound up at a clearing where I could see the Ganges River flowing, flanked by lush greenery. The sun's rays were beaming through with a heavenly mystique. With regained enthusiasm, I dashed up to the clearing and was suddenly greeted by a very calm yogi named Nandadas, who, within moments, pointed down to the ground where another yogi lay dead, partially covered by a cloth. Nandadas reached down and lifted the cloth that was covering the scorched body of this yogi. His body was scorched by the flames of what had probably been a sacred fire ritual. I was overwhelmed by the sight of his burnt corpse, the eyes appeared to be turned upwards, indicating he was in a meditative state, and the rest of the body was severely burnt by the flames. Obviously, this fire ritual had just happened, as there was still some smoke coming off the body.

Without much time to digest this shocking event, I was taken to Rama's cave along the bank of the river, located under a massive rock that had an iron trident on top. I enjoyed some time in meditation inside the cave and noticed that the graphic symbol for the cosmic sound Aum was painted on one of the interior walls of the cave. Nandadas keenly explained that Rama had drawn this smiling Aum with some type of red clay to signify his enlightenment (samadhi). Nandadas continued to explain that an interesting miracle that pertains to the cave. He said that although the cave is submerged under water for several months of the year because of the massive monsoons, the sacred Aum symbol, hand drawn by Rama himself in 1906, still appears.

Sri Swami Rama Tirtha, area near his samadhi cave on the banks of the Ganga (Ganges River) in the Himalayan foothills.

I keep a small piece of stone from this cave site as an auspicious relic on my altar. As is the case whenever I visit any holy site, I sat down to meditate and connect with energies of the cave and Rama. I reflected on some of Rama's words and recited some lines from one of Rama's poems that was a favorite chant of Swami Yogananda's when he first arrived in America[104]. At last, my mind was able to enjoy a deep cleansing, and as I continued to hear the Ganges roar past, my mind became very still.

After departing from Rama's cave, I began listening to, reflecting on, the significance of the experience of the yogi's dead body. I had no expectation of what I would experience at the cave. Much anticipation had grown during my time in India, and certainly experiencing the day of trekking to reach the cave had increased my fervor for visiting this sacred place. Rama's life was so inspiring to many great figures in yoga and to me as well. However, the remainder of my travels throughout India kept my mind focused on other matters and lectures. I did not really sit down and listen to what this experience has to teach me. Finally, some months later after returning home to my regular spiritual routine, I was finally able to introspect and really listen and learn from Rama's cave visit. What I learned from Rama was a very practical point of Vedanta. It had particular importance to me as a former athlete, body builder, and now as a Hatha yogi. During the meditative practice of self-inquiry (vichar), the message came to me as, "The body is not Rama! Death is not Rama!" essentially telling me not to become attached to names and forms. This means that the journey of our life is filled with experiences that we must learn to transcend. Just as prana flows from one living entity to another, life after life, the bodily form comes and goes, and all that remains is the eternal vibration (pranava) that is our true nature as eternal love and joy. This consciousness has no end, no limitation, and thus the mantra of Vedanta is, in order to seek higher consciousness beyond time and space, we must all Realize our true nature.

When Swami Rama Tirtha lectured outside of India, he spoke of India's greatest teaching as Vedanta in a practical form. Vedanta requires cultivating a persevering attitude that blends the living world (prakriti) along with the unmanifest world seamlessly. The art of living Vedanta is applied to dissolve the reactive mind, and to dissolve the conditions that impair the mind from transcending time and space consciousness.

---

104 *Cosmic Chants*, by Paramahansa Yogananda: "Marching Light" and "Ram Tirtha's Song" (Self-Realization Fellowship, Los Angeles).

Outer Forms of Yoga for Inner Transformation

The most common of outer yoga practices today is the postural system that places the body into various positions or gestures to mimic different aspects of the Divine. A great way to start a morning practice is with the iconic sun salutation series. Alternatively, ending the day with moon salutations is ideal, as they are calming and cooling like the night. Concentration develops as one holds any of the poses with an understanding of the meaning and symbolism behind the pose.

For example, if one is practicing cobra pose (bhujangasana), one should concentrate the eyes on a fixed point while reflecting on the ascending energy (prana) along the spine, feeling inspired to overcome the ego and the any negativity in the mind. The snake symbolizes the awakened kundalini (serpent like energy) and practicing cobra pose becomes a vehicle for transcending the senses. Each posture or series of postures should include a period of breathing exercises (pranayama) to expand the energy further into a more subtle form. The series of postures and breathing exercises should be followed by a period of stillness and relaxation (savasana). This completes the outer process. Although postural yoga provides physical benefit with the proper mental attitude, such practices ideally become vehicles for transcending the mind into more sublime states of awareness. In other words, the higher value of asana is to change the mind. This is an example of how the outer practices aim to transform one internally.

The outer paths of yoga are naturally attractive to karma yogis because they enjoy dwelling in action and activity. The highest form of karma yoga is *seva*, selfless service to others. The simple gesture of helping others purifies the mind of the ego. This is because the "I" dentification with the name and form of the body are removed when focusing on acting selflessly for others. Selfless service allows the consciousness to arise to the grander force that is behind the gesture. Any willingness to do good results in feeling good because one allows pure consciousness to flow through them like a spiritual channel. The colossal figure of Indian history, Mahatma Gandhi, was such a selfless person. He performed a multitude of actions for the benefit of so many shackled by the tyrannical oppression of colonialism. The events of his life, as he referred to them, were "experiments with truth."[105] and reflected the humanness of

---

105 *The Story of My Experiments with Truth* is the autobiography of Mohandas K. Gandhi.

his persona that was riddled with imperfections; nevertheless, he continued to strive for a higher good through service to his nation. What matters most is the endeavor to be moral, as A.P.J. Abdul Kalam[106] once said…

> *"Where, there is righteousness in the heart, there is beauty in the character.*
>
> *When there is beauty in the character, there is harmony in the home.*
>
> *Where there is harmony in the home, there is order in the nation.*
>
> *Where there is order in the nation, there is peace in the world."*

The outer paths of yoga are also appealing to wisdom (jnani) yogis who naturally are keen on using their intellect to grow in conscious awareness. This means that regardless of the outer task, such a person can use their mind as a tool for understanding and perceiving the reality behind any experience. It is considered the most difficult of yogic paths as it requires a highly disciplined and concentrated mind.

Whether it be through purification of the senses, selfless service, postural yoga or pilgrimages, the outer paths all provide valid approaches to expanding awareness of the soul. The main intention behind any outer path is in cultivating greater awareness to the point of realizing, "I am not the doer," and as a result, you begin to shift the mindset into a position of observing the ritual, body, and even the mind itself; they all become instruments of the soul. The mind and body become instruments for the soul to enjoy the outer world and you also recognize the all-pervading energy that is behind the objects of the material world. This practical yet powerful technique of Vedanta is known as **vichara,** the inquiry into the nature of our existence, which can be applied at any moment. One form of vichara is to simply question the origin of any thought. Eventually through such investigation, one can realize their essential nature (svarupa). In the broader sense, vichara helps one to distinguish between what is Real, eternal (nityam), and unreal, not lasting (anityam). We are not the mind, thoughts, emotions, intellect, nor even the prana. The very essence of our being is pure consciousness.

Every night when sleeping, one drops any identification with their body, mind, name, and all their responsibilities. Sleep provides a natural purification for the five senses and is an important outer path practice that should not be

---

106 A.P.J. Abdul Kalam was an aerospace scientist before being elected as the 11th president of India in 2002.

overlooked. The pre-sleep moments described earlier are a vital form of outer yoga that can ultimately determine the depth of one's internalization. The internal path of yoga is essentially learning to create a similar experience to the sleeping state, yet one of a more profound level because it happens through your experience of conscious awareness.

Many have mistaken the Hatha Yoga system of the Nath yogis as mainly an outer form. However, Goraksanatha mentions the eightfold system of Patanjali in his great treatise.[107] He defines asana as remaining in one's true state, (asanam-iti svarupe samasannata). Goraksanatha goes on to correlate seated meditation poses like lotus (padmasana) and the cross-legged pose (siddhasana) with the importance of being alert and conscious. Asana begins with learning to be seated in consciousness where one can expand the mind's awareness beyond the senses, thoughts, and all limitations of time and space. The main point to take from this very esoteric teaching is the importance of stilling the body so that the mind has a place to rest. For this reason, holding postures is a signature feature of their practice because it promotes stillness of the mind so the prana can rise in a fluid manner. A still body becomes necessary for anchoring the mind. In contrast, when the mind is filled with fear or anxiety, it most likely indicates fragmentation from the body, a very common characteristic of vata dosha. Raja Yoga is the process of internalizing one's consciousness so that the mind can become fully absorbed in a state of non-duality. Any person who enjoys meditation will most likely be drawn to this royal path (Raja Yoga) because they understand, through their own direct experience, the profound benefits of withdrawing the life force energy away from the senses into the spine. This union of mind and spine is a major movement forward in one's spiritual evolution.

Two Paths of Life

Two paths are available to us. One path flows further into the world like a river that flows out towards the desert where it eventually dries out. Alternatively, another path flows inward toward the ocean of abundance. Ayurveda views the physical body in the same way, seeking abundance and balance of all elements and cosmic intelligence. When the soul chooses a new body to enter through, it does so in a womb filled with water. Gradually, over the

---

107 *Siddhasiddhantapaddhatih*, the foremost treatise on the Natha philosophy.

span of one lifetime, the body goes through three stages, water, fire, and air, drying up in the last stage. Finally, the soul departs the body again to return to the light of supreme consciousness.

Similarly, when one's life purpose is directed outwards toward what society deems as the markers of success in money, sex, materialism, and ego-based outer power, then such a life is likely to be filled with the ups and downs that eventually dry up. These desires come one after the next perpetuating the illusion that the newest desire will bring a better life until, perhaps by chance, a break in our ego-focused consciousness may awaken within us the realization that people, places, and things cannot bring us stability of happiness. The idea of creating stability through objects and outer attainments is an illusion that much of humanity lives in.

On the other hand, one's life purpose can flow towards the ocean of love and abundance in finding contentment within the soul. One flows in this way by cultivating a growing realization of the one consciousness that pervades all living things. This is a type of realignment that occurs over many reincarnations as a person begins to understand the positive feeling that comes from good company, mental discipline, and helping others. This continues to foster and support the positive attributes of their spiritual characteristics and practices.

As sacred rituals are integrated into our lifestyle, our connection to the body, nature and indwelling spirit strengthens. This stronger connection allows for greater control over our mind and its attributes, developing our innate inner powers. Finally, as we expand in our awareness our insights grow beyond ourselves. We realize the interconnectedness we share with all living things and coincidences transform into synchronicities, personal mistakes are seen as lessons, and our understanding of global calamites blossom into new perspectives on life. We even perhaps are given a glimpse into how trifling our troubles are as we recognize the Divine attributes in others.

So, the question we need to ask ourselves is, do we want inner or outer power? While many are flowing towards the desert of the world process, a few are flowing towards the ocean of Divine abundance found in the One. One of the greatest blessings in life, besides the gift of human existence, is the dawning consciousness that sparkles with light and intrigue bringing one closer to the source of knowledge that is endless, eternal, and expands as greater love in the heart.

The outer path of life is defined by the relationship one has with nature. Living in accordance with the cycles of nature as experienced through the four seasons, diet, self-care, good sleep and circulation through exercise, sexuality, and walking are all wisdom expressions of ayurveda and provide ideal methods for balance in the outer life.

The inner path is cultivated through reflection, mantra, meditation, spiritual listening, study, and selfless service. Even though such practices include rituals that involve outer effort, their intention is to reform the mind's relationship with the Self, the inner portion of consciousness within every human being. Evolution is a balance between these two aspects of life as each one supports the other.

Sacred Is Secret

In Vedanta, the concept of sanctity, the sacred, is very important as it supports the individual's preferences or affinities toward divinity. In contrast, each of the major world religions define what is "divine" or "sacred" for all according to the leaders of the religions. For example, in Judaism, the rabbis are the authority figures; within Christianity, authority begins with the Pope and then continues down through bishops, cardinals, and priests; and in Islam, the Mullahs are the leaders.

The Hindu-Vedic tradition does have its monastic order, sanyasa, that preserves and carries on the teachings of a particular lineage (parampara), with each following their own particular image of the Divine. In this current period, we refer to this religion or culture as Vedic or Hindu, however what is important to recognize is this wisdom is universal and eternal, meaning that these truths exist without the labels of religion and culture. The teachings can be applied in all individual's lives; applied scientifically, combining mathematics and devotion. Over millenniums sage's have gathered the inherent intelligence of the cosmos. This intelligence is based on the construction of duality and has been articulated into various expressions that resonate with the four facets (practical, sensitive, intellectual, compassionate) of the human being. Each person chooses their own path and practices that align with them. Thus, the individual defines what is sacred to them depending on which of these four facets is more developed as a result of the laws of karmas.

Each aspirant chooses their own image of the Divine according to the affinity one has. Basically, it's a very individualized approach to spirituality where one chooses what one feels sacred to them. Nature plays an important part in this process, and is also considered sacred, especially for healing. An individual can interpret meaning from symbols that carry Divine energy and can consider abstract images like those in nature, such as a river, mountain, or a tree to be important objects for spiritual transformation. Depending on which yoga energy is predominant in a person, they will be attracted to different forms of the gods or goddesses and to a sadhana (spiritual discipline) that is characteristic to one's energy.

"Sacred" is about giving meaning to the experiences in our life that support a transformational evolutionary movement. Usually, those meaningful experiences include certain objects or images that become vehicles to recreate moments that have shaped our life. This personalization, the way a person defines their path towards the Divine, is in itself sacred and referred to in Sanskrit literature as *svatantra*. Along this sacred path, the aspirant acquires a collection of sacred moments that are saved as part of a series of evolutionary steps that grants the aspirant greater levels of awareness leading to expanded peace, contentment, and happiness. The lesson to remember is that sacred is secret. If not secret, it disturbs the frequency of one's consciousness.

Sharing one's sacred experiences with others (other than your guru or spiritual counselor) can hamper the positive movement toward liberation because it brings the experience to the lower level of the conscious mind.

The most advanced yogis I have met have been humble beyond comparison. In very rare instances an advanced yogi will discuss or describe their own spiritual power; they do so only to make a point to the benefit of those listening, but never share details with those people who remain asleep. Such discussions of one's sacred experiences should be limited to those who are counselors or to the Guru himself because they can help expand them. The greatest of India's yogis remain in seclusion or alternatively work enigmatically with small groups, and they never coat their teachings in sugary sensational displays of their spiritually powerful experiences. Devotees look for the Guru, but the Guru never needs to look for their disciples. When a devotee is attuned to any advanced soul, the devotee can feel the guru's saintly stature vibrating through their humility and kindness.

Creating Sacred Spaces

The outer space one dwells in reflects their inner space. It may be difficult to explain the idea of creating a sacred space to a Western mindset because many have been programmed to think that what is sacred exists outside of them and can only be found in a temple or church, dedicated to a certain God or figure like Jesus. Many people have forgotten that was is sacred is not to be found in the stars or planets, like the moon or mars; instead, the sacred is within our own being, at the very center of feeling in the heart.

This has particular importance regarding the natural elements of water, sunlight, plants and animals. Often when I visit a person's home and see their landscape and their lack of care for their garden, I find lack of care similarly reflected in the relationship they have with their own body and the quality of connection they have with their heart or feeling nature. Obviously, a more intellectually bent person will be less connected to their body, however, this does not have to be the case. Creating sacredness in one's home begins with the outer elements in nature which surround the home and then continues with bringing some of those elements into the home. Caring for the landscape and placing a fountain or saintly statue in a garden area are good for nurturing this balance. The most valuable factors in real estate are the greenery and view of some body of water; it changes the price drastically, for this reason: the way nature makes people feel. Nature and her elements can become a boon to creating a stronger connection to the inner life, the source of all sacredness. Mountains represent a more masculine quality while rivers or bodies of water are more feminine. The origins of this viewpoint can be found in Vedic India. Mount Kailash and is considered the abode of Lord Shiva, while the nearby Lake Mansarovar is the abode of Shakti. These two geographical spots are an example of how nature is regarded as sacred, and so, when one visits these remote places, they are bathed with the blessings of Divine presence.

Making a space feel special enough to contain that sacred energy begins with recognizing that sacred is what is within us as the soul. Any time we make contact with the soul through a practice like meditation or any aspect of a spiritual practice we are awakening the highest potential of humanity. This awakening exudes a vibration of unity that can be best described as calming, peaceful and attractive. A physical space can be classified as sacred because of the feeling it produces as a result of the thoughts and activities that have taken place there.

Sacredness is created when nature's laws and moral behavior come into accordance. Nature, as a vehicle for transformation, is a salient part of the Vedic tradition, and each of the five elements can be used as tools for transformation on many practical levels. One of the main points of this book is to teach us that we need to stop seeing this world as something separate from us. It is pure egoism to think one's actions, even though unique and singular, have no effect on the whole of humanity. All living things are derived from consciousness, and it is for this reason that violence has no place in any society.

Sectarianism and Churchianity

There is an important correlation between secularism and religious movements that cannot be ignored and that shed light on the evolution revolution taking place. The diversification of religious movements and growth of modern societies in both the East and West will most likely continue to increase secularism throughout the world; especially if the governments of major leading economic countries continue to favor one religion over another. When religion does not speak to people, people tend to look away from dogma to secularism or to nature as their religion. As the relationship between spirit and nature within our yoga sub-cultures continue to grow, more people will be drawn toward ayurveda, the religion of natural lifestyle. The yogic and healing systems such as ayurveda teach that one aspect of health is having a purposeful or spiritual life. They teach that a life that adheres to nature's principles may be playing an influential role in the growth of secularism throughout the world. Without spiritually meaningful purpose, a person is left to a lifestyle of basic survival and cultivating their sensory appetite.

As a result of secularism, the spiritual and natural lifestyle movements have become mundane or exoteric, far removed from their original intention or meaning. For this reason alone, integral yoga becomes vital in returning humanity to practicing spiritual rituals in a meaningful manner, one that most resonates with individual's own dispositions. The term, "Churchianity," refers to changes to original teachings of Jesus Christ because of the formation of the Churches during the expansion of the Roman Catholic Church throughout Europe. The churches encouraged societies to begin seeking God on the sabbath day (Sunday) in a church and consequently, the search for spirituality was adapted into an outer process. The consequence of this is the belief that happiness is obtained through external actions and good motivations that are common to all, and publicly judged by our peers and God.

In contrast, Eastern philosophies have always contended that we are made from higher consciousness. One example is the atman-brahman concept that teaches that what is within us is a portion of pure consciousness of that which is outside of us: God or Brahman. The Tantric concept of the chakras within the spinal systems confirms that within us is the church or temple. Integral yoga provides us these four paths to discovering the inner dimensions of our consciousness. Integral healing of the whole being as mind-body and soul is essential now more than ever through the integration of the four aspects of the personality as action, emotion, will, and reason.

The ideal of any great religious movement is self-reformation through knowledge of the true inner Self. Christ himself recognized the many states of consciousness (tamasic, rajasic, sattvic) when he said, "In my Father's house are many mansions."[108] The many mansions are the various qualities of a person's consciousness. The lower chakras (1st and 2nd centers) predominate as inactivity (tamas guna) and a very limited capacity for awareness. At the navel (3rd center), more outward-bound mentality and reactive personality exists, and then from the heart and above (4th – 6th centers), a person's consciousness is reflective and much more supportive of their evolution.[109] Many so-called theologians have interpreted this popular Christian verse about mansions in a more literal manner. They make references related to architecture or even the actual structure Jesus was in during the last supper, but they all have missed the importance of understanding such teachings that use allegory and metaphor.

If we are to grow in our evolution, we must inquire into the nature of certain teachings and how they were derived. Unfortunately, the yogic teachings of Christ were not recognized as Vedic, largely because of the politics of the Roman Empire[110] which launched the start of Churchianity as Jesus was

---

108 John 14:2 King James Version.

109 The chakras, as part of Tantra Yoga, are centers of energy that open through consistent sadhana and lead to awakened prana or kundalini shakti, human potentiality. The seven centers are divided into three distinct regions where the energy can get tied up (granthi). The balance of sun (pingala) and moon (ida) channels, along with heart-centered consciousness, aids in opening all the centers and culminates in liberation, samadhi. The *Bhagavad Gita* refers to these three regions of consciousness as the gunas (tamas, rajas and sattva).

110 Council of Constantinople (A.D. 381). The Roman emperor known as Constantine the Great was the first to convert (he was originally Pagan) to Christianity and subsequently influenced the church to proclaim and recognize Jesus as "The only begotten Son of God." Constantine ordered the First Council of Nicaea in 325, which produced the statement of mainstream Christian belief known

proclaimed God and the savior of humanity. As a result of Roman conquest over the world, this religious decision was politically influenced, and created much of the divisiveness we see today between Judaic, Islamic, and Christian communities.

Jesus as a teacher or guru helped to awaken humanity to the real purpose of life: discovering the kingdom of heaven as something within us, restoring the importance of individual responsibility. It was not an easy time to enter the world and attempt to reform it, especially given what was occurring in the Middle East and Europe. Religious fractures were taking place centuries before Christ was born within Buddhism, Jainism, Sikhism, and then we see the development of Tantra and Hatha yoga systems in the last two millenniums. It is evident that humans are always seeking something regardless of the epoch. Followers of any spiritual path can seek to gain a clear understanding of what the path is and whether it resonates with their own constitution. They may ask, Does it follow patriarchal principles or does it regard the feminine and natural forces equally? Although yoga has evolved over the last two millenniums, and has been adapted to the times, its core principles, such as a personal-God (ishta devata), non-violence (ahimsa), self-discipline (tapasya), and devotion to the Divine (ishwara pranidhana) have always remained intact, regardless of the lineage or Guru. Yoga has always maintained an integral relationship with the natural world and a lifestyle that resonates with every individual.

as the Nicene Creed.

Chapter EIGHT

Listening and the Yoga of Action

When you know how to listen everybody is the guru.

Ram Dass

Esoteric Meaning of Listening

According to the Vedanta philosophy, the entire world is a projection of the mind. The mind is the projector of thoughts onto the screen of life. Projections are created by our recurring thoughts that are essentially subtle energetic vibrations that carry life-force energy. **The thoughts of the mind are projected into the world energetically.** Each thought is like an energy missile that shoots through the ether every time it arises in the mind. The more a thought is carried within the mind, the greater vibratory momentum it carries to manifest as a higher density of molecules and atoms, eventually manifesting into material existence. People who have a powerful mind can make their thoughts manifest very quickly while people who have a less developed mind have to repeat thoughts for perhaps many months or years before they actually manifest. A powerful mind is found in one's capacity to concentrate; thus, a focused mind is very powerful and can be used to create anything attention is placed on.

Through repeated embodiments, the soul carries with it the qualities and patterns of the past life. These appear in each life in the form as habits, many

THE EVOLUTION REVOLUTION *Yoga, Ayurveda, and the Rise of the Soft Power Culture*

of which we become aware of as tendencies and patterns within one's lifestyle. The mind carries these seed impressions or samskaras from one life to the next, particularly the deeply seated ones such as major events and repetitive experiences that shape a person's life. Each impression may lay dormant for months and years until as it continues to ripen (vasana). Eventually, every impression will either manifest into an actual desire (kama) or dissolve itself through spiritual purification practices or sadhana. Life on earth is made up of actions, events, and stories that animate our lives and keep us engaged in the stories of our time. For most of us, these events are important, and shape our attitudes, speech, and influence many of the choices we make. In other words, one's human nature is shaped by the environment one is most exposed to. As our environment changes, we are affected and influenced for better or worse. The interconnectedness of the human spirit with nature is the backbone of yogic thought.

According to the yoga tradition, the universe that we live in on the planet earth exists because of a vibrational field of energy known as **Hiranyagarbha**, the cosmic mind. This vibration is distributed into three parts or aspects that can be correlated to the earth (body), moon (mind), and soul (sun). In some yogic systems they are referred to as dimensions. We live in the world where the illusory power of maya is created by the perpetual cycles of the sun, moon, and earth as they revolve around each other. As they move, they create daytime and nighttime, and the positive and negative polarities that are the foundation for the fundamental laws of life on earth. These three planets can be considered the original factors that gave rise to the human being and the three bodies that make up every human being.

As briefly mentioned in chapter two, this trinity can also be seen in the human brain with hind, or reptilian, brain correlated to the earth, the mid, or emotional, brain correlated to the moon, and the frontal brain, or cerebral cortex, correlated with the sun. These three energies of earth, moon, and sun also make up the quality of the consciousness (gunas) that emanate through the chakras (energy centers along the spine) with the earth ruling the first three chakras, the moon at the heart and the sun at the top, symbolic of illumination. The moon and the heart are interconnected and correlated to the fickleness of the mind. This equates to a personality which lacks commitment and maintains an unsteady nature. The human being is essentially a small replica of the grander universe.

The Vedic culture of India thrived in the exploration of these distinct entities, and the three layers of human existence comprise one of the most fascinating yogic teachings. The study of the body, and the laws of healing the operations of what we call the fleshy body, developed into a unique system of medicine called ayurveda. As I explained in my first book, ***Sun, Moon, and Earth***, the fragmentation of the mind-body relationship is the basis for disease and disorder or what is referred to in ayurveda as ***dosha***. Ayurveda is a science of learning to listen to the body, its needs, signs, and symptoms. For example, even today, modern medical science has discovered the very close inter-relationship the gut shares with the mind and heart.

Listening is the formative power of the soul. Listening becomes the most essential skill with regards to the mind-body relationship. Your body is your little piece of earth, your ecology that you can connect to and listen to. The body is a guru in this sense because it has a language of expressions with different signs and significant symptoms. The body's most subtle form of expression is in the feelings which are interpreted by the neurological and motor systems and then beyond in the thoughts and cognitive aspects of the mind. As feeling is experienced physically through the central nervous system, it is connected to Vata dosha in ayurveda, and for this reason much emphasis is placed on balancing vata. Vata is linked to how one feels, to the nervous system, and to the mind.

If the mind is disturbed, then one can become distracted from the body and potentially ignore messages the body it is trying to communicate. On one level, the capacity we have for feeling comes through of the body. On a higher and more sublime level when feeling is blended with attitude it is referred to as ***bhavana***, one of the most important factors in spiritual evolution. When we blend positive feeling that is derived from the heart with a positive attitude it yokes the head with the heart to produce a thrusting energy of spiritual progression, even though a person's actions may not be consistent. Feeling positive can also be equated with thinking positively. Feeling good begins with how we feel in relationship to our body, and this requires communicating with it. Be careful not to confuse this with listening to the endless sensory demands experienced by the senses that come from mental conditioning.

It's important to distinguish the two: reacting to negative impressions is different from listening to positive feeling.

Whether it is emotional eating, over-eating, or many of the other poor eating habits we bombard the body with, our choices reflect our mental quality; and vice-versa, what one experiences or, better yet, feels in the gut, is indicative of the mind-heart interplay. When a person goes on ignoring the more subtle signals of the gut and signals felt in the heart, the body proceeds to provide increasingly visible signs of disharmony. These symptoms give us something to look at, ponder, and try to understand.

Science has demonstrated that a brain-gut connection exists via the vagus nerve, which serves to control the parasympathetic nervous system. The vagus nerve releases the neurotransmitter norepinephrine into the amygdala which controls our stored emotional experiences in the brain and influences the heart rate variability. The release of norepinephrine into the amygdala occurs when a thought is connected to a prior trauma or experience of the ego. The ego correlates the thought to the past trauma or mental impression and reacts as if the same experience is occurring again, when in actuality, the recent experience has nothing to do with the past one. This is the sad case found in most intimate relationships where one blames the other for things neither person is responsible for. Think of the amygdala part of the brain like soil that can hold water, and the water is made of the tears derived from all types of emotions and traumatic experiences. If one continues to water the soil with emotions, the soil becomes damp enough that things begin to grow and manifest as actual events.

In the drama of life, emotions are energy in motion. These emotions are also responsible for influencing the inner systemic and organ functions of the body. Thus, what ayurveda knew thousands of years ago is now being rediscovered and confirmed by modern medical science, that psychology and biology are interrelated. For example, modern psychotherapy methods such as EMDR[111] release memory of traumatic events stored in the amygdala through repetitive bilateral stimulation in the form of eye movements, taps, or sounds while recalling or focusing on a certain image. This process of left-right stimulation is essentially desensitization of the action-reaction conditioning patterning that perpetuates drama and the entire world process. Both yoga and ayurveda understood the importance of neutralizing (nirodha)

---

111 Eye Movement Desensitization and Reprocessing was developed by psychologist Francine Shapiro in the 1980s as she noticed that bilateral eye movement reduced the reoccurrence of stress events and emotional patterns.

the mind through a balance of two primary forces that are the cornerstone of healing and evolution: this is the balancing of the sun and moon channels, or left and right sides of the brain. Scientific psychotherapy methods such as EMDR have now discovered and applied the principles in practice.

Ayurveda embraces this concept in another way as it aims to balance two forces it refers to as agni (solar) and soma (lunar). Agni (solar) aspect brings balance to pitta dosha imbalances commonly associated with anger. Soma (lunar) aspect brings balance to vata and kapha and their respective imbalances in the form of fear and depression. Through yogic practices, these two aspects of the mind-body complex, or mind-heart-gut dynamic, calm the breath through specialized breathing techniques (pranayama), mantra and meditation, thereby reducing the heart rate. When the breath is calm, the mind becomes more receptive to disengaging from the modifications of the mind as taught in Vedantic philosophy. The techniques that make it easier to gain control over the heart allow for greater management over our emotions, a major factor in the creation or resolution of life's obstacles. All of these principles substantiate that breath control equals self-control. The mind and body (gut) connection is established through a more calm and relaxed state of mind, and this encapsulates one of the basic steps in learning to listen.

By relaxing the heart, a generalized relaxation response is induced; this signal of safety and serenity is distributed through the vagus nerve between the brain, heart, and gut. The relaxation response is a modern term that can be used to describe a bio-neurological function that occurs in the body, induced by the brain, and that produces a reflective mental quality likened to introspection and meditation. The term "relaxation response" was coined by Herbert Benson, a professor at Harvard University, who did research in the 60s and 70s on monks meditating and chanting. However, interestingly enough, this inner process that occurs, this shifting the mind from an active state to a more subdued state, was described as ***pratyahara*** by the great Rishi Patanjali in his Yoga Sutras during the second century B.C.

The healing of the mind comes through the application of the science of yoga, its methods of meditation or concentration, breathing exercises, mantra (primordial sounds), reflection, and introspection. Although yoga also has the profound Hatha Yoga system for healing and preparing the body for attaining higher states of awareness, it is only a small part of a much larger system of evolution. Yoga provides lifestyle efficiency tools to the laws of karma, helping to transform our responses to our suffering, pain, and disharmony. Additionally, through practices of gratitude, devotion, and detachment we can reduce the causes of suffering, pain, and disharmony by simplifying our desires. Emotions are energies, and if properly directed and used in a more efficient manner, emotions can awaken something within us that we never knew existed. Discovering this inner domain of contentment is the promise of yoga because it makes life much simpler.

Salutations to the Earth

According to the laws of karma, we are born into this world, and the experience we call life, simply because we have something to learn and desires to fulfill. In Sanskrit, the planet earth is referred to as a **bhulokha** or the domain of primary consciousness. In more humorous terms, we could call life on earth as kindergarten schooling for humanity because of the perpetual drama (lila) that entertains humans. From the Vedantic perspective, the primary purpose of earthly life is twofold. Firstly, it serves as a place where humans can enjoy themselves and the beauty of Mother Nature as a gift of compassion from God. The second purpose is the remembrance of one's true nature, to experience the true reality hidden behind all human experiences.

This reality, the Divine life force is flowering within nature, in the vibrations of the trees, rivers, animals, and all of creation. Let our spirits be alive in celebration and dance with nature. What perpetuates the drama of life, making it an extended journey with repeated cycles of life and death is the law of maya. Maya has two aspects, avidya (ignorance) and vidya (knowledge). As a result of the spell and delusion of maya, we dwell in avidya, ignoring our true nature, increasing our attachment to objects of life, the people, places, and things. We do this because the mind has associated its happiness with those objects.

Ignorance creates a deep state of delusion (moha). One is deluded to the degree that a multitude of negative forces enter the mind. These are jealousy, greed, anger, pride, along with a constant craving that never ends until all desires are fulfilled; even then, another desire springs up just when we thought we had everything we needed.

Alternatively, when our lives are guided by the pure intelligence that pervades all living things, when we dwell in vidya (knowledge), it becomes much easier to enjoy this world without becoming bound to it. In other words, any form of clinging (abhinivesha) to life is obliterated.

When we hold on to life as if it were the basis for our happiness and content-ment, the fear of death influences many of the decisions we make. In fact, much of the world lives with the attitude of, "I will live forever," and neglects to understand the importance of the impermanence of life.

The practice of yoga helps you develop an ever-growing understanding that, "I am not the body," and you learn to work with your body as a tool. This means taking care of it, so you know you can depend on it when you need it, while at the same time learning to detach from it because it's not who you really are. Isn't that what humanity does unconsciously every day? People use and abuse their bodies day after day and then in sleep, they drop all identification with it. Well, integral yoga teaches us how to create the most efficient path to replicate this beyond-the-body experience, the conscious version of it.

The journey there requires that you develop virtues through activities. The body is a miniature representation of the earth and has been considered, in Vedic-Indic culture, to be a tool for performing many sacred rituals that invoke the Divine within and awaken greater healing potential for dispelling diseases and negativity. That healing potential is the life force (prana).

In the Hindu religion, temple dances like Bharatanatyam and mohiniyattam were sacred dance forms. They were performed by groups of dancers called **devadasis** and offered during many of the religious festivals and other special events correlated to auspicious planetary periods. These performing arts are ascribed to a yogi-sage named Bharata Muni who wrote of them in the Natya Shastra.[112] These two dances hail from the Indic-Sanskrit traditions. Along with many other forms of artistic expression, they were commingled with the Hatha yoga school's teachings, as can be seen in gestures such as the eye gazes, hand gestures (mudras), and many of the standing open leg stance postures. The Natya Shastra also mentions two other dance styles, the **lasya** and **tanadava** and are said to have been created by Parvati and her husband Shiva. Shiva is the great teacher of yoga and the tandava style is derived from ananda tandava, Shiva's dance of bliss as Nataraja, with the symbolic of the force of destruction as seen in his signature stomping of the feet. The lasya style was correlated to the creative force and reflects more feminine fluid movements.

---

112 *Natya Shastra* is a Sanskrit text that compiled by Bharata Muni and presents the world's most comprehensive manual on all the major subjects of the arts including dance, acting, body gestures, music, musical scales and how to integrate music into artistic performances. Dated at approximately 200 B.C., but some date the text more recently, at 200 C.E.

When I first began to explore the connection between postural yoga and dance, I had the impetus to open my first center in Hollywood, California called Dancing Shiva.[113] Even though the center was mostly dedicated to yoga and ayurveda, it was also a cultural center that offered a variety of Indian dance classes. I integrated a fusion of yoga and dance forms into my classes. To me, the center was a tribute to the best of India's wisdom and art traditions, as it offered cooking (ahara vigyan), astrology (jyotish), Vedic architecture (vaastu) classes and more.

Bharatanatya dancer demonstrating various intricate mudras (hand and eye gestures).

The art forms that were an integral part of ancient Indian society and that have continued over the last two millennia, show the use of the body, accompanied by music, to tell stories. This was known as **Abhinaya**, physical storytelling, and always begins with a gesture called **Bhumi Pranam** to honor and offer respect to the earth as the guru. The entire process of the dance arts is designed to convey two elements, **rasa**, the flavor and essence of the story, and **bhava**, the emotional state or mood that listeners may be in while the story is told. The dances tell stories, many of them come from epic scriptures like the Ramayana and Puranic literature.

Like classical dance, classical Indian music (Gandharva) also intends to convey two elements, **raga**, the structure of the melody or scale, and **tala**, the timing or setting. One of the original Vedic texts, the Samaveda, is completely organized in a melodic (raga) manner and the famous Gayatri mantra of the

---

113   The Dancing Shiva Yoga & Ayurveda center (2001-2012).

Rigveda is also embedded with a musical meter. These arts and the multitude of creative forms exist to express human devotion for the Divine presence that exists on earth and within all living beings that inhabit earth.

When one can recognize the earth as sacred, then humanity has the potential to attain a harmonious relationship with the Divine. These teachings are considered to be both artistic and scientific and provide a bridge that separates the human spirit from nature. Humanity has lost its intrinsic connection to nature, in part, because modern science and medicine do not embrace the laws of karma, rebirth, or maya, and they have not fully embraced the importance of prevention as a vital approach to health and wellbeing.

Ayurveda provides an ideal means for educating humanity and teaches us how to live in harmony with nature, her cycles, and to see the human body as a smaller version of the grand universe. The power of listening is an inherent aspect of the mind-body complex, however, it must be accessed and exercised so that its function can serve as a power of the soul. The power of listening is not merely a sensory one but provides a profound discipline for creating spiritual abundance. Ayurveda teaches us how to listen to our personal body and how to listen to the Divine body of the earth. Yoga teaches how to access a more subtle form of listening that allows one to see the energy behind all activities, the intelligence behind all phenomenon, and to gain insight into the force of creativity that embraces the diverse and customized ways one can work toward spiritual evolution.

Listening with the Mind

The power of listening, in the highest sense, is derived through the mind and is otherwise known as intuition. The mind is a powerful instrument that can allow us to create anything we want or need. The mind is more important than the body from the yogic perspective, because the mind is what controls the body, the nervous system, and our senses. All operations of the body are the results, the effects, of the quality of the consciousness that is being cultivated in the mind.

Take care of your body, but take a little more care of your mind, purify it, train it, and expand it beyond its conditioning. The yoga and Vedanta systems have studied and accessed the potentials of the mind unlike any other tradition or culture. The comprehensive and detailed teaching about personal responsibility and the pathway to enlightenment is the culmination of Eastern thought, although during the British Empire's attempt at colonizing the world, the Christian doctrine of an afterlife in heaven or hell slowly expunged this ideal from society. Christian teachings removed the importance of personal responsibility as connected to spiritual evolution because heaven and hell became places that one ends up after death. It contrasts with Vedanta which explains enlightenment as an experience that one can attain while living in the body; you don't have to go anywhere outside of your own existence to attain heaven, you can experience heaven at the very center of your own existence. Feeling heavenly is what we really are meant to be doing, right here and now.

The attainment of a strong, steady, and focused mind is the highest aim of yoga, and is also expressed in Buddhist teachings. In yoga, the mind is used like a flashlight to explore layers or dimensions of consciousness within the body temple. The mind can be utilized for looking within, and through this process of internalization, the mind can expand into new vistas of understanding and for cultivating greater compassion. Initially, the aspirant (sadhaka) may choose to connect to the Divine in either a masculine or feminine form or even as an animal within nature such as the special deity Ganesha (Ganapati). However, as consciousness expands into broader domains of awareness, the form or image is dropped, and the Divine experience becomes about unification with the nameless and formless field of unconditioned consciousness.

The practice of spiritual listening is brought about by shifting the mind into a reflective state of awareness; it is here in this state that can one experience the power of observation. It is powerful because the observed becomes a mere object that has no influence over your mind or life. Through observation, the mind attains the power of nonattachment (vairagya) and creates an inner feeling of freedom, but simultaneously maintains a compassionate connection to the observable world. In such an instance, one can see an object, appreciate it, yet not feel compelled to need it in any way. In this way, the mind can discriminate between actual needs and countless fleeting desires that pass through the mind constantly. Spiritual listening produces the capacity within our consciousness to see the Divine hand behind the things that we don't usually understand. The wisdom of yoga is derived from the broader culture of Vedic knowledge that recognizes that a supreme consciousness exists as **Purusha**, a term that later evolved to **Brahman** (God), as the source of all creation.

The "listening" is a higher form of observing, using the potential of the reflective mind to observe the world. Through observation of the actions in the world and in our own life, we eliminate the distinction between the doer and observer.

Purusha is the formless or passive dimension of consciousness that upholds the cycles of the sun, moon, earth, and the entire cosmology of our solar system. It is the magnetic force that draws humans to pro-create and share in this energy that awakens within us. The power of purusha is within each of us and exists as the capacity we all have to witness the world and cultivate the attitude in life that, "I am not the doer." This is a pathway to understanding the nature of karma and the grander flow of the world cycles. This force moves through us with tremendous power, yet humans struggle with surrendering to it, and characterize it as an energy beyond our control. Even though we use the mind to attain such an inner power of consciousness, we must also realize its limitations when we only use the mind's functions of the ego, thoughts, emotions and senses.

Spiritual listening produces one of the highest virtues: patience. It is the capacity to surrender and trust in the dharma, the higher laws of evolution. Listening is requisite to the attainment of patience. When we listen, we observe the grand drama of the world as a spectator and allow it to guide us, inform us, and move us into proper action. Proper action means living in accordance with nature's laws and in alignment with one's personal purpose according to one's distinct qualities. The best means for the adherence to nature's laws is found in the wisdom of ayurveda. Yoga looks to ayurveda to fulfill this eternal relationship that all humans intrinsically share with nature. The ayurvedic lifestyle creates receptivity with nature, enhancing subtle energetic sensitivities that promote spiritual listening.

Initially, the relationship with nature and her elements begins as a type of purification of earth element and the removal of all gross impurities like foods, body toxins, mucous congestion, and excess fat. Most of these can be addressed with diet, herbs, and spices, and even postural yoga and breathwork (pranayama). This becomes especially important for those body (prakriti) types that are predominant in kapha (earth-water). Ayurveda aims at promoting lightness of the body so that the inner light of awareness, clarity, and insight illumines your entire disposition. As consciousness expands, so does the body's independence from gross food elements to sustain it. Along with this expansion and freedom, immunity (ojas) becomes a vital factor to spiritual evolution. In higher ages of global consciousness, humanity will learn to nourish the body via the breath, the light of the sun, and finer mineral compositions (shilajit)[114] derived from rock and soils that can be combined to create special types of teas and tonics. Herbal tonics go a long way to support the lightness of the body while still nourishing it. Currently, the human body has become a garbage disposal for the reckless violence committed against animal life and our consumption of processed foods.

Ayurvedic living changes the entire vibration and aura of a person, and even beyond that, it supports good skin tone and reduces inner inflammation. Inflammation is commonly seen today in people as they age, because of inorganic or genetically modified foods, meat consumption, alcohol, and prescription medications. These types of food elements put strain on the liver and spleen, thus increasing inner heat that gets trapped inside from an over-burdening of all systemic functions. That inner heat is called pitta in ayurveda and referred to as inflammation in modern health terminology. Attaining the capacity to listen spiritually requires changes to attitude and lifestyle.

Listening to the Body

Let us explore this idea of listening to the body and perhaps understand the many ways that it can serve you. While most of the world is dominated by the outer mind, the desires of their conditioned mind and senses, intuitive listening provides a way to develop the inner mind, by hearing what exists beyond the superficial level. The body speaks to us in three ways and uses the language of what ayurveda calls *tridosha* (balanced health or homeostasis). This system of tridosha is an insightful approach to categorizing the body's biological and systemic functions into three distinct functions. Learning to listen to the body begins with understanding the qualities of each of the elements, air, fire, and water, as related to the doshas.

Air qualities: cool, light, subtle, moving, erratic, rough, dry.

- Vata dosha: controls all circulatory functions in the body; circulation of

---

114 Shilajit is a black rock tar-like substance derived from the Indian Himalayas and other parts of the world. In ayurvedic medicine it is considered an important rasayana (rejuvenative) and used for increasing strength, immunity, and overall vitality. Shilajit is a favorite supplement of the yogis.

fluids like blood, and gases like oxygen. The final step of digestion, the elimination of the bowels, is a function of vata as the stool descends through the colon. Bowel movements are the final process of the digestive system which depends on good circulation for its function.

Fire qualities: hot, sharp, transformative, oily.

• Pitta dosha: controls metabolism and assimilation of foods through the small intestine. The heat of metabolism and the heat of circulating blood produces sweat to cool the body as it disperses heat, cooling the body and removing impurities. Pitta performs all functions of extracting nutrients from food during digestion.

Water qualities: heavy, cold, soft, oily, stable, moist.

• Kapha dosha: is defined as phlegm and is responsible for lubricating the body. Fluids aids in the absorption of nutrients in the stomach, serving as one of the primary steps of digestion. Kapha, as adipose tissue, provides fat to the body and aids in flexibility and mobility of the skeletal system. This function of kapha allows the tissues to grow and become sturdy and strong.

These qualities describe the nature of the elements in the body in their natural state. However, when a person's lifestyle is not in accordance with nature's laws, then the inherent intelligence of nature is blocked, thus producing mind-body fragmentation. When we speak of being out of balance, it means that each of the elements are not equal to one another. In other words, when an element is increased in relationship to the other, this creates an excess referred to as dosha in the body. The doshas create symptoms that create discomfort and may lead to further complications in areas of the body, leading to systemic disorders such as diabetes or gastrointestinal syndromes. The most important area in which to observe doshic function is the digestive process.

Vata should be observed in the colon and represents the final stage of elimination. Pitta governs the small intestine and is responsible for secretion of bile as a part of metabolism between the liver and gall bladder. Kapha is mainly a function of the stomach, however, it is largely also connected to the lungs. Apart from chewing foods, which is considered the first step in good digestion serving to strengthen metabolism, the stomach is the first organ responsible for the initial steps in the lengthy digestive process which can take 3-5 hours to fully complete. This is one of many reasons why a meat-based diet creates a propensity towards obesity, diabetes, and heart disease because meats are heavy and delay the metabolic process (jatharagni).

The first step in listening to the body begins with the stomach because it is where food first settles into the body. It is important to note that the stomach is the most sensitive organ in the body, yet it is the most abused through improper diet and a lack of habituation (satmya). The term **satmya** comes from the root **sat**, meaning truth and **mya**, meaning what is consistent and related to me or mine-ness. So, the basic dietary question to ask yourself is, Are these foods good for me or right for my constitution? Whether it be too many fluids while eating, or improper food combinations, the metabolism gets disturbed, and this can lead to an increase of waste in the body.

If such disturbances to the stomach are ignored, it indicates a lack of listening. Listening is the intrinsic connection given to humanity for avoiding health issues. The stomach loves continuity, especially after the age of 50 when the body enters its most sensitive stage (vata-dosha). The organ of the stomach lies on the left side of the torso just below the rib cage and next to the descending colon. The left side of the body is considered lunar, thus inducing the qualities of the moon-like sensitivity, gentleness, and cool energy. Even though the stomach is somewhat near the descending colon, the food must travel quite a distance before it finally descends out of the colon on the left side of the torso. The way the stomach feels after we eat is an indication of balance or lack of balance. After you eat is a great time to analyze the body's response to food and how it is performing its digestive function. If there is discomfort in the stomach, bloating, nausea, heaviness, or a bulging feeling, then the body is informing us that something is out balance. This indicates that perhaps kapha dosha is in excess in the form of high moisture, dampness, and phlegm.

One of the best things anyone can do after meals to promote balanced (samagni) digestion is to lie for a few minutes, or longer, in a left lateral position as this takes the pressure off the liver and shifts blood flow towards the stomach to aid in assimilation of the newly deposited foods. Walking is also very helpful after meals because when standing up on the feet, it increases the body's temperature (fire element) and increases metabolic strength. Sleeping after eating is one of the worst habits as it weakens digestive fire, increases body fat, and disturbs the mind so that it has trouble entering the deep sleep state.

A weak digestive fire (metabolism) is responsible for most health issues, because food that is not properly digested will leave behind waste elements (ama) in the gastrointestinal tract. Waste elements become toxic and eventually create symptoms in different areas of the body depending on various factors. This residual waste is also responsible for chronic diseases like colon or rectal cancer that begin with the growth of polyps, providing a site for cancer to begin its initial spread through the body. Sadly, cancer has become the second leading cause of death just behind heart disease. Colorectal cancers have one of the highest morbidity rates. According to the latest cancer research,[115] lung cancer has the highest morbidity rate, and colon and rectal cancer have the second highest. In my experience, these illnesses can be thwarted with changes in lifestyle, diet and exercise.

High kapha can increase the risk of lung cancer because of excess dampness and mucous in the lungs. Many factors contribute to this, including lack of exercise, late night eating before sleep, a meat and dairy based diet, diabetes, and toxicity of the blood created by smoking, prescription medication, air pollutants, and other genetic and karmic factors observable in the astrological birth chart.

Sleep and Listening

One of the most essential factors in cultivating a keen capacity to listen to imbalances in the body is sleep. Attaining sound sleep is difficult these days in the age of technology. Sound sleep can be better described as deep, as sleep states can be viewed as being various layers of the mind. The subconscious layer is correlated to the dream state, while the deep sleep state is closest to the unconditioned state of pure consciousness. The main value of deep sleep is attributed to what ayurveda refers to as *ojas*, the primal energy that charges the body so that it can operate, feel lively, and perform its many complex functions. The concept of ojas can most specifically be attributed to immunology.

The average person spends one-third of each day of their life sleeping, yet most of the world is still riddled with health issues. This is because they do not maintain proper immune function to sustain homeostasis. Even though people continue to sleep their lives away, when they awaken, they still have

---

115 Research provided by the National Cancer Institute, 2021.

to deal with the compounded health issues of the body. So, one must question not only what they do in their lifestyle, but also question if they actually have good quality sleep. The fact is that both lifestyle and sleep have become major factors in health today. Good sleep is not merely limited to turning off the senses or exhausting the body through exercise, excessive work, food and alcohol, or even sex, it involves the transcendence of the mind.

Transcending beyond the conscious or waking state and beyond the subconscious or dream state, to the unconscious state, the most subtle layer of deep sleep, is the goal. How can we differentiate between the subconscious and unconscious state of mind? According to Vedanta, the conscious and subconscious mind are correlated to the astral body, while the unconscious and superconscious mind belong to the causal body. The unconscious mind contains the deepest impressions from experiences of many past lives. The unconscious mind is beyond the ego. It has no orientation to name or form and if one enters through yogic practices it can lead to spiritual enlightenment. However, if one is to enter the unconscious mind through sleep, drugs, or as a result of some accidental state, they may be temporarily freed of their problems, but it does not result in evolution. Such an entry into the unconscious is a temporary escape and does not result in real healing because it occurs involuntarily. This is the case with persons who resort to taking what is referred to as "plant medicine"[116] or other hallucinogenic drugs, they experience a temporary freedom and become aware of subtler karmas; however, they are not healing the karmas. The result of experiencing them in this state can do tremendous damage to the brain, nervous system, and stomach. These drugs temporarily cripple the brain and nerves. When the mind is forced to disconnect from these bodily instruments, it creates hallucinations, and this adds another layer of illusion to the force of maya that we are already contending with. The use of these foreign agents is extreme and reflects a desperate attempt for attaining peace of mind. Their use is very detrimental for attaining quality deep sleep.

If a person, through proper natural lifestyle and yogic disciplines, can regularly establish their sleep in the deep sleep state, they are creating a vital platform for attaining the super conscious state of enlightenment. In my view, the sub-

---

116 Ayahuasca is considered a psychoactive hallucinogenic tea-brew prepared by a shaman or curandero (healer) and originated in the Amazon regions as well as other parts of Central and South America such as Ecuador, Colombia, Peru, and Brazil.

conscious mind is one of the most effective forms for teaching oneself how to overcome many shortcomings through the practice of positive affirmations, mantra, concentration techniques, and meditation. The subconscious state is where our habit patterns (samskaras) are stored, and our subconscious mind fills our days with behaviors that do not always necessarily support good immunity.

The unconscious mind contains subtler desires (vasanas) that have yet to manifest into desires (kama). All desire is a result of a previous impression (positive or negative) with negative impressions being influenced as a result of ignoring (avidya) the true purpose of life. Positive impressions are developed through good associations, healthy lifestyle, and yoga practice in general. Good sleep empowers our capacity to listen, feel, and transcend the mind beyond the sensory level to a more refined intuitive level that empowers us to listen. Listening to the body requires developing a sensitivity of the mind that utilizes the nervous system as its instrument for attaining knowledge of what is going on in the body temple.

There are several exercises one can do before sleep to improve our capacity to listen to the body. The ideal state of sleep is to reach the deep sleep state where there is no dreaming or any recollection of being asleep. Deep sleep is so profound that upon waking, one even feels somewhat heavy but very rested; it produces a feeling of having gone far away from the waking world. One feels profoundly rested and attains a lightness in the mind; there is a sense of bewilderment and perhaps even questioning, Where did I go? Good sleep is rarely known anymore except by those who have the proper lifestyle to support it, or more importantly, a broadened level of awareness that is beyond the senses and egoism.

Deep sleep begins with integrating a period of winding down in the evening for one to two hours prior to bedtime. This allows the resting heart rate to decrease and brings greater calmness to the mind. Winding down includes limiting computer use and not engaging in tasks that over burden the mind with too much thinking. The antithesis to an active mind is a focused one. Concentration involves internalizing one's awareness similar to how internalization occurs through the process of meditation. Excessive thinking is the nemesis to good sleep. Even though reading and writing are relaxing and meditative in one aspect, in another aspect, they can trigger imagination and over activate the mind.

Meditation is the most ideal practice to include into your evening routine. This can be a simple silent meditation that emphasizes stillness, or practice can also include reciting a mantra or alternate nostril breathing. One should avoid eating for two to three hours before going to sleep. Drinking some warm milk (according to your preferred type) spiced with ginger, turmeric, and/or saffron is helpful. Herbal tea prior to bedtime can also be helpful and calming to the nervous system, as long as the herbs are not diuretics. Another simple ayurvedic practice is to massage some warm sesame oil or dosha (constitution) specific body oil onto the soles of the feet, ankles, the calves, the ears, and the top of the head.

Subtle Forms of Listening to the Body

Food in ayurvedic medicine is referred to as *ahara*. This concept can also refer to what we take in and how we absorb it. On this more subtle level, ahara signifies the mind as it impressed by outer stimuli and for our health, the stimuli must be nourishing us. If the stimuli are disturbing our state of consciousness, the negativity will lead to ill health. If what you take in throughout the day constitutes junk, such as impressions of negative media, gossip, excessive stimuli of any sort, such as loud and unnatural sounds, then this negativity will likely replicate itself internally within your psychology and eventually physiology.

 Listening to the body may begin on the physical level; however, it must extend to a more subtle form of listening to how one feels with regards to the quality of their consciousness. If one is feeling heavy, dull, depressed, tired, and unmotivated, then this represents the negative forms of consciousness. The negative forms have been perpetuated through excessive materialism, overwhelming sensory stimulation, lack of circulation, lack of exercise, and poor associations. Negative people affect others in the same manner; their vibration, over time, begins to rub off, and unless one has a very strong will and discipline over their mind, negative people become overbearing. Similar to what happens when you walk past a foul-smelling garbage can, someone with a negative attitude influences those around them, and this can change the expression on your face and create a feeling of aversion.

Our environment is everything because everything holds energy and the interplay between your mind and the environment determines the quality of your life. This quality of negative and heavy consciousness is referred to as *tamasic* in the Sanskrit wisdom language and it is what I often refer to as the doubting Thomas syndrome.[117] The body, and especially the mind, are like sponges that absorb everything they are exposed to. Thus, it is important to choose your environment carefully if you want to attain the power of listening.

When the mind is outward bound, overactive, aggressive, or competitive, the true self is hidden, and the ego-mind predominates. Such people may be effective at completing tasks, but they miss out on the hidden language of the Divine intelligence that reverberates within the heart and soul. Their mentality is so engrossed in the outer task at hand that they lose sight of the indwelling consciousness that is sustaining their entire being. Being productive is important, but not at the price of an attitude that fails to contact the sensitive qualities of the heart and soul. This type of energy, the soft power of the heart and soul, is referred to as *rajasic* in Sanskrit.

When the body and mind are settled in the soft power of the soul, energy is fresh and accessible at any time. This real energy is will power and it becomes available at any time; it's merely a matter of where and when it is needed. Will power can be accessed for completing any task. The body becomes like a machine that accesses the battery power (ojas) of the soul in the most efficient manner. The mind relays energy to the body consistently, and depending on the task, it may pause for a break to avoid over heating or exhausting the body. One can learn how to access this primal quality of consciousness while avoiding overburdening the body and its systems. Both the mind and body find perfect efficiency through infinite consciousness.

In Eastern thought, the body is regarded as a temple that holds sacred energy for the pursuit of the supreme Divine experience. This type of communication between the mind and body are referred to as *sattvic* in Sanskrit. The ideal behind the ancient wisdom traditions is that we train the mind how to listen to the body, be aware of it, and recognize that a clear and positive attitude must predominate to keep tamas and rajas in check, promoting their positive qualities: stability and responsible activity.

All three energies (gunas) have a positive purpose; however, the sattvic mind, or higher brain (frontal cortex), must be activated so that it can access

---

117 The phrase 'a doubting Thomas' is a direct reference to the biblical story of the apostle Thomas, who refused to believe that the resurrected Jesus had been seen by the other apostles until he could actually see and feel the wounds Jesus received during his crucifixion.

the intuitive powers of the mind. The brain is the organ, the mind is the instrument, and the soul is the power they borrow energy from in order to operate and live harmoniously in the world. The main point to understand here is that it's natural for the body to feel heavy at times, and such energy serves a purpose in helping us to fall asleep, to feel grounded, to be a stable, and to offer reliable and consistent friendships. However, when this energy becomes blemished by the ego, the energy can turn into negative traits, and this impairs us. We then lose the power of listening because the ego relies on the sensory mind with its vulnerable whims and desires, and ego-based responses are often derived from previous conditioning instead of accessing the fresh and organic insights of the higher or buddhi mind.

Likewise, having the desire to be active, productive, enjoy exercising, these are positive forms of our personality; However, when the ego gets involved, such an outbound energy turns foul as aggression, competition, and even greed. The magic of learning to listen to the body is that one can differentiate between what is enough and what is too much. When the power of the positive mind is accessed and maintains control over tamas and rajas, it promotes a harmonious lifestyle.

The Three Regions of the Body

According to ayurveda, yoga's sister science, the body can be divided into three sections as per the influence of the biological doshas. These three sections of the body are related to the organs and anatomy that are controlled by the doshas, and they are categorized based on their location in correlation to the spinal column. The lower lumbar is influenced by the element of air in the form of vata dosha, the middle or thoracic spine is associated with the element of fire in the form of pitta dosha, and the upper or cervical spine is influenced by the element of water in the form of kapha dosha.

Listening to the spine is another way to connect to the body. Postural yoga is ideal in this regard because it is basically a system of bridging the mind-body relationship through connection to the spine via the postures. Each posture affects the body in a different manner and sends progress reports to the mind about how it feels. This is what differentiates the postural yoga system of the hatha yoga tradition from modern fitness and sports that can be harsh and stressful on the entire body. The foremost yogi of the Nath sect, Goraksna-tha, knew that when you place the body into various postures, extensions, compressions, lateral, twisting etc., it affects both the nervous system and the internal anatomy. The Hatha yoga texts use an esoteric language that describe the realm of the energy body, chakras, and the five pranas. Although, there are some Hatha texts that do describe the therapeutic benefits of postural yoga in a more mundane form.

Listening to Nature

Nature speaks to us with the language of feeling through the elements. Nature is the Goddess herself, inspiring us with her power and beauty in countless ways. Nature controls the great elements through the shifting seasons as a result of the cycles of the moon and earth. Each month, as the moon moves, so does the mind, influencing our thoughts, presenting us with new moods, emotions and our even our sensuality. The changing nature of the moon represents the natural fickleness of the mind. So, a mind without some connection to the body (earth) becomes fleeting like the clouds. Think of the clouds like our thoughts, restless and inconsistent. Therefore, we must be careful with the mind. The mind needs nature, earth, to stay calm and grounded; it must have something in which to be rooted.

In Vedic thought, the head represents the roots of the tree of consciousness; so, in other words, the human body is an upturned tree. This is the symbolism behind the yoga headstand pose where the head becomes planted into the earth. This topsy-turvy practice of the body is meant to ground the mind, reduce depression, improve circulation, and bring lightness to the personality. Often when I come across a person with a sour expression on their face who seems grumpy about some event in their life, I whisper to myself, *If I could only turn you upside down for a few minutes, it would help you clear your mind.* The bulk of society is caught up in the events and stories of life, and the current events so filled with dazzle and frazzle, that egos are kept entertained, yet deluded from the actual reality. This ego-based and mundane storied type of living in the world is a misuse of the mind and the senses. It leads one to become dull-witted.

Listening to nature helps the mind slow down, relax and restore. Nature is filled with activities that can draw our consciousness inward beyond the senses into the sacred space of the heart. The play of Divine Mother's creatures demonstrates different characteristics within us. Animals listen to nature. As the seasons shift, so do their activities, and this reflects their attunement to the grander force that exists. In ayurveda, the four major seasons are linked to the elements, so when the seasons change, the elements change, and so does the human body. Ayurveda encourages us to listen to nature through the seasons and adapt our lifestyle to each season in order to promote balance and harmony in the mind-body relationship.

The spring and fall seasons are largely influenced by the equinoxes[118] when the air element increases, creating dryness, and coolness. A shifting of energy occurs, as seen in the leaves changing colors and falling in September and October, and then, with the new leaves and flowers blooming in March and April. These periods influence the air element or vata dosha in us, and are often the cause of many imbalances related to the mind, nervous system, digestive irregularity, and poor sleep. The teachings that nature is providing humanity during these two major changes are to focus on slowing down, and to adapt our lifestyle in such a way that counterbalances the effects of vata during these two periods.

The winter and summer are influenced by two large shifts referred to as solstices.[119] The winter period influences the water element because of the increase in rain, colder temperatures, and overall dampness (amounts vary depending on where you live). These factors increase water in our body, slowing digestion, and making the mind feel a bit sluggish and on the heavier side. The winter is a period of kapha dosha. The summer heat is a result of the sun's position in the sky; the higher it is, the warmer it gets, and this culminates in the northern hemisphere on or around June 21st. As the outside temperature increases, so does the body's, and this provokes us to naturally search for cooling things like a cool stream to swim in, a large shady tree to meditate under, and some fresh fruits to refresh us. Although these things all seem natural, many people ignore the call of nature and ignore adapting to her changes. They eventually wait until they have created a disorder between the mind and body as a result of purely ignoring nature's presence. If you don't listen to nature, then you have a second opportunity to listen your own physical body because it will always tell you when the elements

---

118 Equinox is a particular time that occurs twice a year in September and March. The sun crosses the celestial equator, making day and night equal in length.

119 The word solstice is derived from the Latin sol, meaning the sun, and indicates two periods when the sun stands still, reaching its highest and lowest points in the sky. Solstices are marked by the longest and shortest days of the year.

are not in balance. However, if one does not listen to either (nature or body) then they are sleepwalking (unconscious) through life. The mind has been programmed by the conditions of society and is affected by the perpetual action and reaction dynamics that allow suffering to endure.

In the same way that one may observe the many creative material inventions that humans have offered to the world, one should also watch and wonder about the creative force that has given rise to all the wonders of nature. The mountains, rivers, trees, plants, animal kingdom, sunsets, sunrises, full moons, and more are all part of Divine Mother's creation, but what is the force that creates it, preserves it and eventually destroys it repeatedly? It is pure consciousness, what all living things are born from. Nature, with all her activities, is telling us something that we don't see, at first. However, she continues to speak, and often repeatedly shares the same point in different ways until finally we say, I hear you now very loud and clear. Although one might question, Where have you been? or, Why didn't you tell me this years ago when I needed to know this?

She responds, My dear child, I have been demonstrating to you everything that you are, everything that you think, say, and perform, but you have not heard me because you were occupied with the sensory pleasures of the world. To listen to Divine Mother's wisdom, one must understand the world as our own projections; that outer world is the world of our own mind. Beyond the mind, its thoughts, ego, and intellect, are the absolute Reality as pure consciousness. That realm is referred to as *sat*, the true Reality, and satsanga brings us closer to that experience. Sat-sanga is made up of two words, *sat*, truth, and *anga*, community or gathering. Satsangs are one of the cornerstones of spiritual evolution, as gathering improves our capacity to listen to nature as the material world of time and space, and we receive the subtle guidance that is available to us. Satsangs are spiritual gatherings where a group of aspirants (sadhakas) come together to hear a discourse on a scripture or topic as expressed by a guru, or dharmic leader, to aid in the purification of the mind. This topic of satsanga prepares us for the next step of learning that promotes evolution which we will cover in the next chapter.

The Language of Listening through Stillness

The highest form of listening occurs through the act of stillness. Through stillness, the mind becomes very calm and present, attentive, and aware. Stillness is the basis for hatha yoga in that, when a physical position is maintained, it brings great benefits to the body; however, more important is what holding still does for the mind. This has been largely overlooked in the postural yoga fitness movement because emphasis is placed on measurement of the body's capacity, but the mind is forgotten about. Stillness is the deepest level of our consciousness and characterizes the supreme state of existence. When the body is trained to be still, we become relaxed as a result of neurological response. When the mind is trained to be still, we feel peace, and the result is a clearer mind.

When discussing the principle of listening, we are not referring to sensory listening. Listening through the realm of deep inner stillness expands the power of awareness through observation. ***In stillness, the mind can engage its power to observe thoughts rather than meddle in them.*** When the mind can engage in observation, it transcends the trigger, the propulsion a thought can have to invoke emotion. Calmness and concentration go hand in hand. A concentrated mind that maintains physical tension does not permit the mind to detach from body consciousness. Although the form of listening that I am describing is derived from a more esoteric perspective, the listening practice begins with the basic listening that occurs in conversation. It can begin with the basic power of attention that every human deserves and appreciates in conversation; the power of attention and listening that reduces human communication errors and promotes understanding. As thoughtfully expressed by Simone Weil, "Attention is the rarest and purist form of generosity; it is given to very few minds to notice that things and beings exist."[120]

Stillness is a language that allows one to learn how to become more detached from the world process. When we listen to what stillness has to stay, we find a doorway into the profound power of forgiveness. We see this reflected in nature. For example, a calm lake has the capacity to reflect everything around it: trees, mountains, and you, when you stand next to the water. However, if the wind blows, the water becomes rippled, and all the reflections disappear. The lake itself is the entire field of the mind, including all the sediments, plants,

---

120 French Philosopher and mystic (1909 – 1942).

and even fish that enjoy living in lake. The wind is the nervous system which controls the how calm the water is. The water in the lake is the content, the thoughts, and the emotions of the mind. When you sit down to meditate next to the water of a still lake, you see your reflection as well as the reflection of all the natural elements that surround you. However, this time, as you are sitting, you realize that the reason you can see the lake, its water, and all the picturesque reflections, is because of the light of the sun shining from above. That light is your consciousness. Even though it appears to play a role in the events at the lake, it is merely allowing you to recognize your own power of reflection, and that the light is the source of your existence. Because the lake waters are completely still, this is possible, similar to the way the mind needs to be to become like the lake. When the mind is completely still it provides its higher language, and it teaches us to realize what is illuminating every aspect of our lives: the light of pure consciousness.

The Highest Listening

As one cultivates the power of listening to the body, this powerful art can also be applied to the entire world. All of life is a series of events and experiences that shape every aspect of the human complex. All of these activities are created and sustained within the laws of karma, also defined as the law of cause and effect. Listening to the world involves gathering guidance from those experiences that can potentially answer the many questions of life's mystery. How does one differentiate between egoistic projection of the mind and a truly transformative insight that provides the next step toward one's evolution? Egoistic projection can lead to supporting the troubles associated with a repeated pattern, and transformative insight can save us much time freeing us of a terrible burden. Cultivating the power of listening to the body comes down to the art of listening and one's level of sensitivity. The Vedantic technique of discernment or **viveka** becomes the secret to distinguishing what is meaningful and divine (shreya) from what is merely delightful and attractive (preya). Discriminative knowledge is intellect that can discern the difference between truth from falsehood, Real or unreal. Viveka provides the aspirant with greater efficiency on the spiritual path as it averts one from pursuing the illusions of the world. Viveka develops one's spiritual sensitivity and capacity to listen so that one can learn from the events and news of the world.

Karma Yoga[121] is an essential part of evolutionary living and one that can lead to liberation as determined by one's actions. At the very least, performing any service (seva) for a cause, organization, or perhaps a specific individual, can be very uplifting if one stays detached. As the yoga of action, Karma Yoga emphasizes performing actions with no self-interest or idea of gaining some reward for performing that action. In fact, one can experience profound joy when acting in such a way, as it removes the ego and attachment to a certain outcome. Although Karma Yoga specifically refers to the actions being performed by a person in service to others. Karma Yoga transforms individual thinking into collective thinking and as this process occurs one gains in attunement and knowledge from the collective consciousness that is operating in the world around you. As this transformation takes place, one's capacity to listen increases in acuity. The actions within the people, places and things taking place are happening for a reason, and it is your responsibility to get the message clear.

Whenever Karma Yoga is taking place in any form, one becomes receptive to hearing the message coming from the world because the ego consciousness is being removed by the action. Karma Yoga is a type of purification that removes the blemishes of the mind so that intuition becomes accessible; in this way, the world process becomes the living guru. Cosmic intelligence (mahat) pervades all living things and becomes an unlimited resource for evolutionary living. When you become aligned with this intelligence and you are able to listen to the world that surrounds you, the obstacles seem to dissolve, challenges become a test of will, and life begins to flow naturally. As Joseph Campbell once said, "Follow your bliss and the universe will open doors for you where there were only walls." Following one's bliss is about purposeful living in that your work and talents are being directed toward a particular task, to the point that one loses identity with the ego. Such work reflects progression in

---

121 Karma Yoga developed as an elaborate form of Karma Kanda, one of the three divisions of the Vedas. This is a result of the many rituals and practices (karma kanda) that were expressed in the Vedas and have gone on to shape the entire spiritual culture that still exists in India, millenniums later. The purpose of these active rituals is to remove impurities (malas) from the mind, such as anger, greed, hate and so on. Upasana Kanda focuses on invoking the Gods, in their many forms, as the Surya, Chandra, Indra, Vayu and many others. Upasana is a blend of two things, devotion, and meditation. The purpose of Upasana is to remove distractions from the mind. This practice aims to reduce the mind's vulnerability to distraction (vikshepa). Jnana Kanda is the portion of the Vedas that deals with wisdom. Vedanta is a result of this wisdom and literally means the end, or culmination of Vedic knowledge.

evolution and brings equal benefit to the recipient. Karma Yoga allows us to Realize that every action influences the whole. Everything we do is shared collectively as part of the cosmic web of consciousness.

Look to the experiences in your life for guidance, listen to what they are saying literally and figuratively. Then wait and allow the lesson to flow through you. If it is clear to you what the message is then it will not appear again. However, if the lesson has not been learned, then it is more than likely that the experience will present itself again. How the Divine intends to communicate will always remain part of the mystery of life.

Chapter NINE

Learning and the Yoga of Knowledge

The chief aim of education should be to help the growing soul to draw out that in itself which is best and make it perfect for a noble use.

Sri Aurobindo

The Importance of Dialogue

Many Vedantic texts are presented in a verse-like (sutra) structure that explain the teachings in a broad and abstract manner. However, several of the epic Indian scriptures are structured in the form of a dialogue between the guru and disciple to highlight the importance of dialogue's structure, the exchange of questions and answers. The dialogues between teacher and student are a type of inquiry where we see the ro/le of mentorship, which is so necessary for growth and development. Language carries knowledge and it is best delivered through a living personality who embodies the wisdom and understanding of advanced teachings. The inquiry process taking place between the teacher and student satisfies the student's desire to know, understand, and comprehend the nature of life. Today, the explosion of podcasts presents a similar structure that many are turning toward as a deeper and more reflective alternative to music. In great scriptures, the teachings were a presented in the form of metaphors and allegory. The famous Bhagavad Gita begins on the eve of a great war[122]

---

122 Kurushektra War took place in northern India. Even though the Bhagavad Gita is written most-

and is written as a dialogue between Lord Krishna, who is a God, king, and yogi, and Arjuna, who is a young warrior prince.

A second example is the Yoga Vasishta which presents a dialogue between Rama and his guru Vasishta structured in layers of stories, stories within stories, in a similar manner as the Gita. Regarding these two texts in particular, there are two important points to recognize: one is that the outer experiences that are taking place in the form of a war or some dilemma with family or society in general; and the second is that the inner afflictions are being experienced internally on the level of the mind. The guru becomes the teacher which demonstrates the correlation between the mind and the outer world. The guru is the discriminative aspect of the mind, its capacity to discern and make effective decisions that promote abundance. Effective decisions include embracing the principle of reciprocity and adhering to one's dharma. These actions promote spiritual evolution.

The primary ayurvedic text, the Charaka Samhita is based on a dialogue between Atreya and Agnivesh and imparts the wisdom of natural living, medicines, and other principles for living in accordance with nature's laws. As a time-honored tradition, Vedic wisdom recognizes what is known as the *guru-shisha*, teacher-student, tradition for its importance in imparting knowledge. The sun is the guru for all who live on the planet earth. In India, traditional schools such as a gurukul provides disciplinary spiritual training for children not merely on superficial topics such as history, algebra, or government, as is the case today in many modern schools. Indian gurukuls teach children the power that lies in a sound mind-body relationship, the use of language, correct use of sexual energy, and rituals that promote a balanced development. The very essence of such schooling is profound because it provides students with the dynamic vehicle of mentorship for the attainment of knowledge, the intelligence that abides within all living things.

Initially the sacred relationships take place in person between two living individuals, a guru and a disciple. Eventually, as the disciple expands their consciousness, the living guru figure is not needed. From that point forward, the teachings or the energy (shakti) that is being transferred through the lineage

---

ly in metaphor and allegory, the author (Veda Vyasa) referred to an actual war that was taking place and used the outer war to demonstrate the projective nature of the mind reflecting the despondency of Arjuna.

becomes the guru. The guru's body is merely a vehicle to transfer the knowledge (jnana) which then becomes the power or motion towards liberation for the student. This is the world wide web of Vedic knowledge that continues to disseminate the wisdom of pure consciousness and remains more and more attractive to yoga enthusiasts and practitioners all over the world. While these guru traditions continue to provide miraculous ways to deconstruct the ego and the mind, the consciousness of the dedicated and consistent aspirant will eventually expand to the point that the entire world becomes the guru.

Dialogue as shared through mentorship, guru, teacher, in whatever form, mimics the intelligence being disseminated by the sun and moon upon its earth child. The role of a mother and father in the human life of a child should never be reduced as the dialogue a child shares with each of his parents provides two different perspectives. Whatever is necessary for the evolution of the person they will manifest through the parents they are born through; therefore, the family unit may not always look the same. As a person develops in their spiritual evolution, so will the parents they are born into. The energy of sun invites reason, confidence, and intelligence, while the energy of the moon provides patience, understanding and compassion. Therefore, two parents are required to raise a child as it supports the balance of life all humans seek.

Dialogue teaches us to connect to the language of the Divine, the force behind all that exists. In other words, to place trust in the world process is a foolish endeavor that will only lead to frustration. Trusting the world process becomes misleading unless one has cultivated the right level of sensitivity to understand the deeper meaning behind the drama. The human mind is the most unstable thing in the world; its mechanics are doomed to fail us unless the knowledge of the mystics is awakened in us. Good dialogue purifies the mind of action-reaction dynamics and uplifts us to feeling as a subtle intuitive function of the soul. Language is an extension of how we feel, thus positive dialogue heightens the mind beyond the limitations of thought, ego, and emotion, and connects us to the heart.

Learning to differentiate what is real and unreal in nature is the very essence of the concept of learning. When a person takes on the role of a sadhaka, one who aspires towards truth (sat), the movement of their consciousness begins to soar toward the absolute reality. A mind that is rooted in *sat* never changes from this higher consciousness and remains unperturbed by the world duality. However, when the mind cannot distinguish between these two domains of real and unreal, it remains in ***asat*** or bound to the realm of time and space. The illusion of time and space is glaring and blinds the mind, preventing it from recognizing the true reality.

Everything in this world continues to change. Natural landscapes change over time, like mountains, rivers, trees, and coastal terrain. The same is true of the body. The physical body that one has at twenty-five years of age is different from the one at sixty-five. This is precisely why the concept of global warming is another illusion of the world process, with the cause of this so-called devastating change in temperature being blamed on human behavior. The world, as a planet, can never be destroyed, as it is upheld by the eternal cosmic intelligence and all of nature contains a portion of consciousness. What is being destroyed is animal and human life, and the potential humans have for transcending their consciousness beyond the trappings of the world. Global warming is another blame game that has no spiritual basis except that perhaps as societies become more compassionate toward nature, they will potentially begin to embrace the attitude of non-violence (ahimsa). Many who claim to be fighting the battle against global warming continue to ignore the importance of non-violence toward all living creatures. How is it that animals are to be excluded from the preservation of earth, as if they play no role in our evolution? Animals speak a language that reflects different temperaments of the One Divine expression. Any human who thinks they can live on the planet without the animal kingdom is misinformed.

The relationship the earth shares with the sun and moon produces the trickery of duality. It's a magic trick that prompts people to search for abundance by hook or by crook, to seek love outside of oneself, and to blame the world as if the phenomena they are unhappy with are completely independent of one's own consciousness. When we follow our truth, it brings complete fullness (purna-midam), the entirety of consciousness and intelligence.

The world process is reflecting the inner most layers of individual and collective consciousness in a type of reciprocal exchange between the projections of the mind stuff: thoughts and their related functions of ego and emotions. All that is observable in life's cinema show is a result of mental projections. What we observe in the world is not the true reality, it is merely a projection of our consciousness that is stained with a bit of ignorance (avidya). Our capacity to learn depends on the ability we have to gain control over the disturbances of the mind as the sage Patanjali stated, ***chitta vritti nirodha***.

Dialogues in the form of discourses, conversations, and being surrounded by members of a conscious community are important ways to remove disturbances from the mind. Without these dialogues, our mind remains confused because what we keep seeing in the world is not coming from the world itself, it is the veil of maya that has been placed over the mind, diluting the vision of pure consciousness (chit). Dialogue is crucial because it allows for the energy of thought and emotion to be expressed outwards for purification in reflection.

Vedanta recognizes the fickleness of the mind and recommends two austerities for overcoming it. One is continuity of effort through various yogic disciplines like mantra, breath-work, and meditation for the purpose of developing greater focus and concentration. The other is emotional detachment (vairagya) from people, places, and things, so that one can establish greater stability and calmness in the mind. As we increase our dispassion for the fluctuating nature of the world, we increase in our compassion and understanding of the true nature of existence. Emotional detachment does not mean one becomes uncaring or selfish; quite the opposite, it means that one begins to realize that the same light that brings awareness comes from the same source of light that gives another being life.

Beyond the world drama there is a field of aware-ness as opposed to aware-mess. The world is messy and is always in flux, but awareness gives us a clear perspective, removing from the mind the triggers of action-reaction dynamics and the perpetual trappings of the ego.

Evolution of Language

Language can be used to learn, while song can be used to love. Language carries the knowledge of soul awareness, while song is language imbued with devotion that arises from the heart. It is important to understand that language carries energy, energy that awakens the power of learning. We can use it to divide us and limit our potential; or alternatively, language can unify us with a grander intelligence. Language is constantly evolving, and, currently, it seems that the world is moving toward one universal language that ideally will reconnect our modern cultures with song, dance, healing rituals, and the understanding of the importance of the planetary cycles. The British empire undermined many of the diverse cultures of the world in their quest to acquire colonies. However, it did leave the world with the gift of bringing the English language to India (and many other parts of the world). This makes possible a more fluid exchange of the Indic wisdom traditions with English speaking cultures. In America, this began in the late nineteenth century with Swami Vivekananda's maiden voyage.

Sanskrit is the original language of India's wisdom traditions including Vedanta, Yoga, Jyotish (Vedic astrology) and many others. Sanskrit provides the most complete form of human expression and influenced the romance[123] and Germanic languages of Europe and the Western world. Sri Aurobindo once said, "*Sanskrit language as has been universally recognized by those competent to form a judgement, is one of the most magnificent, the most perfect, the most prominent and wonderfully sufficient literary instruments developed by the human mind.*"[124]

Sanskrit is a unique language in that two different words can be combined to create a new word and they work together perfectly to create a new meaning. This is a very common practice. As global cultures return to more spiritualistic objectives, they will inevitably be drawn to Sanskrit as a language that resonates with every aspect of human existence and most particularly with our astral body. The 50 letters of the Sanskrit alphabet (16 are vowels and next 34 are consonants) correspond to the petals of the chakras of the astral body and, as the language is spoken or recited during sadhana, it strengthens the frequency of communication and intensifies the meaning, thus creating resonance at the very core of human existence. In other words, the human body is made up of sound-vibrations and channels of energy that have direct links to the breath and beyond.

The human breath creates sound, while the spiritual heart transforms sound into joy, as the eternal song of pure existence (pranava), interconnecting infinity (cosmic vibration) and divinity (love). Anytime joy is felt within, it links the individual with the vibration of all living things. This is the energy that makes plants dance in the sun, animals play, and the energy that prompts the human heart to sparkle with hope for freedom. As language continues its evolution, it will inspire a renaissance for storytelling because the modern world yearns to cultivate a mythology to live by. Mythology creates traditions and shapes a culture so that it can grow in relationship to the cosmic cycles.

---

123 The major romance languages that evolved from Latin are French, Italian, Spanish, Portuguese, and Romanian. English was mostly influenced by the Germanic languages, although it was also an extension of Latin.
124 Sri Aurobindo (A philosophical magazine called Arya. Sri Aurobindo 'Arya', May to September 1920).

Each person has their own cycle that unravels according to the laws of karma, so each person will absorb the lessons of life in a different way. This can transform spoken language into a living language, a language that is spoken through the way a person lives on the planet. The language we speak with the planet earth is reflected in the relationship we share with it. How we speak is how we live, and how we live is reflected in how we feel.

In Vedanta, the soul is referred to as **paratman**, the Supreme Self, which emanates as the original or primal language of cosmic sound. The embodied soul is called *jivatman*, and exists as countless individual expressions of the supreme, like the sun reflecting in water. These two concepts are not separate from each other, and what keeps them connected is the eternal vibrational field. The vibration emanating from the entire cosmos is the eternal Aum (cosmic sound) and epitomizes the unified field of consciousness. All human languages are an expression of the cosmic sound Aum. Humanity, countless jivatmans, has language to use as a way to intersect with the Supreme Soul (paratman). Language also gives us the capacity to understand that any form of separateness is an illusion conjured up by the unpurified mind. Language is a bridge allowing us to stay connected to the Supreme Self.

The concept of illusion, maya, in Vedanta works in very peculiar ways. Even though maya is the illusory force, it has the capacity to move one toward the light of consciousness as an expanding awareness (sattva) or intuitive wisdom. This is because maya, as a product of creation (prakriti), must have a mystical means to transcend it. Maya, as the illusion of appearances experienced through the senses and operated by the human mind, provides a perpetual dismay created by the constant cravings and desires of the impure mind. This usually painful yet clever function of creation is designed to turn us away from the world process. For example, if we desire a person, place, or thing, and after much effort attain it, we then only discover the complexities of having attained it. After enough repetitions, we develop negative feelings, such as dismay and dissatisfaction, about the process.

Having nowhere else to turn, one begins to shift their mindset toward an inner process of inquiry. As this inner movement continues, perpetually enforced by maya, the developing energy becomes transformed into self-discipline (tapasya) and spiritual practice (sadhana) aimed toward subtle inner experiences, and is no longer used to attain outer things. Along the way, one may get stuck, confused, and even feel shame. At times, a person may feel like giving the world another go; however, it is most important to continue the inner process of inquiry by connecting to a language that will purify the negative aspects of one's personality.

Through language, the capacity to learn will continue expanding; however, it does so side-by-side with our past negative tendencies. Gradually, through sustained effort and individual responsibility, positive associations and discipline, the impurities (malas) of the mind fall away, one by one. As knowledge of one's higher nature increases, even though at times it may be unclear because it's like trying to find the sky on an overcast day, one's use of language will most likely evolve. The language of learning is a positive and more subtle language, called **vidya**. Vidya is drawing in greater knowledge of the Reality in the form of pure consciousness. This evolutionary movement is magnanimous; it is the basis for the law of attraction. The soul is like a magnet that attracts everything it puts out. As the soul moves towards unity, then everything that we encounter in daily life is there to teach us valuable lessons.

Responsibility and Learning

Life on earth is like being in a school where a person can discover their true nature through the experiences, relationships, and community that surrounds their lives. Life is filled with many different types of relationships, but the ones that we value the most are the ones that provide us unconditional love and knowledge. One form of gaining knowledge is through conscious dialogue between two individuals, where one of these individuals (the guru or teacher) has attained the knowledge of pure consciousness that affords them the capacity for understanding the nature of life, resolving differences, and expressing compassion in all circumstances. As you live in the school of life, important points to consider are who you gather information from, what you are reading, and who you are surrounding yourself with.

In modern society, when a person feels unhappy or is confronted with a personal challenge that disturbs their conditioned state of mind, they may go to see a psychotherapist and discuss the issues at hand. Other choices a person may make to change their state of mind is to resort to alcohol, or they may try to cope by changing their outer environment. However, regardless of what one does or where one goes, the disturbances of the mind go along. The true problem is not the world or what anyone may have done to you, but instead is the mind and the conditioning you have acquired based on external objects, relationships, and experiences. Even though dialogue with a therapist may initially be helpful in gaining some perspective on life's situations, it is the way the mind is being used that must inevitably change.

We have to change what the mind is projecting outwards in order to be able to create positive change in the world. The mind must be cleansed of all negativities, gossip, and criticism, because as long as a person takes the stance of pointing the finger at others' blemishes, they will never take responsibility for the battlefield they have created in their own mind. Learning yoga is not enough, it must be combined with an understanding of how evolution works, and this is where philosophy comes in. Vedantic philosophy employs allegory, mythology, and other techniques for learning how to behave and unfold the true Reality. As Ramakrishna's signature motto implies, "Paths there are many, Truth is One."

When there is a thorough study of the mind as has been taught through Vedantic philosophy, one can gain an understanding of the source of life's experiences and be able to learn from one's mistakes. The foundation for learning must begin with taking complete responsibility for one's own life. By the law of karma people create their own destiny. Some of these karmic patterns are obvious, and others are much more hidden, sometimes referred to as chronic in that hidden karmas keep repeating. Other karmas lay dormant within our subconscious waiting to ripen and manifest into our life according to the Divine laws. Therefore, we must never take the stance that everything will always be perfect, falling into a passive state of mind that is not progressive. Proactive evolution means you must have continuity of effort and self-care as an act of prevention and preparation. Through personal responsibility, you take ownership for your life and cultivate a fearless attitude that promotes positivity.

Knowledge from the Light

To paint a big picture of this cosmology we need to begin with the energies of the seven major planets[125] that carry cosmic intelligence. The light of the

---

125 Sun, Moon, Mars, Mercury, Jupiter, Venus, and Saturn are the major planets, each of which signify the seven days of the week. Additionally, Vedic astrology recognizes two nodes (Rahu & Ketu) of the moon that exist as a result of eclipses. They have no mass and are referred to as the "illusory planets" and deal with the mystical, the spiritual and the transcendental aspects of life. Rahu,

planets shapes the quality and major characteristics of the twelve signs of the zodiac, giving each of them unique features. In other words, each of the planets share a relationship with each of the zodiacal signs. There are twelve signs of the zodiac, and it is for this reason that we have a twelve-month year. Each is assigned to one of the major elements (earth, water, fire and air). Vedic astrology, *Jyotish*, means the study of the light and comes from the root *jyoti*. The light of the planets shines through the different signs and emanates, influencing all aspects of life on earth.

The study of how light influences us is important to the evolution of humanity. From the yogic perspective, if a person has little light entering their consciousness, they will likely behave with a limited understanding of human nature, express a territorial attitude, and will be primarily interested in sensory pleasures. This is referred to as tamas guna. For those individuals that have a moderate amount of light illuminating their consciousness, their approach to life includes an increased call to action, they are more expressive, communicative, and extroverted in general, and their behavior can lean toward being reactive and proactive. Their choices, in general, are intended to fulfill a combination of their own personal needs and motives with a consideration of others' needs and motives.

When the divine light enters one's consciousness without much resistance from the mind, it transforms the personality from passionate to compassionate and there is an organic understanding that how one behaves influences the collective whole around us. This sattvic, awakened intellect, allows a person to make choices that promote evolution and supports integral yoga, a union with the diverse aspects of the divine in all living things. The light of consciousness transforms the way the aspirant lives in the world. The entire world process becomes a vehicle to ascend towards oneness, increasing one's capacity to see the light of consciousness in all living things.

According to Vedic astrology when a person is born, where the planets and the signs are located in particular houses are significant indicators of the person's traits, karma, and constitution. The houses correspond to different aspects of life. For example, the first house is correlated with the body because it marks

---

is known as the "Dragon's Head" and Ketu as the "Dragon's Tail." They generate such power that they are elevated to the status of planets. Rahu and Ketu deal with the secret, hidden, and spiritual dimensions of life.

the soul's point of entry into the world. This rising sign, lagna, is the sign that appears in the eastern horizon at the time of birth. The lagna plays a major role in shaping a person's body and their personality. This unique feature of the Vedic system becomes a tremendous boon for ayurvedic counselors who use the first house to understand a person's constitutional traits as related to the body and mind. These three major factors (planets, signs and houses) shape every individual in their unique way according to a person's karma. This is precisely why two children born of the same parents can be completely different with both positive and negative characteristics that will dominate their personalities.

As the planets go on constantly moving into different signs, they invoke different energies according to the relationships the planets have with each other and the signs they are moving through. This ever-shifting process corresponds to the effect of constantly changing events in a human's experience on the planet earth. The shifts provide the potential for evolution as the light of knowledge continues to unfold in every living being. Change is the only constant on this planet, and as we say in ayurveda, Stagnation is death, and circulation is life.

Prana is the positive side of vata dosha and exists as good circulation. Tejas is the positive form of fire, or light, as consciousness and awareness, providing an attractive vibration in the personality. When both prana (life force) and tejas (light of awareness) are bountiful, they rest in the container of ojas as immunity or reserved energy that supports the body's defense system against bacterial and viral intrusions. Ojas filled with prana and tejas, gives a person tremendous will power and the motivation to evolve. From the esoteric perspective, this primal energy (ojas) gives us the impetus to aspire and to become a sadhaka (yogi) living for the highest purpose of self-realization.

At birth both the signs and the planets are arranged in the twelve houses of an astrology chart according to the soul's past karma. In accordance with the law of synchronicity, the light of consciousness is reflected onto the fetus as it exits the womb of the mother. Subsequently, the light of cosmic intelligence is also imparted on the child through the mother and father (egg and sperm) and influences the quality of the relationship the parents will have with the child. Another additional perspective that is important to note is that in a normal, birth the fetus exits the womb and enters the world headfirst; thus, the first house of the chart is assigned to the head as the first part of the body.

The first house represents the entire body and its main features, personality, ego, and general characteristics. The remaining eleven houses correspond to the rest of the body in descending order. Simply put, the twelves houses (bhavas), each with their own respective sign, are assigned to one of the main sections and organ functions of the body, finally ending at the feet which are assigned to the twelfth house.

Before birth, the development of the fetus in the womb during its nine months is uniquely tied to the planetary system of Vedic astrology in that the trimesters are correlated to three phases influenced by the ayurvedic doshas (kapha, pitta, vata). According to ayurveda, the fetus goes through the developmental process and aligns with each of the three doshas. The mother, as the carrier of the fetus, will experience these phases within her own physical body. In general, there is predominance of kapha in the first trimester, pitta in the second trimester, and vata in the last trimester. Kapha in the first trimester increases moisture, weight, and heaviness in the body. In the second trimester, pitta brings in nausea and increased appetite. The third trimester begins with pitta blended with kapha and increases chorionic villus.[126] The nine major planets of Vedic astrology can also be correlated to the nine-month period of pregnancy.

From an esoteric perspective, the light of consciousness presents conception as a spark of the Divine light that gives rise to prakriti (mind-body constitution) and prana through cosmic intelligence (mahat) which combine breath and life into a human form. The power to breathe gives us life, while the breath can also lead us to supreme freedom or samadhi (nirvakalpa). According to Hatha-Tantra yoga, the breath serves as a link to the light of higher consciousness. This means that how you breathe influences how you think and determines the level of connection you have to your body. When the mind is filled with fear, it increases the heart rate and disrupts a person's connection to their body. Fear also blocks the subtle nerve channels (nadis) around the heart and blocks the light of consciousness from entering the astral body. A lack of orientation to the mind and body leads to fragmentation and a lack of control.

---

126 Most of the villi consist of connective tissues that contain blood vessels. Chorionic villi are a rich source of stem cells. Two forms can be considered, either floating villi float freely in the inter-villous space or anchoring (stem) villi that stabilize mechanical integrity of the placental-maternal interface. In modern medicine, chorionic villus sampling (CVS) is a procedure of prenatal testing in which a sample of chorionic villi is removed from the placenta for testing.

ASTROLOGY SIGNS AND THE TWELVE PARTS OF THE BODY

1st House, Aries
Head, skull & brain
life, personality, whole body

2nd House, Taurus
Face, eyes, nose & mouth
family, wealth

3rd House, Gemini
Shoulders & arm, dexterity
siblings, communication

7th House, Libra
Lower abdomen,
large intestines & kidneys
relationships, marriage

4th House, Cancer
Chest, heart, lungs
mother, emotions

8th House, Scorpio
Lower trunk, genitals,
anus elimination
death, longevity,
unexpected occurrences,
learning from the past

5th House, Leo
Liver, stomach &
spleen, diaphragm
children, education, intelligence

9th House, Sagittarius
Upper legs & thighs
spiritual-life purpose (dharma)

6th House, Virgo
Hips & small intestines
extracting nutrition,
service (seva),
problem solving, &
medical diagnosis, enemies

11th House, Aquarius
Calves, shins
fruits of our actions, income, gains

10th House, Capricorn
Legs & knees
practical matters, career

12th House, Pisces
Calves, ankles, feet
surrender, spiritual liberation

Zodiac body shows how the signs of the zodiac correspond to specific areas of the human body.
Each sign is ruled or influenced by one of the seven major planets.

When a person lacks control over their mind or body it leads to acting irresponsibly. Irresponsible behavior is simply a block of the light of awareness, leading to a lack of proper judgment. Inevitably, a person without the light of consciousness is not capable of learning from the world, one's relationships and experiences.

According to the universal laws of cosmology, every soul attracts their parents. Every soul is assigned a vehicle in which to enter the world depending on their individual karma and the relationships they have shared in prior lives. The new relationship dynamic between parent and child provides a new opportunity for evolution. Each person in the family is holding a mirror for the others to reflect upon, indicating the karmas that need to be learned.

I find this scenario admirable: a person who lacks the capacity or knowledge for completing a certain task they are about to begin, and, after a moment of introspection, surrenders and asks for support from another knowledgeable person. When one puts aside their ego, they attain the power to learn. As a result of recognizing that she/he doesn't know everything, and seeking someone who can teach him/her, it creates an opportunity for learning. Anyone can be our teacher if we welcome the light of their knowledge into our consciousness; however, we must create the space for it.

We have so much to learn from the world, but humanity has become blinded. Many cannot see the wisdom consciousness that is available through nature. The great guru Sri Ramakrishna was able to recognize the light of higher consciousness in his devotees and often encouraged them to shine their light in service to others. A willingness to serve others is a high attribute of the soul. Gauri Ma was a very advanced female devotee of Ramakrishna's, and, recognizing her spiritual strength and fearlessness, Ramakrishna encouraged her at a young age to help educate women, empowering them to play a more prominent role in society. Imagine taking on this task in 19th century India? Initially, she resisted, but eventually, after her guru's passing, she created the Sri Sri Saradeshwari Ashrama[127] for women. Ramakrishna told Gauri Ma "Your life was meant for serving women, the living goddesses." As was the custom in Vedic tradition, she held classes under a tree, and over one hundred years later, her work continues to help women rise in society. Ramakrishna's life message was a combination of action, knowledge, and devotion, all of which led to a peaceful life.

Learning is not merely an intellectual process of memorization of principles and mechanical practices of spiritual exercises; it must be adopted within the heart. When we learn something, it has to feel right, not just seem intellectually right. Intellect is only converted into knowledge when the mind is

---

127 Located in Calcutta (now Kolkatta), India.

merged into the heart. Otherwise, intellect remains a clutter of information in the brain. The head and the heart must work together for mindfulness to exist, otherwise life remains a mechanical process.

At the very heart of our existence is a light, the light of the individualized soul (jiva). Good concentration is necessary for achieving any task, and it brings efficiency and success. When the mind is focused, the light of awareness is directed at a single object or task, and it brings great capacity for knowledge because the distractions that normally cloud the mind are removed, leaving pure awareness. As the world remains asleep to life's true purpose, still, unbeknownst to them, many aspects of people's lives are intermingled with the mystical energy that supports life. The exercise enthusiast loves things that make his cardiac and circulatory systems pulse with energy and when hearing the sounds of breathing they experience a soothing vibration in the mind. The athlete often says that whenever they workout it feels like a meditation. As a result of the mind being focused on a single task, the mind and body function harmoniously and uplift the consciousness beyond the flutter of disturbing thoughts. Therefore, a distracted mind can lead to many disorders; too many impressions bombard the mental body disturbing the flow of prana between the mind and heart. This is essentially the basis for mind-body fragmentation, it exists as a divorce of the mind from the heart and leads to a lack of discernment. When a person relies solely on intellect as gathered information it produces what is called stress.

According to yoga, the breath produces a subtle sound unheard by the ears, although it is heard by the mind, that is merely its mechanical function. If people were to understand the mystical nature of life, they would realize that a profound energy sustains them, keeping them inspired to do what makes them feel alive. This aliveness is life's purpose, to be awake and alive is a blessing more are enjoying. In this level of awareness, the plants dance, animals invoke purity of the heart, and every person appears as an expression of light. The breath is a key to the light, it awakens our higher nature and expands our capacity to observe the material world as illusory.

The Importance of Scriptures

Much of the world and, most particularly, the modern Western world has no mythology to live by. Without myths to live by, humanity loses it sense of purpose and becomes confused and devoid of inner contentment because of an over-externalized mind. Dharma can be defined as the duty and responsibility every human being has to seek their truth, the nature of one's existence. Mythologies serve this purpose through the use of metaphor and allegory so that one can shift their identity from focusing on their own life, body, and name, to focusing on aspiring and transcending the limitations created by the mind and body. Knowledge, as derived from the field of pure consciousness, has no limitations. The cornerstone of all great scriptures is detachment (anasakti), the result of a life integrated with even-mindedness (titiksha). Most of what we see in the world is turmoil created from attachment (asakti). The entire world process is designed to teach us that nothing is ours to claim. "I" or "mineness" is the very cause of greed that perpetuates the desire to cling to material objects and to life itself.

Although humanity is relying upon the knowledge of the East, India should be seen as a metaphor for us. We turn towards the East where the rising sun is a symbol of our yearning for transformation from human love to Divine love, from passion to compassion, and from working for income to serving one another as children of the universe. What I mean by this is that rather than just becoming aware of the inner search that arrives in our consciousness as curiosity, increased sensitivity, and even dissatisfaction with the mundane pattern of life, we must be compelled to do something about it. We can take action by redesigning the structure of our lives, creating a new set of initiatives that align with this inner movement of inquiry. As consciousness continues to shift inside of you, you must do something about it and overcome the fear of departing from identification with the mind and body.

Let me describe a short scene to explain this important point on the path to learning. One day, you are sitting on a dock witnessing the vast and limitless nature of the ocean. You have been waiting for hours for a boat to arrive to take you to fulfill a specific mission you have planned to accomplish. As you continue to relish in the magic of the ocean, you witness that the boat is there in the distance, slowly approaching the dock. Suddenly, a playful seagull flies by and captures your attention. Before you know it, you realize the boat has already left the dock without you, and the seagull has floated off along with a fresh gust of wind.

In this scene, your specific mission you have planned to accomplish is the earnest desire to be enlightened. Observing the ocean is the mind's power to discern and see beyond the limited nature of the ego-mind. The boat is the vehicle of action (karma), and the dock is the illusion of stability of the mind-body. The seagull is the distracting potential of thoughts. The scene illustrates that we must be careful not to ignore the power of awakened consciousness so that we do not miss opportunities when they arise to venture off beyond the limitations of the dock, as the mind and body. We must stay focused on our goal of self-realization and be careful not to become distracted by our thoughts or the impulses of the senses. In this way, we can continue to embark on the boat of practice and self-discipline by taking initiative and staying focused on departing from the dock, the limiting nature of the mind-body. Scriptures awaken this higher power within us and help us to know when to take action and change our ways beyond the superficial safety of people, places, and things. Some of us stay on the dock with our minds floating away like a bird, while others embark on the boat of action to explore learning from the greater knowledge available in the vast sea of pure consciousness.

Learning and the Art of Sacred Language

The importance of language cannot be overvalued as it contains the evolution of culture and the expression of love. Spoken language is humanity's main form of communication and it continues to evolve as societies become filled with greater social and economic complexities. The world contains hundreds of languages with which to communicate and hopefully understand each other better. However, language has divided our cultures in many ways, leading to misunderstanding. This is because languages lack spiritual essence and are developed into mundane forms, expressing the more indelicate aspects of life. An ideal use of language is to use it for uplifting consciousness by unifying our cultures. I am not rejecting the beauty of cultural diversity, but rather encouraging us to understand the underlying fabric from which all languages are derived. For this to happen, language must contain an energetic value that can enhance one's Divine potential.

For this reason, the yoga tradition is founded on the Sanskrit language. Sanskrit mantras have a special capacity of sticking to the unconscious mind where they undo the fetters that restrain our evolution and lead to the creation of more karma. Mantras afford the aspirant with a greater sense of mental freedom. Mantras unbind the mind and are a tremendous boon to the entire mental field (chitta). If yoga aims to unify our consciousness, then naturally it must be based on the very essence of our existence: energy. Sanskrit is derived from the sounds of the astral body. The astral body is another way to define the mental field in which the chakras are contained. The distinct sounds of Sanskrit originate from cosmic sound, the field of pure consciousness (Mantra Purusha).

Secondly, these primal sounds and contain the original elements that gave rise to human existence. Each chakra vibrates and produces a frequency according to the five elements, beginning with earth, and proceeding up into water, fire, air, and ether. Each of the 50 letters of the Sanskrit alphabet represent the petals within the energy centers (chakras) in the astral spinal channel. Each of these sounds is linked is to a current of prana (life force energy) that gives life, health, and magnanimous energy to the human complex.

Use of the Sanskrit language for healing is important because it provides an integral experience that is not limited to a physical sensory sensation. This means that when a person learns something, it is not merely on the level of the intellect. Learning through the Sanskrit language is the original form of sound therapy. In other words, whatever is learned through Sanskrit transcends the intellectual level, becoming knowledge as the vibration of the sounds penetrates the physical body and enters the astral (mental) body, thus making it an integral experience.

This transcendental experience can be produced through repetition of the Sanskrit mantras that shift the mind's attention inward, beyond the senses and tissues, to where attention is eventually re-connected with the inner astral body. This is where the petals of each chakra begin to open just like a lotus flower that gracefully opens to the rays of sunlight. Mantra allows the sunlight of Divine consciousness to enter one's being to illuminate the moon qualities in our personality as compassion and positive feeling. Recitation of specific mantras while counting them on a beaded necklace called mala, is the most common use of mantra which is referred to as japa mantra. The word mala in ayurveda means impurity, so in a different context, relating more to the mind, one may experience impurities of negativity beginning to leave the mind through consistent recitation of these sacred sounds.

The significant impact of a mantra lies in having an affinity for how the mantra sounds, what it means, and what it symbolizes in relationship to your own consciousness. Because the Sanskrit language is derived from primal sound, it has a tremendous capacity for promoting harmony and balance of the entire mind-body complex. Dr James Hartzell, a neuroscientist and postdoctoral researcher, coined the term, 'The Sanskrit Effect' and prepared an innovative project that measured the capacity the Sanskrit language has for stimulating brain function and memory.[128] He found that chanting the Sanskrit mantras activated important parts of the brain responsible for cognition and memorization, both of which are necessary for acquiring knowledge.

Professor Rama Jayasundar from the All India Institute of Medical Sciences in Delhi makes an interesting point about Sanskrit. "It's a language which had been developed in a very scientific way and the sound takes the highest priority in Sanskrit language and the pronunciation is very important. There are rigorous rules about intonations, the tone, the stress, the rhythm. It's actually a science of sound."[129] While the orthodox Vedic tradition as well as Hindu, considers pronunciation of primary importance, it is only one aspect of how this language can be applied as a tool for spiritual evolution. I share here a wonderful dialogue with Swami Jyotirmayananda on this topic that I believe provides clarity on the practice of Sanskrit.

After reading a quote from Sri Sivananda Maharaj (his guru) to him, "The Japa of a Mantra can bring to the practitioner realization of his highest goal though he may not possess knowledge of the meaning of the Mantra. Such a mechanical Japa may take a little more time in realization than when it is practiced with knowledge of the meaning."

Swami Jyotirmayananda eloquently responded by saying, "It is important to practice Mantra Japa according to the rules, meaning and good pronunciation. This is the kindergarten stage. As one advances, Bhavana (mental attitude) behind Japa becomes more important. Ritual stage continues with spontaneity. Thus, defect in pronunciation does not matter; your Love for God continues to lead you to enlightenment!"

---

128 The Sanskrit Effect project was funded by the India-Trento Partnership for Advanced Research, a program between India's Department of Science and Technology (DST) and Italy's province of Trentino and University of Trento. It compared the brains of 21 male participants with those of 21 professional Vedic Sanskrit Pandits who had memorized the *Yajurveda Saṃhitā* text, a discipline that begins in early childhood and can extend into adult-life. These 3,000-year-old texts originate from a vast oral tradition, some of which range up to 100,000 words in length. The study found increased thickness in the Pandits' cortical regions as well as their grey matter density. Dr. Hartzell found, "In the cerebellum - which is the back lower part of the brain which coordinates both motor and cognitive functions… 33% of the Pandits' cerebellum grey matter was denser or more increased compared to the [other participants], which was remarkable." Imaging demonstrated increased volume in the hippocampus, which is related to how the brain uses memory.
129 Resource: Interview with SBS Hindi.

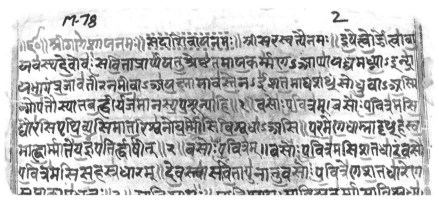

Yajurveda Samhita-Sanskrit text

Our sound environment is important and plays an important role in how the mind functions. If the language of Sanskrit can influence the function of the cerebellum (lower part of the brain) which manages both motor and cognitive operations, then we can conclude that it provides a positive impression (samskara) on the mind, linking the mind to its cosmic source or cosmic mind (Hiranyagarbha). The other form of healing that can occur through language is that of vibration, the exposure to different tones and meters. Instead of actively repeating a particular mantra, one could take a more passive approach by relaxing the mind and allowing the sound of these mantras or musical instruments to penetrate the consciousness as a type of sound treatment.

In many postural yoga classes, the 'Aum' mantra is commonly practiced, reminding practitioners of yoga's purpose, attaining a unified state of consciousness. 'Aum' as the vibration of this universe, is the primal sound of all mantras and languages and is the supreme portal for attaining a unified state of awareness. Aum is the supreme mantra of yoga and resonates on the inner level of our being in three distinct aspects. Each letter contains a specific vibratory frequency that resonates with the astral body. The letter A resonates at the third chakra (manipura) and is correlated to the physical body, representing the primary level of consciousness. The letter U resonates at the heart center (anahata) and represents the astral body, what is referred to as Hiranyagarbha, the cosmic mind. The letter M resonates at the third eye chakra (ajna) and reflects the higher domains of consciousness that obliterate the male/female

Photo Credit: Ms Sarah Welch - Own work, CC BY-SA 4.0,

duality and break all limitations of time and space. These three letters can also be considered a type of yantra (sacred image) for concentrating one's attention. The Aum symbolizes eternity, or Brahman, as pure consciousness; therefore, if an aspirant applies concentration combined with meaning and devotion, one's consciousness can transcend towards higher domains. Yogis also visualize this Sanskrit symbol while concentrating on each of the chakras for expanding consciousness beyond the body and mind.

AUM

The basic point to understand is that sound impacts not only the mind and whatever environment one is most exposed too, but it aids in disentangling the consciousness from the shackles of the body, mind, ego, thoughts, and intellect. Sound shapes the quality of consciousness. Every person and every culture are products of their environment.

Let's transport ourselves back to ancient India for a moment in order to understand how mantra was being practiced. Imagine a small band of yogis or a village community gathering either under a tree or in a shaded grove. Depending on the time of the year, such rituals may take place around a fire. Together they would chant various sacred sounds for hours combined with breathing exercises that gradually drew their consciousness inward into a calm meditative state of peace. As these sacred sounds were being recited, they were also combined with prayers as a type of sacrificial rite or *yajna* intended to burn up egoistic obstacles created by the mind. The main intention was in purifying the mind, ridding it of the sensory distractions and thoughts and to arrive at the inner realms of consciousness that have direct links to pure consciousness. Mantric sound is a vehicle that carries the mind beyond the blemishes of the ego and its conditions.

Mantra Alone is Not Enough

Yogic wisdom teaches us that our environment is our greatest influence; indeed, it is the most powerful factor in anyone's life. The aspirant begins to learn that community is an important factor that supports one's spiritual evolution, and for this reason satsanga, gatherings of truth, have always been an essential counterpart to sadhana. Any discipline like mantra or meditation can be very powerful if one has the community (sangha) to sustain it. Yoga, mantra, or any spiritual practice (sadhana), is not enough without sangha. Sadly, in most cases, the world of pleasures will win and pull one back into the belief systems that influence people to follow the pack.

Learning and living the yogic life is not about creating an extraordinary life. Quite the opposite, it involves years, and perhaps lifetimes, of removing the "extra" in order to live simply with ordinary. A simple life means living in a manner that does not keep validating the ego, mind, and body. These are the very things that have driven humans to suffer and live aimlessly for thousands of births like a programmed machine. Simple living promotes high thinking in the form of reflection and inquiry into the nature of one's words, actions, and thoughts that have shaped one's life. A person can chant their life away with very powerful mantras, but unless their environment is pure, spiritual, and natural (sattvic), the mind will have to fight battle after battle to attain any progress. In fact, such a contrast between spiritual practices and proper environment can lead to much mental unrest as the mind is pulled in and out and up and down like a yoyo, never having a place to settle and expand. Positive associations provide space for the mind to expand and gain knowledge (jnana), fostering opportunities to perform uplifting service (karma yoga) for others. When we surround ourselves with spiritual community, we are naturally uplifted without having to do much, because, purely on the level of vibration, it impacts our entire being.

The Highest Learning

Learning anything can be one of the most rewarding aspects of life. Learning opportunities come in spontaneous moments, chosen adventures, and can appear as circumstances that never seem to go away. Learning is often correlated with the memorization of facts and principles that overtime only end up being antiquated or they disappear without having much use in our lives. However, learning can produce some of the greatest gifts, extracted from the most challenging moments in our life. Learning, from the perspective of Yoga, has profound implications if you are able to apply your sensitive capacity toward any event of life and link it into the realm of knowing as pure awareness. This level of knowing is directly linked to the *jnana* path of yoga and is an inherent divine power within each person.

While listening is the first step to evolutionary living, learning is the second step, and it requires proper use of the mind. Pure knowledge provides the capacity to distinguish between what is real and unreal and is directly linked to the power of intuition. There is no greater teacher than the world itself as it provides insights into layers upon layers of the mental complexities hidden behind the mind and its devices, primarily functioning through the ego. Some simple daily exercises for developing the capacity to learn or developing in the path of knowledge are: reading, especially spiritual books; meditation; journaling at the end of each day and asking yourself the question, What have I learned today? or What can I learn from this experience? Always be willing to explore new places and learn from any person, place, or object that has crossed your path. One should always be a student, and the spirit of learning should always continue without interruption. The more you learn, the more the ego's transparency grows. This is the real dissemination of pure knowledge (vidya). **Humility makes one a worthy aspirant.**

Life is a school that should be used to develop the knowledge of the light that pervades all of existence. As one increases in knowledge, one learns to live more efficiently by reducing their desire for superficial pleasures. Desires create impulses that lead to mental impressions where one thinks something outside of themselves is needed in order to live a fulfilling life. Reflection is required to develop in the power of learning. as awareness increases and becomes a tremendous thrust in the Godward direction, the path of knowledge provides an important power, shakti. The power of knowledge is referred to as *jnanashakti* which requires a necessary amount of devotion if one is to keep moving toward the heights of liberation.[130]

As Krishna states in the Bhagavad Gita, *"The Jnani who is ever united with God, and therefore, one-pointed in his devotion to God, is the best. I Am supremely dear to the man of wisdom (jnani), and he is dear to Me."*[131]

---

130 Swami Jyotirmayananda refers to this trinity of shakti, bhakti and mukti as Shabhamu.
131 Chapter Seven, Verse 17, *The Bhagavad Gita*, Commentary by Swami Jyotirmayananda, (Yoga Research Foundation, Miami, FL).

Chapter TEN

Love and the Yoga of Devotion

One of God's Names is Love.
He Himself resides within all, at every moment, everywhere.

Sri Anandamayi Ma

Life's Driving Force

Love is a profound word with broad implications that spans all four major aspects of life.[132] ***Love spelled backwards is evol, the root word in the word evolution, and therefore, without love there is no evolution.*** Love is what sustains all relationships, friendships, and families, and is the impetus behind intimacy and the pleasure of affection. The affectionate aspect of human life is referred to as *kama*. Each of us pursues the joy of working in a vocation that satisfies us on a heartfelt level. I'm not speaking about a job that one performs with a sour attitude, but rather vocation (artha) is that craft that appeals most to your personality and talents and is designed for you. When you love what you do, it never feels like work because it allows your mind to concentrate and be present within the heart. When a person is in their right vocation, the mind becomes so immersed in the task that it transcends thought; so much so that the joyful work becomes an experience beyond the limits of time.

---

132 Dharma, artha, kama and moksha.

If love is not in your work, then your work will never lead you to love. Your work will take you away from the heart, create stress, and become a series of monotonous and mechanical chores that exhaust you, and draining your prime energy resource (ojas). Much of the adrenal burnout (also known as chronic fatigue syndrome) we see today, is a result of heartless work that does not support evolution. There must be pleasure and meaning in your vocation, whatever it may be. For anyone to grow beyond the ego's limitations, their work must be inspired by a selfless attitude. Otherwise, love develops conditions because there is an expectation of being rewarded.

Love is the underlying force that sustains purposeful living based on the law of dharma. Without love, the higher aim of selfless service becomes shallow, and our actions become selfish and driven by greed. The deadliest disease in the world is greed, and it is being sustained by the virus called egoism (asmita). Adherence to dharma (higher duty) produces a blend of positive feeling (bhavana) and joyful activity when working in our heartfelt vocation (artha). When our artha and dharma are aligned, we are living and working in a way that leaves the gentlest footprint on the earth, and nonviolence is the highest form of dharma.

Moksha, liberation, is the highest aim of life and is the cornerstone of all religions. Love for God is what ignites the fire of the soul seeking self-realization and unity with the source of all knowledge, beauty, and existence. That source is Brahman, pure consciousness. Many have often asked me to clarify this salient ideal of Hinduism. Practically speaking, it means that one fully Realizes, through a direct and personal experience, that the very essence of who you are is within, and pure consciousness does not exist separately or outside of you. Each soul is distinct but is not separate from life or the world. The light of consciousness that exists within you is a portion, a wave or reflection, of the same consciousness that upholds all living things.

Integral to this very ideal is the principle of non-violence, in that hurting anyone or damaging Mother nature is only hurting yourself. As a result of the laws of karma, anything that you do has an equal reaction; hence, Sri Swami Sivananda's adage, "Do good, Be Good! Ideally, we want love to be the driving force behind these four aspects of our life, dharma, artha, kama, moksha, so that we may grow in an integral manner. When we speak of the whole person, these four aims are what define the universal ideology of Vedanta. As one approaches these aspects of their life with the right understanding (sanmati), love becomes the highest intention, nourishing our zeal for life and affording the body with the best form of immunity, protecting us from the worst viruses and diseases.

Creating Affinity for Divinity

One of great features of the Hindu-Vedic tradition is the plethora of images representing the different aspects of Divinity. Each person has their own distinct qualities as a result of the choices (karma) and experiences that have shaped their consciousness and personality. Their jyotish[133] birth chart indicates the astrological sign that a person is born under and their alignment with one of the major elements (earth, water, fire, air). The certain qualities of that particular sign, its mythology, and the planet (lord) connected to that sign is indicative of their consciousness and personality in this lifetime. For example, libra is an air sign, so a person born under a libra sky influences them to be creative, have lightness, and, because libra is ruled by the planet Venus, the person will be attracted to beauty and design. Astrologically speaking, in Vedic astrology, it is the moon sign that is important, as is the case in Asian cultures. This is because the moon defines our inner nature, emotions, and the mind in general. Therefore, if you want to get to know more about yourself, or the person you are attracted to, discover, and study the moon sign and its respective star qualities (nakshatra).

Begin to ask yourself, How is it that I am attracted to the Divine? To whom, on a personal level, or to what, on an abstract level, do I turn when my mind is dark with the clouds of illusions, my broken heart is prodding me to expand, and when I am yearning for answers?

A good place to begin is to distinguish whether the vibration (feeling) of your inner heart is more lunar (feminine) or solar (masculine). Or perhaps you are drawn to nature and her many delightful and alluring forms. This is the initial process for personalizing your relationship with the Divine. For some, this may be difficult if they were raised in a specific religious tradition that worships a masculine figurehead or God, which is very common in this era as a result of historical events and the calendar change during the second millennium B.C.

---

133 Sanskrit term for Vedic Astrology.

Evidently, the major world religions, with the exclusion of Hinduism, all worship the Divine as masculine and favor the masculine force in some way or another. This has created a partition between humans and the natural world and her animals. Without human connection to her (prakriti), human potential is very limited. Perhaps this is one reason why humans keep killing animals and justifying it in the name of survival or to maintain enough protein in their diet. Wherever humans go, life is barely sustained or perishes; literally speaking, human beings are the most destructive living entities on the planet earth. History shows humanity's shame in this regard. This destruction is a result of a solar dominated world that promotes a focus on individual feelings and ego. The Western world's culture has disregarded the moon's presence, nature, women, motherhood, selfcare and devotion to the divine. Such devotion cannot be packaged, taught, and followed in a predictive and prescriptive manner, as this would fail to embrace the true meaning of love beyond conditions. Love is not something we acquire or receive from others, instead, it is our very essential nature. When we are in love, devoted to the Divine, we are anchored in that essence that enlivens the power of attraction and sublimates hatred, fear, greed, and other egoistic illusions.

Personalizing Your Relationship with God

Once you have a clearer idea of how you feel toward God, you can bring in more specific imagery upon which to focus your attention. I was once sitting with one of my spiritual counselors, Swami Anandamoy, and he asked me, "How do you see God?"

I replied, "Well, God is everywhere and in everything!"

He said, "Yes, I know, but how do *you* see him?"

Suddenly, as I began to explore within my mind and heart, I became more and more silent and could not answer his question.

Finally, he said, "That is what you have to explore! It will help you tremendously."

After some time, I began to explore how I felt about the different aspects of God: male, female, Guru, living, or nonliving. In the depths of my meditations, it came to me through my heart. I felt waves of energy that kept emanating from my heart and the feeling swept across my entire being. At last, mentally I whispered, "Jai Guru, Om Guru." Since then, I have been blessed to experience this sweet feeling of joy in most of my meditations.

Discovering your affinity for divinity opens the door to higher consciousness. Consider this metaphor: if you want to open the door to your house, you have to know where to put the key; the key socket is the preferred image of God; and the key is the mantra or breathing (pranayama) technique. Without knowing where to put the key or where to direct one's attention, you will aimlessly look at the door of your heart without knowing how to open it. Obviously, the key has to fit inside the chamber to unlock the bolt, and so the aspirant must have the right mantra, referred to as *ishta* mantra. The ishta mantra brings a mystic connection between the verbal letters and your psychic personality. Your ishta mantra becomes your key to the door of higher consciousness as it removes the maladies of the mind such as excessive thinking, misjudgments, sensory addictions, and inflammation of the ego. As Krishna states, "Whatever Divine form a devotee wishes to worship with faith, I intensify and make unflinching his faith in that very form."[134]

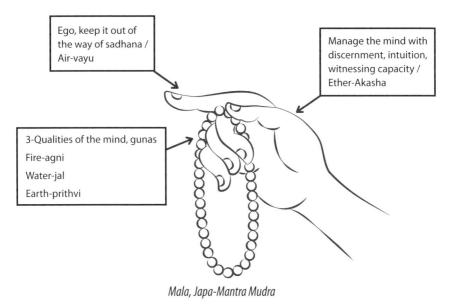

Ego, keep it out of the way of sadhana / Air-vayu

Manage the mind with discernment, intuition, witnessing capacity / Ether-Akasha

3-Qualities of the mind, gunas
Fire-agni
Water-jal
Earth-prithvi

Mala, Japa-Mantra Mudra

---

134 *Bhagavad Gita*, chapter 7, verse 21. *The Bhagavad Gita, Commentary*, by Swami Jyotir-mayananda (Yoga Research Foundation, Miami, FL).

If subtle desires (vasanas) or seed impressions (samskaras) are purified, your personality is drawn toward good associations, people, and communities that will uplift your consciousness to new heights. Then, as one begins to replace these mental maladies with consistent positive affirmations, the light of the soul begins to shine through. The sound of the mantra then becomes linked to the image in the mind. One can start recitation of the mantra while observing a beautiful picture of the preferred image, statue, or any other form one chooses. Once good concentration is established, and the intensity increases, one can begin to close the eyes while still visualizing the image at the third eye, the ajna chakra center. When both the mantra and the image are linked, it empowers the process of mental purification. Until this process begins, love will remain obscured from view, like dust on a window, and one's enjoyment of the world is felt through the dirty glass of the ego rather than the clear perspective of the soul that is pure love. Pure love has no glass to see through, it is the fresh joy and compassion that emanates from the heart within.

Converting Emotion into Devotion

Let us interpret the word emotion to serve our understanding. The *e* in e-motion stands for the sum of one's past ***experiences*** that have become part of the conditioned or subconscious mind; and the second part of the word emotion is ***motion***. So, we can think of emotions as past experiences being put into motion. Emotions are a byproduct of the mind. The negative connotation of emotion comes from how they prompt behavioral reactions that can have negative consequences. The emotional aspect of the mind can create irrational behavior. This the basis for what I refer to in my counseling practice as action-reaction dynamics. These dynamics are what perpetuate the entire world process, the ego, and the cycles of birth and death (samsara).

On the positive side, emotions are a type of energy that, when transformed, become spiritual boons. Rather than acting out these mental conditions, emotions can be used to complete an important task, overcome an obstacle, or perform spiritual disciplines (sadhana), all of which create positive impressions on the mind. Eventually, this process obliterates the emotion, and the aspirant uses purified intellect (buddhi) to perform their duties in the world.

When emotions are transmuted into devotion toward God, they become Bhakti Yoga. Bhakti Yoga takes emotional energy and converts it to love. Devotion to God increases the state of being in love. Typically, when a person says, "I am in love," it's understood that their love, in some form, is being directed towards another person or object. However, love cannot be given, no one can give you love. Instead, a person can express compassion or kindness to another living being, but love is not something that can be received from anyone except from within oneself; it has to be experienced within the heart. One cannot fill another with love, otherwise a Jesus or a Krishna would have filled everyone they encountered with love, and their disciples would have continued the process; however, obviously, that has not been the case. Like any great guru or avatar, they demonstrate the way to experience love. We can grow to experience love in our relationship with the natural world and in the manner in which one treats others. It is One love that everyone is seeking, the same in India as it is in America, and every living being has access to the same domain within their heart. In the yoga tradition, the heart center[135] is where devotion for God emanates from.

There are several ways that recurring emotions can be transformed into the devotional power of Bhakti Yoga. Three predominant emotions exist and can be associated with the Ayurvedic doshas: vata (fear), pitta (anger), and kapha (sadness).

Fear Into Flow

Fear is correlated with vata, the air element, and it influences the region below the navel to the base of the spine. When fear grips the mind, it creates a knot that inhibits will power and limits everything a person can do. For this reason, people who are fearful display a hit and run approach to life that perpetuates violence because they fear being hurt. This can also be witnessed in a person who does not observe the law of ahimsa or nonviolence in diet by continuing to support the brutal slaughter of animals. Such a person subconsciously turns a blind eye to this, and feels, on a very superficial level, they are in control, and/or they feel they are above the animals in importance. If you observe such individuals around animals, they demonstrate fear or a sense of

---

135 It is important to differentiate the physical heart as an organ from the heart center as a chakra, a portal for higher compassionate consciousness. The chakra system is an expression of the Tantra Yoga tradition where great insights into the astral-light body are presented. The system provides an exploration into how prana, mantra, and the powers of the Goddess can be awakened to heal the conditions of the mind. There are seven centers within the astral body and each one reflects a different level of awareness or consciousness.

discomfort if a dog, for example, is not on a leash. Fear, in the human mind, converts them into behaving like territorial animals that will fight even to protect their bowl of food.

When fear is transformed, prana begins to flow, promoting circulation and synergy among all systemic functions. Fear breeds stagnation that increases the imbalance of the doshas, thus promoting disease and all types of disorders. Healthy circulation maintains the essential balance between intake (ahara) and output (vihara) that promotes life and vitality. To begin transmuting the energy of emotional fear into devotion, one should first focus on the image of Divine Mother Durga who controls will power at the navel center. Mother Durga is depicted riding a lion and is a fierce and powerful warrior who wages war on ego and the primal conditions reflected through the lower chakras. She is commonly known as the Goddess of protection and will power. She is defined as energy at the navel center known as *kriya*-shakti, the power to ascend, to arise in consciousness. Her mantra is **Aum Dum Durgayei Namaha** and can be recited with concentration at the navel center while holding her image in the mind.

Anger Into Initiative

When the mind is raging with anger, it heats the entire body and especially the head. The body becomes red like the planet Mars, and it becomes a very destructive and dangerous energy when expressed outwards. Anger is notoriously associated with high pitta and can eventually manifest into cancers, high blood pressure, hypertension, and other diseases of the heart and liver.

On the other hand, anger can provide a tremendous impetus for opening the heart for the purpose of awakening its positive side: devotion. When anger is transformed, it implodes a tremendous capacity for taking initiative in order to fulfill any desire or overcome great life challenges. When devotion is awakened, it leads to the practice of Bhakti Yoga. Every ritual in life can become fragrant with devotion, whether it be cooking, chanting, dancing, or prayer, it is love that brings abundance and the rewards of compassion and love for others beyond one's close relatives. The Goddess Lakshmi resides at the heart center to usher into your personality Bhakti, as love and devotion. Bhakti replaces anger as the capacity to have compassion, patience, and understanding. Once consciousness is more present in the heart, it becomes much easier to overcome the selfish demands of the senses and perform acts of service (seva). Lakshmi is commonly depicted standing on a giant beautiful lotus flower and its opening is symbolic of an ever-expanding awareness, just as the lotus flower opens gradually to the rays of sunshine moving across the sky. While visualizing her image at the heart center, one can chant her mantra as **Aum Shreem Maha Lakshmiyei Namaha** while deepening the feeling of love at the heart. Mother Lakshmi controls the power of devotion, called icha-shakti, which opens the heart.

Sadness Into Stability

Finally, the heaviness of sadness (or depression) is commonly correlated with kapha, along with congestion in the upper respiratory tract, slumping of the shoulders, and increased fat on the body. Sadness is overcome with attention at the spiritual eye while the aspirant engages the energies of shakti (will power) and bhakti (devotion) to awaken wisdom (vidya) as the highest level of consciousness. This intuitional channel provides profound levels of right understanding (sanmati) and knowledge (jnana) directly from the soul, as opposed to empirical knowledge that is based on sensory observation or memorization. Goddess Saraswati controls chit-jnana shakti, the power of knowledge. When sadness is transcended, it brings stability and strength to one's personality. Stability is established when knowledge is derived from the true Self, not the ego. When a person recognizes the truth of their existence, it brings great consistency of effort as discipline for sadhana. The Goddess Saraswati plays an instrument called the veena, and she awakens creativity and intuitive knowledge. She inspires wisdom to pour through your personality, leading the aspirant to liberation, mukti. Her mantra is **Aum Aim Saraswatayei Namaha** and can be recited while concentrating at the spiritual eye and visualizing her image there.

It's important to avoid interpreting liberation as living in a state of carelessness or liberal supremacy where one claims to be free; as the state of enlightenment, mukti is much higher than this. Working with the energy of emotions is a primary step in a long process of expanding consciousness. The goal is to abide in the experience of being in love rather than in the motion of action-reaction dynamics that perpetuates this world. Such work is not mastered in a weekend workshop or perhaps even in a few months, it must be practiced consistently until it becomes fully integrated in a natural way on a moment-to-moment basis. When integral yoga is applied, it becomes like the sacred Ganges River (Ganga Devi) where shakti, bhakti and mukti flow like an electrical current that illumines the personality with inspiration, positivity, and serenity (shama).

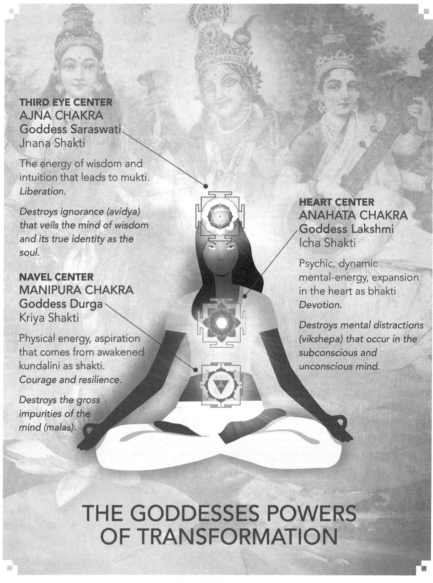

THIRD EYE CENTER
AJNA CHAKRA
Goddess Saraswati
Jnana Shakti

The energy of wisdom and intuition that leads to mukti. *Liberation.*

Destroys ignorance (avidya) that veils the mind of wisdom and its true identity as the soul.

NAVEL CENTER
MANIPURA CHAKRA
Goddess Durga
Kriya Shakti

Physical energy, aspiration that comes from awakened kundalini as shakti. *Courage and resilience.*

Destroys the gross impurities of the mind (malas).

HEART CENTER
ANAHATA CHAKRA
Goddess Lakshmi
Icha Shakti

Psychic, dynamic mental-energy, expansion in the heart as bhakti *Devotion.*

Destroys mental distractions (vikshepa) that occur in the subconscious and unconscious mind.

THE GODDESSES POWERS OF TRANSFORMATION

Three Goddess Centers:
Vital regions in the subtle body for transforming consciousness.

Mantra sparks the light of awareness and devotion, expanding the two in the heart, the two go together to increase the power of learning. The practice of mantras or affirmations is an essential part of yoga and any auspicious spiritual path, and it is a powerful way to expands one's consciousness as the obstacles of the mind are suppressed or moved aside. Think of mantras as words that contain energy and when they are repeated out loud or silently, they have a positive effect on the mind because they recondition the brain to operate in a manner that produces the positive result of inner contentment. ***The power of inner love must replace the love for outer power.*** This cannot be attained without creating a new programming for the brain that is activated by clearing the mind of its conditioned limitations. These changes must be integrated into our lifestyle gradually. They cannot be immediately realized through outer experiences or substances.

These limitations are the basis for egoism and cloud the light of awareness. They block our capacity to feel and learn from our lessons, and learning is requisite to being in love. Emotions such as anxiety and fear paralyze the mind from learning. Anyone can benefit from reciting mantras or devotional song; however, one will benefit much more if they understand how they work and what the words mean. Therefore, this process as of sha-bha-mu, the merging of shakti (will-power), bhakti (devotion), and mukti (freedom), must eventually lead to surrender, the essence of all spiritual practices and the bedrock of the four yogas. Shiva symbolizes the obliteration of the dualistic world or the feeling of being separate from the pure consciousness that upholds human existence. Shiva symbolizes merging of our individual consciousness with pure consciousness. This mergence is attained through the integral process of yoga as well as adherence to the natural ayurvedic principles that allows us to dance harmoniously with nature.

Eventually, all modifications of the mind must be transcended in order for love to expand. As Ramana Maharshi once said, "Descending from the head to the heart is the beginning of spiritual sadhana." Both yoga and ayurveda play vital roles in purifying the mind so that it can abide in the heart. Shiva symbolizes destruction of mind, ego, intellect, emotions, and the conquering of all sense impulses, as this brings us to surrender to the process of evolution. In the process, what gets negated is our association with any name or form.

There are no shortcuts on the spiritual path; each person's evolution is like a mathematical equation that contains two equal sides. Call these two sides sun-moon, male-female or Shiva-Shakti, as long as they are equal. Every person is a manifestation of the creative force we call spirit, and nature is the womb of the creation. Science and quantum physics (mechanics) is still perplexed by the idea that these two aspects of life (time-space) and the domain of pure consciousness are interconnected. As long as this separation exists, it will continue to perpetuate a lack in love. Love, not the mind and intellectualism, is required to understand the mysteries of creation and to improve the improve the quality of life. The sum total of any action (cause) has an equal measure (effect), in order for unification to occur one must abolish the patterns of fickle desires. As the sages say, "The swan, *hamsa,*[136] flies on the two wings of knowledge and action." One wing is Karma and relates to self-effort as a means of purification of mental and physical impurities. The other wing is Jnana and reflects knowledge of the goal of life. With both wings aloft, there is the power of surrender!

With the power of surrender, all actions are not futile, all mantras or words are not ineffective, all our thoughts are not unproductive. They are all surrendered to this Divine equation. How long it takes to complete evolution no one knows. Life's equation is a play between the wind and the sea. The wind is the restless nature of the mind, and the ocean is the settled portion of consciousness that exists in every living molecule, every cell of living matter. Pure consciousness is settled and stable and never in flux, unlike the mind or doshas. When the mind is windy, it is likened to a monkey mind, and that leads to behavior that moves us from tree to tree according to our desires. Likewise, in this mindset, we move from body to body over lifetimes, perpetuating the cycles of birth and death over and over again. Listening, learning, and loving, all require a certain amount of surrender, a letting go, in order for evolution to take place.

When, by the mysticism of synchronicity, things align within the world of time and space, then one is able to convert thoughts – that trigger past conditions of the mind as emotions – into devotion, and in this way, become Hanuman. Hanuman is a central figure in the Ramayana and represents the inner power one can attain when they overcome the restless mind. Mind, thought, emo-

---

136 In the Hindu tradition, *Hamsa* is term that signifies the two aspects of the cosmic sound Aum and is also added as a name or title of one who has attained the highest Realization such as Parama-*hamsa* Yogananda or Sri Ramakrishna Parama*hamsa*. In other religions such as Islam, the Hamsa is known as the Hand of Fatima, named after the daughter of Muhammad. The downward facing hand symbolizes femininity and protection, and is also connected to Judaic and Christian traditions.

tion, and breath are all interconnected and mastered through the techniques of yoga and the Vedanta philosophy. When one becomes a master of the wind, a master of the breath – so that thoughts that float across the mental sky become more transparent – Reality is revealed. The epic Hindu text, **The Ramayana**, depicts Hanuman as the monkey God. The monkey-aspect of Hanuman is symbolic of the mind's fickleness. Ravana, as the ten-headed king of the demons (rakshasas), symbolizes the many demonic aspects of an unpurified personality. In the story, Ravana abducts Rama's wife, Sita, and takes her to the island of Lanka. In order to rescue Sita, Rama has to cross the bridge to the island with his army of apes and monkeys. This allegory teaches the aspirant to transcend (crossing the bridge) the limitations of body and mind so that they can finally abide in the heart of devotion. This crossing represents Rama awakening our love and devotion so that we can accomplish the task of overcoming our tests. This leads us to the final step, surrender. Surrender is the bedrock of all yogas. Letting go is an ongoing process of trusting the Divine to flow through us in all the moments of our life. As we progress in our sensitivity to listen and expand our depth of learning, eventually we arrive at being in love.

The Highest Love

Every living being is imbued with the capacity to love. Life is perpetuated by the illusion that love is something we acquire or receive from others rather than feeling it as the very essence of who we are. The highest love is devotion for God and defines the path of Bhakti Yoga. Love is the purest state of our existence and is ever renewing as the expansion of our awareness. Love is beyond the commotions of emotions, beyond the stupidity of cupidity and the entanglements of marriage and religion. Love is the magnet of the soul. When we follow the heart, it leads us to our dharma, bringing meaning and purpose as the foundations of real contentment. As the great poet Rumi expressed, "Your heart knows the way. Run in that direction."

Discovery of love in the Self requires stilling the mind through sadhana; a restless mind is forgetful of the heart. When we abide in the heart, our conscience is free from the disturbances of the world process. Feeling love begins with the many selfcare practices of ayurveda like abhyanga, self-massage with herbal oils. Following a plant-based diet can also bring a greater synergy with the cycles and energies of Mother Nature. Caring for animals also attunes our senses and expands the feeling in the heart that increases our natural intelligence. Behind every miracle is love. The heaviness of a milky white winter is transformed as Spring smiles through the colorful flower blossoms. This blossoming inspires us as we seen them through summer's glistening rays of light, and then they fall back eventually into her bosom again. Our true nature is love, the feeling we have in Her presence is always near, but only if our heart stays near and dear. Love culminates in detachment and the capacity to let go of the people, places, and things we shared, knowing that nothing is ours to keep, leaving us to surrender to the Divine hand.

Chapter ELEVEN

Surrender and the Royal Path of Yoga

*Internally dedicate all your problems and worries of the mind to God within you. Feel
that the Divine Hand is taking care of the burden of your life and is gently leading you
on to the spiritual goal--Liberation. Let your every action be an act of Divine worship.
Though working in a noisy world, enjoy an inner sense of silence and serenity.*

Sri Swami Jyotirmayananda

Letting Go

Surrender is the cornerstone of all major paths of yoga and represents the
supreme virtue of the spiritual life. The capacity to surrender, or to let go,
indicates that an aspirant has developed complete faith in the divine process.
One lets go wholeheartedly, having given their best in any circumstance, thus
allowing the Divine hand to determine the result of any outcome. One who
surrenders trusts that no matter what the outcome of any experience is, it was
intended to demonstrate some lesson, an opportunity to learn where one's
love for God may be only partial. The practice of surrender demonstrates that
one understands that there are higher laws of karma in place from previous
lives. No matter how much effort is given toward the preferred outcome of
certain events or challenging life situations, some courses cannot be altered,
nor can one prevent specific results.

Although a specific event occurred and efforts to deter it were unsuccessful, two important factors will have changed. Firstly, positive intention is not lost. Whatever spiritual or disciplinary effort a person makes toward changing any event or blemish in their personality is always for the better. The intention and efforts become stored as positive impressions in the mind so that when the stars align according to a person's evolutionary cycle the impressions can manifest in a manner originally intended. In other words, things don't happen when we want them to, they happen when God decides it is best for us, in support of our spiritual evolution. Secondly, such efforts teach us that life must embrace a sacred relationship that exists between two distinct aspects of creation, that of individual human existence and the realm of pure consciousness that sustains all living things.

The practice of integral yoga develops the power of surrender, allowing a person to change their destiny. The royal path of yoga (Raja) can be referred to as the supreme, or integral, path because it focuses on the importance of transcending the senses through mental discipline and presents a methodology for establishing direct connection with the soul. Raja Yoga teaches the practice of meditation as the ideal method for internalizing one's consciousness. As the aspirant expands their awareness within the inner dimensions of one's being, his or her capacity to surrender will naturally increase. Destiny becomes a fixed equation when the mind or intellect is highly conditioned, programmed like a robot. Raja Yoga aims to transcend the programming by cultivating the mind's capacity to expand in awareness. Intellect that exists without spiritual aspiration remains impure, limiting a person's capacity for evolution. Spiritual progress depends open purity of intellect. The potential of intellect is that it can become intuitional. This transformation of the mind is precisely the intention of Raja Yoga. The process of purifying the intellect in daily life requires consistent observation and discipline and occurs in the form of tests and challenges.

Raja Yoga, as one path of integral yoga, focuses on cultivating the inner life, the capacity to surrender, and the importance of social responsibility. The importance of social responsibility cannot be separated from living an evolutionary life. The way we live in the world and the relationships one shares with others and the natural world is a reflection of their evolution. Social responsibility is a steppingstone to the higher practice of surrender. From the perspective of yoga, social responsibility is characterized by the primary principles of the eight-limbed system called yamas.[137] The second set of principles called niyamas[138] are developed through our personal relationship and trust with God including our capacity to surrender. The niyamas emphasize the importance of surrender and Divine devotion as ishwara pranidhana. Both sets of principles define the balance between our inner and outer life. Patanjali Maharishi enumerates these ideals in his Ashtanga Yoga Sutras[139] and he codified these as moral and ethical values for promoting an evolutionary life.

Surrender is the greatest quality the aspirant can attain in their consciousness. Having the capacity to surrender to God demonstrates that one has attained the fire of knowledge (jnanagni). Jnanagni provides the aspirant with a sure-footed dharmic life and continuous insights into the supreme Reality. A thirst for knowledge, for the mysteries of the world, is a great virtue, filling one with a courageous approach to life. If one can acquire this understanding: "You are an instrument in Divine hands,"[140] then one's fear will be removed. Fear works in us like Kryptonite weakened the comic book hero, Superman. The ultimate weakness is fear, because it weakens the entire mind-body complex and obstructs us from being in love.

Fear must be abolished before one can attain the full capacity to surrender. When one lives in the world of time and space, and especially today with the corruption in politics and propaganda in the media, one's attempts to be courageous are being undermined with the tactic of fear mongering. Propaganda entices viewers to stay engaged in the world's lila (drama). Anytime a person chases anything it runs from them faster and farther. One can embrace Vedanta when one stops chasing and Realizes what exists within themselves is always there and is everything they have been looking for. Chasing what is outside of oneself is a result of a deluded mind that has become conditioned by the senses, materialism, negativity, and lack of wisdom. Most human errors

---

137 Yamas: Ahimsa (non-violence), Satya (truth), Brahmacharya (abstinence), Asteya (non-stealing), and Aparigraha (non-possessiveness).
138 Niyamas: Shaucha (purity), Santosha (contentment), Tapas (austerity-self-discipline), Svadhyaya (self-analysis-reflection), and Ishvarapranidhana (Divine surrender).
139 Yama and Niyama are presented as the primary and secondary steps of the Ashtanga *Yoga Sutras*. Patanjali Maharshi codified these as core principles of the *Yoga Darsana*, yoga philosophy.
140 *tasmāt tvam uttiṣṭha yaśho labhasva, jitvā śhatrūn bhuṅkṣhva rājyaṁ samṛiddham mayaivaite nihatāḥ pūrvam eva, nimitta-mātraṁ bhava savya-sāchin*, Therefore, arise and attain honor! Conquer your foes and enjoy prosperous rulership. These warriors stand already slain by me, and you will only be an instrument of my work, O expert archer." Bhagavad Gita: Chapter 11, Verse 33, Commentary by Swami Mukundananda.

are repeated many times before change takes place, although change is not always in the right direction, towards the heart.

Understanding the Laws of Karma

Most people understand the word karma to mean something associated with any action they take and the resulting repercussions. Furthermore, the term is typically used with a negative undertone, as if karmic consequences can be used as a threatening warning: Behave, or else! However, good karmas play an important role in cultivating the power of letting go. To be clear, I use the terms 'letting go' and 'surrender' synonymously. Our actions shape our capacity to surrender, in both a practical sense – dealing with mundane aspects of our lifestyle – and actions related to the more poignant moments in our life. Such moments arise within acts of generosity and self-discipline and they promote evolutionary living, the simple life.

The capacity to surrender is an inner process that produces an outer result. These outer results include natural living, abiding by the principles of ayurveda. Raja yoga provides the ideal pathway towards cultivating that inner process through meditation and natural living, enhancing the overall mental attitude (bhavana) one carries throughout their life. Bhavana, feeling combined with positive attitude, promotes a selfless attitude that prevents us from getting entangled in life's dramas and the perpetual illusion that obtaining something new or better will change everything. Simply put, expectations lead to conflict and suffering.

Three main forms of karma exist, latent (sanchitta) past actions that are awaiting to manifest at the right time and place, present moment (kriyamana) actions that will determine one's future and actions or events that are going to happen and cannot be changed (prarabdha). Of the three, most people worry about the last one because prarabdha karma is, as Swami Sivananda said, "The arrow, which has already left the bow, which cannot return, which must hit the target." As they are bound to happen, these are the events and experiences that become opportunities for growth.

The path of Raja Yoga prepares us for the karmas that are bound to happen by increasing our power of surrender. The most practical forms of karma are the present moment actions (kriyamana) because they allow us to take responsibility for our life and determine the type of future we would like to manifest. The actions of the present moment allow us to shape our lives, and surrender is applied through vairagya, by maintaining a neutral or stable state of mind as we perform our activities. This evenness of mind is one of the building blocks to surrender. Vairagya teaches us to avoid dependence on a world that is unreliable. It is the natural movement of the mind to discover what one is really desiring: soul realization. Vairagya, dispassion, appears to the egoistic mind (sleepwalker) as a display of being cold or callous; however, to an awakened being or yogi, Vairagya is the process of developing greater control over the mind and senses.

Other prerequisites that lead one to attaining the art of surrender are referred to in the eighth chapter of the Bhagavad Gita; these prerequisites pertain to the paths of knowledge (jnana) and action (karma). Krishna explains to his disciple Arjuna that while the self should renounce their actions (sanyasa), it is also important to renounce the fruits of our actions (tyaga). As these epic scriptures elucidate truths in fascinating and profound allegory, so we must understand the teachings and apply them all to our actions. How? By listening to the moments in our life and those in the world around us. Listening provides us with the opportunity to learn and grow in love, leading to evolutionary living. For healing to take place, we must be willing to let go of the past.

Creating a Meditation Practice

All that has been introduced in prior chapters supports the practice of classical meditation which is characterized by stillness of body and mind, and awareness of breath. Creating a comfortable sitting position, one that supports the hips and helps to maintain a straight spine, is important. Practice of postural yoga is ideal before meditation but not always required. The practice should be planned according to one's mind-body type (prakriti) and seasonal factors. If one has practiced what I call their *prakriti poses*, at least several times within the span of a week, the practice will provide residual value, and the postures will be not required every time you sit down to meditate. This is especially the case after many years of consistent practice.

Meditating outdoors is also very supportive if the conditions are good with respect to weather and sound. Ideally, natural environments can provide profound support for internalizing the mind because the natural elements aid in purifying the senses. Real peace rarely exists where noise is prevalent. Noise produced by modern machinery or vehicles are characterized as outer projections (rajas) that can be very disturbing for the mind; however, if a person's consciousness is highly developed, then disturbances will not matter much. Meditation begins with stillness of the physical body, and it best to minimize all physical movements during meditation. Meditating in spaces with good energy is helpful, as is meditating with friends or meditators, especially if they are more developed in their practice, as this will deepen your experience. This is experienced as a feeling of peace and calmness that one can enjoy without any concept of time. It is not how long one meditates, but how deeply and consistently one practices; the depth of the experience is created in meditation through consistent practice and then eventually one enjoys meditating for longer periods.

Breathwork in Meditation

Since one of the primary aims of meditation is the stilling of the mind and heart, it is best to apply the correct breathing techniques in order to support stillness. Before meditating, is important to try to reduce congestion, because difficulty breathing will affect mental acuity, one's ability to relax, and the uplifting of the eyes to the third eye center (ajna chakra). To address sinus congestion, it is ideal to flush the nostrils with saline water using a neti cup. Once the nostrils are cleared, ayurvedic healers recommend applying nasal drops.

Next, to enliven the mind, improve focus, and ignite the power of the life force (pranashakti), it is good to practice combinations of forceful exhalations through the nose (kapalabhati) and bellows breathing (bastrika). I recommend applying a 2:1 ratio when employing these two breathing techniques. A simple approach would be 12 repetitions of kapalabhati followed by 6 repetitions of bastrika. One can conclude with a deep inhalation followed by a complete exhalation; this is characterized by the full expansion and depletion of the lungs.

After this process, it is ideal to relax in stillness while maintaining an upward gaze, because this directs the awakened life force energy (prana) up through the spinal centers. These three steps present a unique formula and were presented and systemized by Patanjali as Asana (the seat of meditation), Pranayama (energy control-breathing techniques) and Pratyahara (relaxation where sensory energy is withdrawn). These three steps are primary, they are practiced before beginning meditation, however they are also an integral part of the entire process of meditating.

Another subtle technique that can be added to the seated position (asana) is the tensing of the entire body, as this helps to relax the nervous system. The practice is simple, but the effects are profound. Begin this by taking a slow, long, and deep inhalation until your lungs are full, then hold the breath and begin tensing all the muscles of the entire body. Hold the tension for a slow count of three. While you hold the tension, the eyes can be turned upwards towards the spiritual eye (shambhavi mudra), indicating where the prana should go. This gaze is auspiciously connected to Lord Shiva and is one of his thousand names. Shiva symbolizes Supreme Consciousness. Shiva is the destroyer of duality, time and space thinking, and the spiritual eye is where duality is transcended.

The practice of tensing the body is a signature feature of the Paramahansa Yogananda energization system; although he added a double respiration (inhale and exhale) as a precursor to the practice. The double breath is a very mystical form of breathing; it has a remarkable capacity for awakening prana-shakti and piercing the subtle body. The double breathing technique can be practiced repetitively in either a lying or seated position for several minutes. The lying position is much more relaxing and can be used for more therapeutic purposes. The seated variation can be used as a preparation for deepening meditation.

The practice involves double inhalation (one short-one long) through the nose, followed by a double exhalation (one short-one long) through the mouth. The idea is to direct the second and longer inhalation upwards towards the heart center. With each second inhale, the longer one, the person draws energy from the lower chakras upwards to the higher centers. This is an important intention to set because the exercise is useful for not only awakening the prana-shakti, but for establishing a higher state of awareness. One can access the mind's capacity to discern and witness. The length of practice can range from 1 to 10-20 minutes depending on one's level of purification and meditation practice. In some cases, just a few practices of double breathing with or without tension can internalize one's consciousness and a relaxed and peaceful feeling is experienced.

Alternate nostril breathing is also another effective breathing exercise to balance the solar and lunar energies of the mind-body complex. When practiced slowly, it slows the resting heart rate, induces withdrawal of the senses (pratyahara), and helps to manage vata dosha on the mental level. This technique is profound as it directly influences the two aspects of the brain (as discussed in chapter three). Alternate nostril breathing desensitizes the storehouse of emotions in the moon-brain's amygdala and is considered an important precursor to meditation. I often recommend this technique to my counseling clients who want to deepen their sleep.

Similar breathing techniques[141] were explored during the American counterculture movement of the 1960s and early 1970s. However, they did not comprise a comprehensive system or aim toward the goals of Indian Raja Yoga, Tantra, and Kashmiri Shaivism systems, and so they did not maintain a following.

In today's modern breathing practices, we find many who continue to explore the remarkable power of breathing. Some people sensationalize it, adding the practice of plunging into cold water after breathing practice. Again, these methods claim to bring many benefits for changing a person's mental state; however, without devotion and a cultural lifestyle to sustain them, they become another fad of modern times.

I want to distinguish the yogic forms of breathing from these modern movements with the clear objectives of transcendence and spiritual liberation. Any yogic pranayama should be done in short increments overtime in order to properly purify the gross body and gradually awaken higher dimensions of the astral body. The measure of success is one's increased stillness. Concentration and is attained through consistent practice of pranayama. Increased stillness and concentration are strong foundations upon which to establish a sound meditation practice.

Mantra in Meditation

Mantra is an expression of sound or vibration through the instrument of language. In the Vedas, language is extolled as a tool, found within the forces of nature, for revering the Divine. I want to emphasize two aspects of mantra as a tool for propagating an evolutionary lifestyle. One is the role of the feminine Divine and her distinct Goddess forms, Durga, Lakshmi, and Saraswati, that

---

141 Holotropic breathwork was developed by psychiatrists Stanislav and Christina Grof in the 1970s. They implemented an open mouth repetitive breathing exercise in order to experience entering different dimensions of consciousness. The results provided many physical and mental-emotional healing benefits.

I discussed in chapter nine. The second aspect is mantra as cosmic vibration, particularly the supreme mantra, Aum. The Upanishads state that Aum alone is enough to unify the soul with God.[142] When Aum is chanted properly, it produces three distinct vibrations: the A, pronounced "aaa" can be felt at the solar plexus; the U, pronounced "ooo" can be felt as the throat vibrates; and on the third syllable M, pronounced "mmm" the top of the head vibrates.[143] For the recitation of mantra, a mala or Hindu rosary is used. The mala[144] contains 108 beads to aid in counting one's repetition of the chosen mantra while one focuses on placing emphasis on the meaning and symbolism of each word.

When reciting mantras for the feminine Divine and her distinct Goddess forms, it is helpful to have a visual representation of each Goddess in the form of an image or statue. For this particular exercise, it is not necessary to recite each of the mantras 108 times, but rather, one must focus on the energy of each mantra and the image of the Goddess. This can be done either with eyes open, or while visualizing her internally.

Begin with Mother Durga at the navel center (manipura chakra). While internally concentrating there, mentally repeat Aum Durga while feeling and resonating with her qualities as the power of initiative, protection, courage, and confidence. Alternatively, one can recite the complete mantra **Om Dhum Durgayei Namaha** and feel her qualities arise in your being; then after a few moments, enjoy some silence and stillness. Then feel Ma Durga's energy rising up and connecting you to the heart center where her energy expands into the qualities of Mother Lakshmi: sensitivity; abundance; generosity; love; devotion; and compassion. As you visualize her image, mentally recite Aum Lakshmi, or the longer version **Aum Shreem Maha Lakshmiyei Namaha.** Enjoy the expanded feeling of joy in your heart and the abundance of being connected with the beauty of nature and the play of her animals, and appreciate the gifts that your spiritual practices have brought you.

---

142 *Mundaka Upanishad* (Translation by Swami Gambhirananda), *"Aum is the bow; the atman is the arrow; Brahman is said to be the mark. It is to be struck by an undistracted mind. Then the atman becomes one with Brahma, as the arrow with the target."*
143 *Dancing with Siva*, by Satguru Sivaya Subramuniyaswami (Himalayan Academy India-USA).
144 Shiva mala are made of multi-faced, reddish-brown seeds called Rudraksha, meaning the "Eye of Rudra" (as Shiva). India's scriptural heritage ascribes the first rudraksha tree to God's tear that fell from the heavens out of compassion for humanity. The tree that grew produces this sacred seed worn by yogis as a symbol of their commitment to transcend the world of time and space through the practice of mantra, the recitation of the Divine names.

As you focus at the third eye center (ajna chakra), visualize Mother Saraswati and while feeling her virtues as wisdom, creativity, and intuition, mentally recite Aum Saraswati or the longer version **Aum Aim Saraswatiyei Namaha.** Now that the spinal centers have been energized, allow the lifeforce, prana, to reach its culmination at the thousand petaled lotus chakra at the top of the head. *Visualize the full moon in all its glory, recognizing that the moon is not visible or empowered without the light of the sun. That soft moonlight is the sun illuminating your personality with the power of surrender.*

As you silently mentally recite Aum repeatedly, your trust in God grows beyond names and forms, beyond nature and all forms of duality. Your consciousness enters the abode of freedom, washing away all worries, thoughts, emotions, and the limitations of the ego. Enjoy increasing the length of your meditation as this practice becomes more consistent in your lifestyle, integrating the qualities of the feminine Divine into every aspect of your life. Bring her into your relationships as patience, care, and affection. Allow her to flourish in your work as tenacity and gratitude. Feel her guiding your life's purpose (dharma) as an internal knowing. Trust that liberation (moksha) will come when you recognize that the One you seek is the shimmer behind all eyes, is in the dance and splendor of nature, and is the optimism in every ray of the sun.

Let meditation be simple by recognizing that what is within you is outside of you. Be in the moment. Let go of the past, and truth will inspire every moment of your life. Another mantra that is most auspiciously correlated to the concept of surrender is attributed to Lord Shiva, the destroyer of the little self (ego). The mantra is **Aum Namah Shivaya.** As it is recited, one can visualize the dancing Lord Shiva as Nataraja, the one who dances in a ring of fire and who can be assimilated into your life as a halo located above your head, illuminating your consciousness. That ring of fire is *agni*, the sacred fire that provides abundance and awakens the boundless virtues of the soul, such as discipline over mind and body, the power of to negate and overcome attachments to thoughts or false associations.

Aum Namah Shivaya[145] is probably the most significant mantra associated with

---

145 *Aum* is the cosmic sound of the universe; *Na* is 'no' or to negate; *Ma* means me or mine-ness; *Shi* is correlated to the Goddess Lakshmi and the cultivation of spiritual wealth; *Vaa* is the expansion of consciousness; and Ya is the root letter of the heart and so indicates communion with the heart. It is also known as the mantra of the five elements as Na Ma Shi Va Ya are the five syllables correlated to the five elements. Chanting of this mantra helps to integrate individualized consciousness with Shiva

surrendering to compassion. It is a nectar of glorious energies. The purpose of this mantra, and any other mantra, is purifying the consciousness from its animalistic (instinctual) state, beyond the mental (intellectual) state, and into the supreme state of super consciousness. Any of the mantras written here can be used independently if one feels a strong resonance with one in particular. This exercise should not replace one's regular and consistent practice of their personal (ishta) japa-mantra. These three Goddesses are celebrated each year in India in the autumn and are recognized throughout the world during Navaratri, the celebration of the nine nights, with each of the three Goddesses being celebrated for three nights. The celebration culminates on the tenth day (Vijayadashami), with the tripartite Goddess's triumphant victory over the demon of darkness. The demon of darkness is the false self, the ego. The Goddess's light of awareness prevails.

Vedantic Meditation in Five Steps

Meditation needs a framework in which to function effectively, otherwise one's practice can devolve and never transform beyond the superficial level of sitting still. There are five steps that comprise a framework to support one's mediation practice.

- **Invocation**

The energy of space, **bhutaksha**, is considered the primary level of preparing one's consciousness in Vedanta. The energy of one's mediation space can influence the quality of one's mind and general practice of meditation. The first stage of meditation is invocation, where the space is made sacred through purification of the ether by ringing a bell, burning incense, or lighting a candle. These sound, smell, and light elements can be waived throughout the space, or the entire room, to clear the air, the ether, of any negative vibrations and to invite the light.

- **Breathwork**

Secondly, breathwork can be practiced as we just discussed in chapter ten, as

---

Tattva or the principle of the all-pervasive energy consciousness. Sri Sri Ravi Shankar says that the Dancing Shiva (Dancer) is consciousness-purusha, and the dance is the Prakriti-Nature, (Creation). These two can never be separated.

per your needs or dosha type. Stronger, more rajasic and activating techniques, such as bellows (bastrika) or forceful exhalations through the nose (kapalabhati), can be applied when a person needs stimulation, nasal clearing, and energization. When a person needs calming, they should apply the alternate nostril breathing combined with breath retentions at the top of the inhalation.

- **Mantra**

Then, in the third step, one uses mantra as the subtler energy that deepens one's inner state of awareness, withdrawing attention away from the outer world of the senses. After mantra practice is complete, after a substantial level of stillness is present in body, mind, and breath, then this stillness becomes the cue for the fourth step of meditation. This readiness is confirmed by a magnetic and peaceful feeling of being drawn inward.

- **Meditation**

In meditation, there is nothing to do anymore except enjoy being still, although it is a good habit to check the gaze of the eyes, making sure they are uplifted to the spiritual eye center. Anyone new to meditation will notice their eyes may have a tendency of dropping downward; however, with regular practice, the optic nerves and muscles become trained to hold the concentration at this very sublime point. Initially, when one starts these steps, the most important factor is exercising the practice of physical stillness because this helps set the proper foundation for calming the breath and mind.

- **Prayer**

The last step of meditation is prayer, the technique for invoking the grace of God. Prayer becomes an effective means for establishing personal and direct communion with the Divine through your ishta devata, your personal aspect of the Lord. Divine presence is the most comforting feeling one could ever want. As Divine grace (kripa) is invoked through prayer, it satisfies every desire. Prayer becomes effective when one makes actual contact with the Inner Self, the *Antar-atman*; this Self is the soul. Most people give up on prayer because they have never learned how to properly overcome the obstacles of the body-mind complex, nor have they learned to listen to the voice of God.

Deep and effective prayer leads to grace. As Swami Satyamayananda146 says, "Grace and God are one. Grace allows us to move from an ego-centric life to a God centered life." Grace also flows through our actions, our karma yoga. When we are generous and selfless, grace increases and flows ceaselessly. Meditation, as an inner-life practice, provides a direct path to cultivating surrender. From the practical action-oriented outer side of life, Karma Yoga can be enacted to enhance the amount of grace we want to experience. One can choose the inner way or the outer way, or both, and enjoy the realization that all steps lead to letting go!

The Miraculous Way of the Royal Path

Integral Yoga is an approach to spiritual evolution that has been presented by the stalwarts of these ancient Vedic traditions for millenniums for one important reason: Integral Yoga is a methodology that manifests the promise of enlightenment. These practices have been tested repeatedly over millenniums. They have been written about in numerous scriptures, and their teachings continue to inspire people and their civilizations to evolve. Because Raja Yoga is a path that leads to liberation as the supreme purpose of life, it is the path taken by those who have a clear understanding of life's purpose.

In this age of materialism, humans continue to strive for material abundance. However, as many awaken in the dawn of an evolution revolution, they question the doctrines of societal norms and prioritize how they are living on earth. Many now are discovering a new means of using currency, such as those derived through Blockchain technologies that are basically decentralizing the traditional financial banking industry and aligning to the higher laws that embrace reciprocity and redefine what it means to have abundance. Such changes are reflected in the relationship humans are having with the living world, and even with their own religion. These changes are happening for many people because a lifestyle that embraces health, harmony, and individual responsibility is reverberating in their own consciousness under the resolute proclamation of unity, unity! Anything done with a unified vision that recognizes one supreme truth, one love that pervades all hearts, is a movement toward evolution.

---

146 Monk of the Ramakrishna Order / Vedanta Society

Vedantic philosophy encourages us to view life's challenges as Divinely or-chestrated occasions. Through our challenges, we are encouraged to grow in love; however, we must listen and learn before being able to love. One great example from scripture is Vasudeva, the father of Krishna, who had to remain pragmatic even while he and his wife Devaki were imprisoned by King Kansa and their seven children were murdered. Finally, when Krishna was born, Sun in Leo, Kansa's attempt to destroy Krishna failed. This was as an act of grace. Krishna's birth represents turning the misfortunes of life into lessons. The power of love is what allows us to awaken to the teachings.

In life, surrender is necessary in every step. Without the capacity to let go, the grace of God (karunamayi rasa) cannot exist. Many of the complex events of human life present a higher message and when we interpret their meaning, love blossoms and keeps us moving towards liberation. The path of integral yoga, applied as listening, learning, loving, and letting go, can provide an aspirant with tools for living and enjoying the world while not becoming attached to the results of our actions. In this way, we live in the world, but do not become controlled by it. Consider these four aspects of listening, learning, loving, and letting go to be the keys that open all the doors to the mysteries of life. These mysteries are treasures that, for most people, remain to be discovered.

The history of India abounds with miraculous stories of yogis who have, through the mastery of Raja Yoga, attained the eight *siddhis*, eight powers of the soul. One of the most famous books of modern times that tells of these powers is the ***Autobiography of a Yogi***, by Paramahansa Yogananda. The powers written about in this book and the remarkable acts demonstrated by yogis are not meant to entertain or embellish their egos or any other person's ego, but rather, to prod the aspirant to awaken their own human potential. These powers are quiescent and meant to be aroused with integral yoga to bring the soul into unity with the limitless potential of pure consciousness.

Imagine attaining the power of silence and never feeling the need to speak using the voice. Many modern yogis such as Meher Baba and Baba Hari Dass took vows of silence for most of their lives. I once enjoyed some sublime moments of silence with Baba Hari Dass, and after telling him of my work in integral yoga and ayurveda, he gestured with his hands saying, "The roots are the same," and I understood him perfectly well. This active silence symbolizes the great realm of silence attained in meditation or mauna. Such a yogi becomes a *muni*, and, having attained freedom from the bondage of the five elements, this silence can carry one's consciousness beyond prana and the mind.

While in India, I had the privilege of visiting the ashram of a great yogi-saint and poet named Jnaneshwari who was born in 1275 in the small village of Alandi, Maharastra. Jnaneshwari was known to have many remarkable powers. His life's work is an important commentary of the Bhagavad Gita in Marathi, the language of that region. This commentary inspired generations to follow the path of devotion to Krishna through Bhakti Yoga. His version is a remarkable teaching in that it is the oldest known Marathi text and is comprised of 9,000 verses, even though the Gita only has 700 verses. It is written using a unique rhythmic prose that can be chanted. This is one reason why it provided much influence in the Bhakti path, and his work influenced other notable Hindu saints such as Tukaram and Namdev.

I was invited to Alandi by one of the trustees of the ashram board on a very auspicious day celebrating Jnaneshwari's birthday. I was able to view the original version of his text that is carefully preserved and highly guarded. The energy at this ashram is profoundly strong yet playful, and I felt especially devotional when I was taken to walk over to the entryway of Jnaneshwari's entombment. After the completion of his great scripture, Jnaneshwari asked to be buried alive at the age of 21 and has been left there ever since. It is believed that he remains alive and preserves his body in a specialized state of meditation known as jivan samadhi. Centuries after his entombment, a devotee was summoned by Jnaneshwari so that this devotee should open his samadhi mandir (tomb of meditation). He explained to his devotee that the roots of the tree just above his earthly sanctuary were beginning to encroach on his body, and even beginning to strangle him. Naturally, the devotee proceeded with the task of pruning this old tree, cutting the roots that were intruding on Jnaneshwari's meditation seat. The devotee cleared the way so that Jnaneshwari could continue with his work of channeling light and prayers to humanity.

Such individuals do much for the salvation of the world, as their consciousness is rooted in the astral realm. They become continuous channels of pure light and conduits for devotion that continues to permeate the land of India. Once the root clearing task was completed, Jnaneshawari asked to be left alone again, and his visitor obligingly departed. The only person who happened to ever see Jnaneshwari since his enshrinement was Eknath,[147] another great

---

147 Eknath (1544-1599) was born in Maharashtra, India, and was a disciple of Janardan Swami. Eknath was best known for his translations of the *Bhagavata Purana* and composed his own version of the *Ramayana*, known as *Bhavarth Ramayan*.

Marathi saint and devotee of Krishna that carried on much of the work that was initiated by Jnaneshwari.

Many stories of yogis with the powers of Raja Yoga exist, like the miracles of Trailanga Swami[148] who lived to about 300 years in the same body. He would sometimes remain under water for days at a time, use telepathy, and change his body size. He was highly revered and respected by Ramakrishna, Vivekananda, Lahiri Mahasaya, Swami Abhedananda, and many others. In one instance, he was seen entering the very sacred Kashi Vishwanath where he defecated and urinated on the Shiva lingam (holy stone of Shiva). Although this would be considered sacrilegious, Swami was able to transform the waste products of the body into Ganga jal (water), honey, ghee, jaggary, flowers, and incense. After being lambasted and taken away by the temple priest, later that evening, the King of Kashi dreamt of Mahadeva (one of many names of Shiva) who appeared and proclaimed that Sri Trailanga Swami is Shiva and that Shiva is in him.

Sage Patanjali, in his **Yoga Sutras**, enumerates how the eight miraculous powers (siddhis) develop conquest over the five elements (bhutajaya) as cultivated through sadhana of Raja Yoga. Raja Yoga is essentially presenting a mastery over the mind, both in the practice of still meditation and as accessible through practical awareness. Raja Yoga provides the aspirant the capacity to direct the life force via the instruments of the mind and breath. What is presented here is a very brief summary. Raja Yoga allows one to access an extensive series of techniques or actions (kriya), harnessing an awakened power of energy through concentration of the mind on the breath within the channel of the spinal centers (chakras). Sacred sound in the form of the Aum mantra aids in converting the power of prana in each of the lower chakras (muladhara, svadhisthana, and manipura) into shakti as the subtler form of feeling (bhavana).

So basically, the techniques focus the energy of these three lower centers and transmutes energy into devotion in the heart. With continuity of practice, the prana gains enough momentum to open the petals of devotion (Bhakti Yoga) as expanded feeling or devotion for God in the heart. This is a very

---

148 Born Sivarama in Holia at Vizianagaram, in the state of Andhra Pradesh 1607 (approx.) and lived mostly in the holy city of Varanasi. He was said to be an incarnation of Lord Shiva and left his body on December 26, 1887. Much of his life's events are recorded in a biography titled, *Umacharan Mukhopadhyay*.

transcendental experience that is beyond the senses. As concentration and stillness deepen, this sacred life force energy is directed to the higher regions in the spine where pure knowledge (jnana yoga) is disseminated and leads the aspirant towards spiritual freedom (mukti). Raja Yoga integrates shakti-bhakti-mukti to promote integral evolution.

Vedanta and Raja Yoga Meditations

One might ask, if Vedanta provides the culminating philosophical expression of the Vedas, then how can it be practiced in the waking state? This becomes the outer living form of Vedantic wisdom that must be integrated into the moments of our life. Whether it be in work, in conversations or interactions with others, or during the decisions that challenge our intellect, Vedanta must be practical and not merely a theoretical system for entertaining debates. On the other hand, the path of Raja Yoga guides the aspirant inward, beyond the senses, towards the centers of consciousness to arouse the higher and usually dormant faculties of inquiry (vichar), discrimination (viveka), and the enriching insights brought forth from the witnessing (sakshi) power of consciousness. If one can watch the show of life while avoiding attachment to it, they can be instantly freed of the cycles of birth and death (samsara).

When we are presented with a challenging moment, Vedanta affords us the ease of waiting because of the trust we have in the Divine hand of surrender. Through this trusting and patient inner power, we avoid reacting to what may appear as an unfavorable circumstance. It could be providing us with clues into faults in our personality. By waiting, one can allow the practice of watching (witnessing awareness) to unfold in order to discover how we should respond. These moments of observation allow us to inquire into the nature of our experience, and eventually leads to the higher level of awareness, from which we can respond. Again, the basic point is to avoid reactive behavior or actions that are spawned by the conditioned mind. This type of awareness is not limited to the physical layers of what one can see, but entails discerning the deeper implications behind such moments.

The Highest Surrender

The highest surrender exists when the aspirant transcends searching and transforms into Realizing the Supreme Reality. One's mind will become fully aligned with the Divine. Every circumstance is guided with the sweetness of surrendering to God's grace as the Guru within as the discerning faculty of pure consciousness (Brahman). Attaining such a sublime virtue means that a person has naturally developed this quality through lives committed to sadhana. For practical purposes, the initial movement toward letting go is developed through nature. Accordance with nature exists both through the five elements and all the basic lifestyle factors the body and mind find stability in. Additionally, accordance with nature exists also when one transcends the basics as they grow to discover that the inherent intelligence that exists within Mother Nature's kingdom is the same intelligence that sustains his or her own consciousness. The power to surrender is developed through sadhana. Those same disciplines that can often feel laborious sustain one's capacity to let go and trust in the Divine process. Spiritual disciplines, as prescribed by the guru and supported by their respective lineages, keep the soul walking on the straight and narrow path.

When life challenges arise, we are given the opportunity to practice letting go, after we have listened and learned from the experience that has challenged us. Once those steps have been completed, the mind is receptive having cultivated a positive attitude, and the heart is also receptive with positive feelings. Through attunement of the mind and heart, the power to let go has no resistance. Growth on the spiritual path is stunted when fear and attachment grip the mind; for this reason, we cannot just expect that any person can easily surrender, even when, from our own perspective, it seems very natural. The process leading to surrender is tedious and timely and relies much on the art of listening and learning from the world. When you know the guru is alive in all the moments of your life you can love the world as you own, always trusting the Divine process is at hand. In modern times, abundance has been reinterpreted to mean financial and material gains. However, abundance from the perspective of evolution or movements toward spiritual liberation (moksha) follows a life of dharma, or God-first living. Seeking Divinity first is the most generous act anyone can engage in because the rewards benefit all. This is in contrast to seeking money first, which has limited benefits that are not enduring. Evolution requires an integral approach to yoga and life; it is only a matter of practice.

Chapter TWELVE

Listen, Learn, Love and...Let Go!

Lord, change no circumstance in my life change me.

Sri Gyanamata

Integrating the Four Methods

Living the path of integral yoga requires various behavioral attributes. A person needs first to recognize them and then to gradually develop consistent behavioral choices. Karma Yoga, in many ways, is the primary path for spiritual evolution because it is both influenced by, and influences, how we act in the world. Our actions do speak louder than our words because actions are dramatic. Because we become aware of our own energy as expressed through thoughts, speech, and actions, we are encouraged to live more responsibly in the world. As depicted in the epic scriptures, these *lilas* (dramas) have something to teach us if we are willing to, and capable of, listening.

Listening and learning requires one to develop greater awareness, to cultivate the capacity to inquire as to nature of one's actions. We must attend to not merely the action itself, but also the manner in which it is done. Understanding the intention behind the action is more important than the action itself. This inquiry requires the technique of *vichara* which includes having a more sensitive awareness of the connection between mind and body. Developing the capacity to listen begins with our own body-mind relationship. This listening supports a type of intimacy, in that one begins to feel consciousness flowing through a connected mind and body. After much spiritual talk at dinner with a new friend about the promise of integral yoga, we both stood up to shake hands as he departed and he said, "*Ahar, Vihar, Achar!*" These three words summarize the entirety of the integral yoga:

- Ahar - Take in the wisdom of the world.

- Vihar - Remove all that is negative and useless to you.

- Achar - Build your character and master yourself through discipline (tapasya), reflection (svadhya), and surrender (ishwara pranidhana).

The supreme form of purification for the mind-body complex begins with embracing the path of Karma Yoga. We can use our arms to cook for others, our legs to walk with others, our strength to carry things, and we can perform activities that connect us with mother nature. We must perform our actions with meaning, purpose, and a higher intention that allow us to be guided by the higher power of God's grace. Firstly, whatever path one chooses in life should align with their constitution, skills, and talents. This is where jyotish (vedic astrology) can be very helpful for those who do not have a clear sense of direction. One's rising sign, the sign that appeared in the eastern horizon at the exact time of one's birth, defines a person's relationship to their own body, the ego, general personality traits, and skills. The star and sign under which one comes into the world must be studied; it helps a person avoid getting trapped in jobs or commitments that do not resonate with who one's authentic identity.

As one begins the path of Karma Yoga, it is important to ask the questions, Who am I? and What are my strengths and weaknesses? **When we Wonder, life on earth becomes wonderful; when we wander, a soul becomes lost in the world of illusions.** Without knowing what work, a commitment, or a relationship mean to you and the role it plays on the path of evolution, all actions become mechanical gestures that entangle the mind in its projections. The projections have nothing to do with who you are behind all your conditions because of this wandering, this lack of knowing the Real purpose of life.

Listening: Commitment, Concentration and Consistency

The theme of evolutionary living, as presented in this book, is aligned with the universal message presented in the epic stories of *The Ramayana*, *The*

Bhagavad Gita and *The Mahabharata*. The universal message is that of seeking one's dharma, learning to always be in love. Dharma leads you to victory. Victory is freedom from the ego and all the limitations of mind, body, and the world process. If one listens to the drama of life, it repeatedly spurs one to ask the question, Am I following the path of dharma? This is determined with only one proof: love of God. Progress in dharma is characterized by your increasing devotion; devotion for the Divine to your heart's content, and as compassion for all living things, animals, and nature. The depth of devotion is based on feeling and thinking with the heart. In Bhakti Yoga, listening is referred to as **shravana**, and reflects a certain quality of attentiveness. The art of listening in its highest form, can be further refined by developing three special aspects: commitment, concentration, and consistency.

- **Commitment**

The first is Commitment. This is a kind of initiation (diksha) that sparks the evolutionary path, sanctifying your life's actions with a willingness to listen. Your initiation is a commitment that can easily be done by lighting a candle in front of your preferred image of the Divine, holding your rosary (mala), and affirming that, "From this moment forward, I am making a commitment to live a Godward life for the rest of my life." This process can be in the form of this affirmation or something you may want to personally write yourself. You could also use your mantra or even a certain song, as long as the intention of commitment is clearly behind it.

This willingness begins as a renewed commitment towards God when you recognize that it is Divine intelligence that is trying to guide your life. Imagine being able to hear the soft whisper of Divine mother as you enjoy the splendor of her creation. Spiritual commitment is an initiation taking place between you and the Divine, and by making a commitment you are willing to take on the attitude that you are now an instrument (nimitta-mātra) in Divine hands. Commitment allows you to be an instrument because you have an understanding; either you understand why you are performing certain actions, or you understand why certain circumstances are occurring in your life, or perhaps both.

 If the spiritual path is trivialized, then it becomes like anything else in the mundane world: lost in the translation. If no commitment is made, the world will no longer be a channel for guidance toward the light. As you work, secretly sing, Listen to my heart. As you perform your sadhana sing, Listen to my soul.

The lack of commitment that individuals express and receive is rooted in poor understandings of who we are and what we truly need in our lives. These days, there are so many distractions enticing us to fulfill every desire, and so we find it difficult to make a commitment. The options are excessive. Our society influences us to believe that we need much more than that which we already have within us. Therefore, before making a commitment to someone or a commitment to attaining a goal, it is very important to be clear regarding who and what we are committing to and also understand what we are seeking within ourselves as part of the process. The soul is constantly craving its reunion with the source of existence as pure consciousness. However, if your life is dominated by egoism, then your choices are driven by old impressions (samskaras). Samskaras will throw you into the patterns of attraction (raga) and aversion (dvesha) as a cycle of pleasure and pain.

Sometimes we realize that we have made an incorrect commitment. For example, many people born into strong religious families make commitments to marry based on religious affiliation or their cultural background. If the commitment to marry has not been made on the basis of compatibility, a person may come to eventually realize that you don't fall in love with a religion but with a soul, hopefully with a person who shares similar lifestyle interests and the goal of attaining higher consciousness. Wisdom and spiritual evolution come when everything we do on the spiritual path and in our lives begins with a commitment to ourselves; this means we must learn how to be loyal to the inner Self.

Many may see this loyalty to the inner Self as selfish because the practice of learning to be loyal to ourselves requires a substantial amount of time and dedication to knowing who we are. We may do such things as reading quality books, writing or journaling, meditation, and contemplative practices. These activities allow us the time and experience when we can look inwards and understand ourselves. This is valuable because any resulting commitment we make will have the loyalty to support it. Without knowing the inner Self, the commitments we make will not last.

Among the characteristics that distinguish the yogi from a layperson practitioner are the yogi's commitment to a journey of self-improvement and, most importantly, the yogi's loyalty to the God-sent guru. For the layperson, commitment to the journey is difficult because so many aspects of our culture promote passionate individualistic desires driven by the ego's quest for attachment and false senses of security. Eventually for the layperson, during times of emotional uncertainty or stress, their patterns of seeking outward fulfillment must change. If not he or she will keep being pulled down by the negative (tamasic) energies in life that can create greater pain and suffering.

All that we need lies within and the solutions come when we make the **commitment** to know ourselves as one with the universe. I learned this from one of my counselors during a period of learning period in my life. He said to direct pain and the struggles for happiness towards the divine, to give it all to the Highest One. He meant that we should see the periods of hardship and uncertainty as opportunities for finding inner resolution through a deeper relationship with God. We must surrender to this inner calling. Our outer struggles and obstacles are signs and symbols of the need for a new direction, a new perspective or vision that destroys the ego's **me-mine** mentality, transforming it into a intention of letting go, saying, "Now I will surrender to something beyond reason or the thinking mind."

This is the great message in the mantra, "Om Namah Shivaya." When it is chanted, the devotee appeals to God in the aspect of the destroyer. Swami Sivananda Radha says, "Self-centeredness cannot be mastered by sheer will-power; we must surrender and ask for divine help. The Aum Namah Shivaya mantra is a call upon God to eliminate our negative qualities, and to destroy the obstacles to higher spiritual life." We must be committed to allowing the destruction of the obstacles to our spiritual progress. That commitment begins and ends with the Most High and it takes time and repeated effort for a lifetime. Benjamin Franklin once said, "Experience keeps a dear school, but fools will learn in no other, and scarce in that."[149] Our lessons often come to us because of foolish behavior, and it is uncommon that one learns a lesson the first time around.

- **Concentration**

The second principle for refining the art of listening is Concentration (Dharana). The importance of concentration cannot be ignored, and it becomes enhanced as one increases their capacity for attentiveness. The quality of our life is determined by our capacity for attention. To pay attention, we must

---

149 *Poor Richard's Almanack*, by Benjamin Franklin, is a collection of his timeless maxims, rules, and aphorisms, and was first published December 28th, 1732.

slow down. As long as we are chasing things of the external world with the idea that things will bring us greater happiness, we are losing our capacity to listen. Ayurvedic lifestyle and the daily and seasonal health care practices are of tremendous value because they support us in prioritizing our health and wellness, and this increases our harmony with nature. Postural yoga, breathing techniques, mantra, and meditation are all great practices for increasing our power of attention. I have found that certain daily life choices improve the capacity to calm the mind, which, in turn, create a greater capacity to concentrate. These choices include reducing time spent using technology and walking more or using a bicycle as a means for transportation instead of driving everywhere.

Concentration produces greater efficiency, and it also leads to refining our sensitivity. Not only can we listen to the world through the ears, but we refine our capacity to feel the essence of each moment. There is so much joy in being present. In being present, we can manifest abundant joy and show those we are present with how wonderfully contagious this state of being is! When we can hold our attention long enough to sustain our focused attention on whatever the person with us may need, when we can hear them, a person feels welcomed and appreciated. Being heard is often what most people are seeking in interactions. What we can say to them is often not as important as that we are willing and capable of listening deeply to them. After you have made a commitment to living an evolutionary life, it is time to take that initiative and apply your attention to the moments and interactions of your life with the utmost concentration. ***Be present and feel what it means to be alive.***

Concentration is essentially a level of focus. Our ability to focus is dependent on many factors including the dosha type (mind-body constitution), lifestyle, environment, and even the astrology of the individual. Concentration is the ability to apply quality attention for a given period of time. Ayurvedically, it's the fire (pitta) types that have a tremendous ability to concentrate and achieve. The yogis use concentration to focus attention on a particular sacred point on the body or sometimes on an image or symbol outside of the self until that focus can be directed inwards.

No task can be completed without some level of concentration. In conversations, I see that people find it difficult to stay focused, to maintain eye contact, and to maintain an effective level of presence. For the mind to be able to concentrate, it must be calm; a fast mind is usually a distracted one. A good practice for developing good quality concentration is to focus on completing one task at a time. Do not let the mind shift to anything else until the original task is completed. Try for example, cooking a meal, or reading, writing, or helping someone with a task. It doesn't really matter what it is, but rather how we do it. What is important is keeping a steady level of focus, keeping the mind present until the task is finished. This may take some practice, but eventually you will come to realize that multitasking is actually less efficient than working on one thing at a time. When our concentration improves, the quality of our work improves. This is because we become more efficient. This is commonly expressed in the idea "quality verses quantity." Swami Rama Tirtha says, "The greatest worker, when he is at the height of his work, when he is doing his best, mark him. This incessant work unwittingly leads you to the highest yoga." Perhaps in the eyes of others, this work seems to be a strain, stressful, a struggle. However, this deep quality of focus on tasks achieves the destruction of the ego concept of, "I am working," and there exists a perfect oneness, freedom, and peace that comes from concentration.

- **Consistency**

The third principle for deepening your power of listening is Consistency. As with anything in life, the capacity to strengthen your commitment and concentration is influenced by how consistently you do it. Yoga practices prove to be most efficacious when they are done with regularity. Two terms in the Sanskrit literature that are applied in Vedanta and related to the principle of consistency are *abhyasa* and *tapasya*. The first, *abhyasa*, is defined as the continuity of one's effort towards attaining the goal of liberation. The second, *tapasya*, indicates a form of discipline, the willingness to control or manage one's actions. The quality of tapasya allows us to transform austerities into positive attributes in our personality. The quality of abhyasa manifests in the practices that we know are good for us naturally, and the more consistently we enact them, the more we increase our willingness to perform anything with consistency; this can be seen as a cycle of positive reinforcement. Doing things in a consistent manner helps us to recognize God's love and compassion by always listening to that Divine presence in every living moment. Listening to the world is not a matter of convenience, but instead, as we recognize every moment of our life is a sacred opportunity for learning, we should listen consistently. Listening to world requires taking initiative, it must be active in the sense of being aware and having a concentrated mind. But listening must also be passive in the sense that we should surrender to the process that is taking place and not resist it or become defensive. In this way, we practice consistency: a continuous exchange between the head (awareness), hand (activity), and heart (trust and surrender).

There is nothing more valuable on the spiritual path than our ability to be consistent. The nature of who we are and who we will become is solely dependent on how consistently we do things. It is the continuity of our efforts that brings us the real fruits of success. The law of karma is very simple: what you do the most is what you shall become. The greatest of struggles in life are those where we try to restore or maintain balance. We have all heard in the adage, "I have to get back into balance," and the key to balance is endorsing a practical approach 'to doing' (our activity) and 'to being' (meditation).

We are more mentally active these days. Media keeps us entertained and we have many more toys than people did during the Industrial Revolution. In this period during the late 18th and early 19th centuries, major changes in agriculture, manufacturing, and transportation had a profound effect on the socioeconomic and cultural conditions in Europe, the Americas, and the changes eventually influenced the entire world. During this Industrial period, work was much more physically laborious and the relationship between the use of the body and the use of the mind was strongly exercised. This created a synchronicity of body and mind. However, much has changed since then with regards to consciousness. Learning to be **consistent** needs to begin with re-uniting the body and the mind so that they are in a working relationship that not only serves the physical body but also the mind.

The modern approaches to health commonly practiced in gyms wherein the body does one thing, and the mind is somewhere else, either on the phone or staring at a television, results in mind-body fragmentation. This practice further divides the mind and the body until eventually the body and the mind no longer know how to communicate with each other. The power of both yoga and ayurveda is derived from its continuity, the unification of body and mind as a way of life. Going to a yoga class a few times per week is where it may begin for many, but this practice needs to include other hours in the day dedicated to small intervals of sitting in silence, frequent introspection, and active moments in service to others. Any continuous effort to improve ourselves does lead to a better quality of life.

Commitment, Concentration, and Consistency are the three practices that refine the art of listening. When following our dharma, the important tasks in our lives, we must make the commitment, make the time for action. Once that step has been taken, we are able to focus the power of attention to create real concentration. If practiced consistently, it's a formula for spiritual evolution that never fails.

Enhance Learning with Solitude, Stillness, and Silence

The path of evolutionary living requires embracing a life that includes not only moments of solitude, but a perspective that comes from your own soul. In the early stages, after your consciousness is awakened and you are centered outside of egoism, you may experience loneliness and a distinct feeling of being different, distinct from the world of time and space, family, and friends. You are now questioning those who live without guidance from their own souls. This is an early movement away from the course of the river that flows to the desert.

These experiences mark the start of your journey on the path of self-knowledge, following the the course of the river that flows to the ocean. Throughout one's lifetime, there are many opportunities for living an evolutionary life. They usually appear when difficult situations arise, like a health issue, a divorce, or a financial loss; these are some of the experiences that prompt people to search for help. As a result of life's turning points, one may call on friends who are spiritually inclined or emotionally supportive, or perhaps one may take up yoga, or read self-help books. This is a good start, but sadly, for most, this progress does not last.

The new directions in listening to their soul may end when they attach to a new intimate relationship, get a new job, etc. Many return to the old conditioned habits, leaving the lessons they have begun to learn behind. Learning requires constant nurturing. The goal is to find solutions directly from being in the solitude of the soul where your consciousness grows, and realizations take place. This marks the expansion of jnana, pure knowledge, and these moments serve to fortify one's movement towards liberation. It may appear as if the world and those closest to you are opposing you, challenging you, and persuading you to stay with them, to follow their path. These moments may extend for years, even, perhaps, lifetimes.

- **Solitude**

When we have the courage to step away from the world and its processes, we gain the space and energy for developing the witnessing power of the mind known as *sakshi*. There is no question that the power of solitude exposes our luminescent inner qualities. Yogananda once said that, "Solitude is the price of greatness," because it serves to recharge mind and body with the soul's magnetic energy. The root of the word solitude, *sol*, means the sun in Latin, and it also can be found in the word, *solve*. The phrase, "to solve," refers to being with the One. Life is a gift; we are given the opportunity to solve a mystery and most search for something outside of the self that is never found. This dilemma is resolved when one discovers that the person, place, or thing we are looking for is right in our heart.

A bold distinction needs to be made between the meaning of solitude and that of loneliness. They are both often associated with a negative connotation. However, the practice of solitude is the farthest experience from that of feeling alone. Choosing solitude in your day is essentially choosing to be one with the essence of our being, that is Brahman (God). When we practice solitude, we remove our mind and body from the disturbing vibrations of society that continuously pull the senses outward and drain the energy. Solitude in nature is one of the best ways to restore the mind-body relationship and bring about greater balance.

Therefore, solitude is a positive way to improve our wellness and it gives us a chance to shift the mind into a more reflective state, creating an act of sensory purification. The practice of solitude is very different from taking a stimulating vacation filled with mindless activities and socializing. True solitude also requires turning off the multi-media world in which we now live. We can approach the existentialist perspective even though our world now is far different from the time when Henry David Thoreau went to Walden to reflect, write in his journal, and study himself through the lens of mother nature. Thoreau wrote of the value he found in one of India's greatest scriptures, The Bhagavad-Gita. "In the morning I bathe my intellect in the stupendous and cosmogonal philosophy of the Bhagavad-Gita, in comparison with which our modern world and its literature seems puny and trivial." In so doing, Thoreau etched the importance of solitude in the literary culture of America.

- **Stillness**

Solitude promotes one's capacity to slow the mind down, and to bring about stillness, just as the still wind allows one to discern the clear reflection of the moon in water. Solitude invokes the purest reflection of the self, and fosters the power of discrimination, ***viveka***. In solitude, one develops the capacity to attain mental stillness, manifesting tremendous power for learning. According to ayurveda, stillness or balance of the mind, is a prerequisite to health and wellness. Yoga asana and pranayama have great capacity to help one create this yogic state referred to as ***anubhava***, pure being.

On a teaching trip to rural Georgia in the southeastern part of the United States, I had a realization related to the power of anubhava. While I was approaching the country home of a couple who hosted me for a series of classes, I noticed a deer standing near the house. I later came to learn that this deer had become a pet they called Luna. I have always been fond of deer, such gentle creatures, and I often see them when hiking in the mountains. Luna held a soft and steady gaze like that of the moon. As I sat next to her for some time, I was able to peer deep into her eyes and experience a profound understanding of pure awareness. Through this little creature, I was given a glimpse of the Divine connection into all living things. "This is Brahman (God)," I exclaimed. I felt that I was looking into the universe. This pure stillness is within us and is the universe itself.

There is a great story about Krishna that explains this truth. As a child, Krishna was a very mischievous boy who loved butter. He often stole butter from other houses and many of the other parents came to Yashoda[150] to complain of this. Krishna, while playing with his friends in the fields, ate some dirt in while in a quarrel with some friends. Yashoda, hearing of this, went to scold Krishna and tied him to a grinding stone, then she asked him to open his mouth. There she saw the Seven Oceans, the entire Universe with its vast expanse of the mountains, the planets, air, fire, moon, and the stars. There also

---

150 Yashoda, the foster-mother of Krishna and a wife of Nanda. Krishna was born to Devaki but was given to Yashoda and Nanda in Gokul by Krishna's father Vasudeva on the night of his birth, for his protection from Devaki's brother, the king of Mathura, Kansa. Repeatedly, Kansa's army tried using demonic weapons to destroy Krishna, however Krishna plays the bamboo flute (bansuri) which symbolizes strength. Krishna can call on the cows, who are symbols of the wisdom and the grace of Divine Mother. The flute is an allegorical expression of allowing your personality to become a channel of God's will.

was Narayana, Almighty Lord in the form of Vishnu, seated upon Adishesha, The Divine Snake. Narayana was being attended upon by his beloved consort Maha Lakshmi, the Goddess of abundance and prosperity. What Yashoda saw within Krishna's mouth was what is also within us: the vast unmanifest realm of pure consciousness. This realm, this profound source, exists within the heart. It is for this reason that the heart chakra is called **anahata**, meaning unstruck. The heart center is where the realm of pure consciousness can be found as the supreme abode of peace and stillness.

In the yoga sutras, sage Patanjali describes a triune: concentration, meditation, and enlightenment. In such exalted stillness, one reaches the highest degree of consciousness because all identification with body, mind, time, and space is completely annihilated. Becoming still requires a calm mind. Maintaining stillness requires the power of attention. Both a calm mind and stillness can be supported by following the path of integral yoga. Each aspect of our personality can be cleansed of its gross impurities, malas, such as jealousy, pride, and anger, making our minds calm and still.

Purification of the mind, the removal of gross impurities takes place through selfless service to humanity, Karma Yoga. More subtle impurities of the mind exist through the ego; however, the ego requires much more effort to overcome. The Vedantic scriptures recommend Upasana, the art of devout devotion, being wholeheartedly devoted to God through meditation. Thus, the term Upasana implies the combination of devotion and meditation as the merging of the head into the heart. The cause of all impurities is ignorance of our Divine nature. When we forget the true Self within us, we also depart from our relationship with Mother Nature. The ego does not get along well with nature, it resists it and sees it as separate or distinct even though the five elements remain active as inner forces (doshas).

- **Silence**

The discipline of observing silence, mauna, is one of the oldest spiritual practices. Silence enhances meditation because it serves as a spiritual fast. Speaking is one of the most taxing things we can do and it can engage the mind strongly in the attitude of "I"-ness. Silence is observed in a postural yoga practice as a teacher leads the class, thus allowing the practitioner to increase focus and concentration on the body and breath. Many yogis such as Meher Baba, Mahatma Gandhi, and Baba Hari Das, all practiced silence for extended periods of time and some for a lifetime. Silence speaks in more powerful ways than words can, because, through silence, we can become more attuned to the energy of expression through the eyes and gestures of the face. Practicing silence is a way to confront the ego and diminish it.

I remember a client who came to see me about various struggles in her life ranging from her career to personal relationships. As I often do in such cases, I recommended practicing more meditation and silence. She decided to take a short retreat at an ashram. It is customary to practice silence during one's stay to enhance the power of reflection. Well, when it came down to the first meal and she sat down with everyone at the table in complete silence, she did not know what to do. She explained to me that as everyone was seated her discomfort grew and grew so much inside that she started staring at her food to avoid making eye contact and to maintain silence. She wished she could hide underneath a piece of lettuce. As the meal continued, she became more restless, as eye contact and facial gestures continued in glances across the table without any words. She finally got up and walked away. After hearing all of this, I chuckled because I knew it was so good for her. I asked her, "Who felt uncomfortable?" She said, "I did." I responded by asking, "Who is the "I?" She looked at me with a sincere smile. She got it. The silence was making her ego uncomfortable. The silence was exposing her to an aspect of herself that she had lost connection to for many years. I'm not suggesting that everyone needs to go to an ashram to practice silence, but it can be very helpful for enhancing the capacity for learning.

In the yogic sense, there are two types of practice (sadhana). One is to control the thought waves (vrittis), developing mental will power through practices like solitude, silence, and stillness in meditation or through pranayama, breath control. If one does not have good strength of will then practices like solitude, silence, and stillness in meditation can be very helpful for developing the mind's power over the restless thoughts. But even such lifestyle practices as solitude and silence can be too difficult and discomforting for people to start with. Secondly, the multitudes of breathing techniques of the Hatha Yoga system are excellent tools for thought control.

In the Buddhist Zazen traditions, walking meditation is done by linking each step with each breath as a moving meditation that prepares the mind for greater stillness in the more traditional seated position. Integrating some silence and solitude into our exercise routines, like a walk, a bike ride, or yoga practice,

THE EVOLUTION REVOLUTION *Yoga, Ayurveda, and the Rise of the Soft Power Culture*

can be a very powerful measure for purifying the mind of the subtle vrittis, thought disturbances. Sssshhh your way into deeper and deeper peace and well-being and find yourself with a lot more energy at the end of the day than had you been speaking all day. When we lose our balance and peace of mind, we forget how simple it can be to bring back our natural qualities reflected in a still or sattvic mind. When the mind can arrive in a more consistent state of sattva, then a great purification has occurred in your life. Krishna states in the Bhagavad Gita, "Be still and know that I am God." I think that says a lot about what being still really means. Yogic stillness is equated with God consciousness.

Expanding the Domain of Silence

The natural world, untouched by humans, is permeated with the song of the earth and that of Mother Nature's five elements. Now, with billions of human inhabitants, the frequencies are changing and disrupting the mind's capacity to remain connected to the super mind of Aum. Additionally, our eco systems have been altered and nature is in disarray. As discussed in chapter eleven, the primal sound is Aum and the vibrations illuminate the mind. The grandest vibratory spere is that of the universe as recognized in yoga-Vedanta as the eternal AUM.[151] All humans are born with a capacity to connect with this realm and to choose a pathway that is natural and attractive as per their astrological energies. Some may be more drawn to abstract forms of meditation like meditating on Aum or the Sun, and others may have a more definitive affinity for the Divine, perhaps in masculine or feminine aspects. Each person can also become more aligned with one of the four branches of yoga (Karma, Bhakti, Jnana, Raja) that seems most accessible for opening the door to universal consciousness. Once the door is open then the other features of the personality begin to develop integrally, leading us to a renewing and expanding joy of awareness, pranava, as referred to in Raja Yoga.

As humans continue their evolutionary journey, they begin to live in a more efficient manner and enjoy the sacredness of silence. Silence is the also the state of emptiness where the mind is free of thought. As one develops in their evolution they begin to realize and appreciate silence. Silence begins through

---

151 *Mandukya Upanishad* (Translation by Swami Nikhilananda) verse 1 states, "*All that is past, present and future is, indeed, Aum. And whatever else there is, beyond the three-fold division of time-that also is truly Aum.*"

quieting the need to speak. As one speaks less this allows the mind greater power of reflection and promotes detachment from the senses. Speaking is a result of the air element (vayu) that is controlled by the vocal cords; the sounds are shaped with the tongue and mouth. The practice of vocal silence is requisite to inner silence and promotes restoration.

One does not realize how exhausting speaking can be until they are ill, and they feel naturally more withdrawn so they may preserve their energy. Ayurvedically speaking, vata types chatter, pittas interrupt, and kaphas abstain in a general sense. If you take a moment to listen to most conversations, you can easily witness the three doshas represented. When a pitta type is frustrated or agitated, they will speak at you and often the volume of the voice is heightened much more than is necessary given the proximity of others. Vata types jump from thought to thought and their conversations flows like a snake, erratic, quick, and unpredictable. Kaphas are the best listeners; however, they can lack clarity in communication because the water-earth tendency influences retention. All these are general considerations that depend on many factors and whether or not a person is in balance.

I often recommend to my counseling clients that they observe how the constitution (mind-body type) influences their speech. This is a way to learn how to better manage dosha forces as they operate through the mind and body. We want to make the purified intellect, the higher mind, the controller of these elemental forces, as opposed to the conditioned consciousness as it operates through the ego. Eventually, as silence is enjoyed within, one seeks to be with people and in spaces that honor and cultivate a serene atmosphere. The noisier a space is, the further it is away from serenity. Ultimately, as the aspirant attains that Divine connection with the supreme supplier of peace, it will not matter much where one goes. Higher consciousness becomes ubiquitous and is the attractive source that all seek. Silence is energy that, like a magnet, attracts the serene. Chatter and gossip attract more of the ego, more of the conditioned consciousness. Meditation is a wonderful practice that teaches us to learn how to enjoy the serenity that is within.

Increasing Capacity for Love

After having listened and learned from the world or the particular circumstance to which you are applying these teachings, it is love that is expressed in the third stage. The path of Bhakti Yoga provides many methods for expressing love. However, one must make sure the individual obstructions are removed. These obstacles are barriers that each person has created according to their karmas. It is helpful to understand the workings of the world process. Understanding will support removing the obstacles and will increase one's capacity for being in love. When one expresses the words, "I love you," it does not mean that the person is actually abiding in love. Love, from the yogic perspective, is characterized as love for the Divine in all forms.

As a result of the influences created by the world process, the mind becomes afflicted with what Yoga-Vedanta refers to as the five afflictions (kleshas). As long as the mind is afflicted, there exist obstacles that prevent us from being in love. The five kleshas are:

1. Avidya – Ignorance, the fountainhead of all problems.
2. Asmita – Egoism, associations with names and forms (namarupa).
3. Raga – Attachment, created by the impressions of superficial pleasures.
4. Dwesha – Hatred or Aversion, arising from impressions of pain.
5. Abhinivesha – Clinging to life and the idea that this is my only life. This perpetuates fear of dying and increases a false need for the things of the world.

The practice of yoga aids in purifying the mind of its many obstacles, and ayurveda teaches us to find harmony and develop sensitivities through natural living. Vedanta presents to us a unifying message that draws the aspirant closer to truth regardless of the path upon which one starts their spiritual movement. The good listener finds ease in the activities that harmonize the head, hand, and heart. Those with good reasoning capabilities will naturally be good decision makers, are turned to for advice, and enjoy the wisdom that can be deciphered from worldly experiences. Others have tremendous will power and the strength to manage the mind, senses, and withdraw from the world through the peaceful practice of meditation. The lover simply wants to love and enjoys this path in various ways. The Bhakti Yoga path provides the devotee Nine Methods of Devotion (Navadha Bhakti).[152]

---

152 *Applied Yoga*, Swami Jyotirmayananda (Yoga Research Foundation, Miami, FL).

1. Love can be expansive through listening (shravana) to the stories of great mythologies or the great spiritual scriptures of India.

2. *Kirtana* or devotional singing, dancing and thoughts of the Divine is a popular path for those who enjoy the creative arts. One way that Westerners who do not speak Hindi or Sanskrit can connect with the power (shakti) of Vedic culture is through the many bhajans, devotional songs that invoke devotion, foster feeling for all living things and aid in moving one's consciousness in a Godward direction. God becomes interested in entering our heart.

3. The practice of meditation is valuable not merely for its mechanical benefits on the mind and senses, but also to create a constant memory of God (samarana) that is carried into the daily life, even during the difficult moments that tend to pull us away.

4. Serving humanity in any form is a way to recognize the Divinity in all. In the more orthodox sense this practice implies service to the Guru image of Brahman. Service (seva) is a profound practice that can change even those who are filled with anger and resentment.

5. Flowers make the world a more colorful place. Offering (archana) them to the God in others or to guru images on the altar recognizes God's presence blossoming through the flower as the smile of Divine Mother.

6. *Vandana* is the adoration of the Divine in all living things. As one practices this in daily life, they can begin to experience the insignificance of one's little life. It becomes a transforming practice of becoming a spiritual nobody wherein one no longer identifies him or herself with the body or conditions of the mind.

7. Yielding, *Dasyam*, to a higher force elevates one's capacity for love through recognition that love comes from God, and that love is the source of all existence.

8. Sakhyam is the practice of making God your best friend.

9. The highest form of love is complete surrender to the God as the supreme beloved (atmanivedana).

Therefore, when we analyze the reasons for not feeling accelerated in our love, ignorance (avidya) is at the very core of it. Avidya perpetuates both the world process and the cycles of birth and death and becomes the source for mental afflictions that block the love that is emanating from the indwelling soul. So much importance in the world is given to birth, life, and the many gratifying moments that the ego becomes associated with in the form of worldly accomplishments, experiences, and relationships; however, so little time is given to manifesting love from its real source. What about death and celebrating the moment we are to leave this world? Imagine, if at the time of birth each person was presented with a certificate that provided both the time of entry and the time of departure. Ponder this idea for a moment, would life be different if you knew the exact day and time when you were to depart and dump the body again?

When the mind draws a connection to this field of awareness there is no limitation to the capacity of our mind. When the mind becomes capable, the heart opens to love. Being in love begins when the world process is unraveled. Love must not be conceptualized, rather, it is an experience that transcends conditional thinking. Real love must arise from reciprocity and rise beyond the sentimental level. Love is within you, and you can experience it by removing associations with thoughts, emotions, and transcending the ego. Love is found in the inner-most Self.

The journey of loving in evolutionary living begins with a low sense of love. It is mistakenly defined as an obsession or an infatuation with a person and is influenced by external factors such as beauty, financial status, or societal prominence. This type of love throws one into the cycles of mental impurities such as anger, jealousy, and attachment. The ideal of evolution, as taught in Vedanta, is to arrive in the experience of being in love beyond names and forms. For this reason, Divine love is defined as being in love with God, not limited to one form, but beyond, into the experience of being in it, to the degree that one can affirm, ***aham prema***, I am love. Patience is necessary as the aspirant moves through the various stages of developing devotion as listed below:

- Faith (shraddha)
- Good company (sangha)
- Remembrance-meditation of the Divine (smarana)
- Removal of obstacles of negativity in all forms (anartha nivritti)

- Firmness or stability of devotion (nishtha)
- Pleasure in meditating and hearing about God through spiritual stories (ruchi)
- Growing attachment to God (asakti)
- Divine Feelings (bhava)
- Divine love (prem)

Yogi or Bhogi

A yogi that is immersed in sensory pleasures cannot learn to watch the mind. The outer sensory pleasures, bhoga, keep the mind outward bound and far away from the real source of contentment (santosh). True wealth is measured by how well contented the mind is. The world of bhoga is viewed as the world of calamities because it is simply bogus. The world does not give any Real support. We must firstly surrender to the Goddess in nature as **bhumi-devi**, or any feminine aspect of the Divine, to invoke the power of surrender. There is no medicine better than love and the feeling of being cared for. It changes the endocrine function and hormones are released that promote strong immunity, increasing the level of mental radiance (tejas). Physically, a luster appears.

When someone enters the hospital for any reason, the real healing comes not from the sterile atmosphere but mostly from the feeling of being cared for by nurses, family, and friends. In my experience, one of the most healing aspects of integral yoga comes from the "mood or attitude" **bhava** that one feels. According to the personality and temperament, a person develops a type of **bhava** that reflects one's awareness. These modes of feeling are levels of devotional feeling that eventually culminate with the lover and the beloved becoming one. Any of the nine modes of Bhakti Yoga can aid in cultivating the right bhava.

When attention is placed on connecting the heart center (anahata) to the third eye (ajna) through calm stillness, the experience of truly being is attained, **Anu-bhava**. Therefore, bhava of the mind reflects the ability to "feel" not in a sensory manner but feeling as the higher mind's capacity to intuit. It is this higher intuitive aspect of the mind which can only be cultivated by regular practice of meditation and creating a pure inner environment, (**shaucha**).

Letting Go through the Royal Path of Yoga

What was at one time considered the norm for both genders, even a few decades ago, has changed due to the pace of our solar-dominated societies in addition to the changes in cultural revolutions (agricultural, industrial, cognitive, and technological). The Agricultural Revolution was between man and nature's resources. The Industrial Revolution was between mankind and machinery for the purpose of advancing materialism and efficiency. The Cognitive Revolution was an intellectual study of psychology and the mind that subsequently led to major developments in technology. The cognitive revolution, that began in the mid-twentieth century, has begun a gradual shift in focus on independence, individual freedom, ecology, and transparency in business practices.

As a result, in my view, we are at the dawn of an Evolution Revolution which marks a clearer movement towards self-realization and the need for dharmic living. This evolutionary cycle will continue to include advancements in technology and financial systems, the dissolution of currencies, and changes in dietetics and increases in plant-based lifestyles. We will see greater use of astrology for interpreting specific events and promoting the integrative ecological systems that bridge the gap between humans and nature. What we have witnessed over the last few centuries with respect to definitions of masculinity and femininity has changed substantially, reflecting a broader cultural digression from patriarchal systems and their aggressive influences over society and lifestyle. The Vedantic-yogic ideal of surrender is derived from nature as mankind learns to develop a sacred relationship with nature. A yogi aspirant recognizes that surrender is the highest part of the evolutionary equation as is reflected within human reciprocity and the recognition that consciousness and nature are fully integrated.

Women have adapted towards more masculine tasks and roles by taking on more diverse positions in the workplace, performing in competitive athletics and even dressing more like men, wearing caps, tank tops, and hairstyles rarely seen before the technological era of the later twentieth century. In India, men commonly dress in clothing that is much more feminine than that of the Western world. In India and Asia, men commonly wear sandals (chapels) that expose their feet, and they wear loose clothing like wraps called dhotis. Many of the Eastern (moon) societies influenced cultural norms that eventually traveled west into Europe. This included men wearing high heels, stockings, gowns, wigs or maintaining long hair, and, in general, men were much more ostentatious.

The notion of a "revolution" is difficult to define in any consistent manner, especially given the differences between Western and Asian cultures. Revolutions are described in terms of the changes seen in the material (social) world, how humans live and interact with each other, and the use of nature as a commodity. Many people appear to be a product of the current age and environment, influenced by global and cultural factors such as government policy and international relations, commerce, fashion, diet, and general lifestyle.

Indian Man Wearing Feminine Clothing as Perceived by Western Standards/ Image Courtesy Sasi *Edavarad*

However, the inner revolution of the soul is a silent thrust that begins to appear in the relationship that each soul has with nature, diet, and lifestyle. The current evolution revolution is measured mainly on the basis of the inner aspects of human consciousness and the perspective one has with the entirety of life itself. This means one's view of life is profound in a transparent way, beyond the sensational and tarnished expectations of the ego. One feels alive in every moment and has an appreciation for even the smallest moments of life; for example, a flower blossoming with color becomes a majestic event for celebrating the magic of living a mystical life. The evolution or Godward motion is the inner movement of the soul toward its source in pure consciousness as defined by Vedanta as truth. This inner revolution is the royal path of yoga (Raja) that is defined by individual will power, control of the mind and senses, meditation, and the power to surrender by allowing the mind and body to become instruments in Divine hands.

One may come to wonder what the concept of a cultural (evolutionary) revolution has to do with the practice of surrender or letting go and the royal path of yoga. Hopefully, as you can surmise by this point in the book, and in your witnessing of how violently things are changing in the world, you know that our world communities can no longer continue such a course of imbalance. Most of our civilizations are perishing. Perhaps this time in history is similar to the great floods and droughts of the past. Humanity's relationship with the natural world does not promote real success because it fails to recognize that human consciousness is the same consciousness that sustains our world. When we not only ignore her but also fail to recognize that we are all intricately woven into her creation we insult the Divine Mother. The inner path guides us to enhance the power of surrender and thus display an appreciation for life. We can embrace the idea that nothing occurs by accident, but instead, life is embedded in the law of synchronicity.

The advanced approach to living in accordance with the practice of surrender invites us to incorporate several factors in our daily lives. First is the relationship we have with the external world. This includes, nature, animals, human relationships, and our individual behavior with respect to society. These relationships are primary and are founded on living a life of ahimsa (non-violence), and adhering to dharma, the laws imposed by the universe and the creative force of Brahman (God).

Dharma is the cornerstone of living an evolutionary life. In the Indian-Aryan culture, dharma is the basis of human progress. If one does not live according to one's dharma, then one cannot make real progress in evolution. In other words, if you are following the spiritual path, God provides all types of associations (synchronistic moments) for the betterment of your life and evolution. Yogananda once said, "It works like mathematics; it cannot fail."[153] Dharma nourishes our life. The Sanskrit literature defines the primary syllable "Da" in correlation to three positive qualities: 1) *Dhama*, which indicates controlling

---

153 This comment was made to one of his direct disciples, Swami Anandamoy, and in reference to a Kriya Yoga breathing technique as the premier expression of the Raja Yoga path. This quote draws from the correlation of human life with the laws of karma and rebirth. Human life is intrinsically tied to the cosmology of the entire universe, and most particularly, the solar system, in which the planet earth exists. The seven major planets are correlated to the seven days of the week, and the moon cycles around the earth twelve times within a year, giving birth to the "month." The human breath (inhalation and exhalation) are microcosmic features of the cycles of the sun and moon. Thus, in the yogic view, breath is equated to one's quality of consciousness and one's capacity to unravel the magical illusion of maya.

the mind and senses, a salient principle of Raja Yoga to support internalization of the mind; 2) **Dhana** which is charity as expressed in reciprocity; and 3) **Daya**, living a life with compassion and humility.

As you apply the ancient yet practical wisdom of integral yoga into the moments of your life as the special time-tested prescription of Listen, Learn, Love and Let Go, may it bring you the true success of inner happiness that the soul yearns to express. I want to leave you with a personal affirmation that has been dear to my heart for many years. It can be used as a daily mantra, or it can be used as a prayer before starting your day. Best of all, may you use it as a reminder of who you truly are and what you can do for this world.

"I am a bright shining light, I am filled with love, my true essence is peace. And everywhere that I go, and in everything that I do, I will share, and I will shine, my Divine qualities, always, always."

Chapter THIRTEEN

Awakened India

In India the mother is the center of the family and our highest ideal.
She is to us the representative of God, as God is the mother of the Universe.

Sri Swami Vivekananda

A Universal Wisdom for Modern Times

An awakened India cannot be stopped and will change the world from the inside out. An awakened India (Prabuddha Bharata) is a term coined by Sri Swami Vivekananda that signifies the rise in India's consciousness as is reflected in the growing demand for truth through the practice of integral yoga and the integration of values that promote evolution. When we speak of dharma in this context, we mean that truth must prevail, and will do so through humankind's changing relationship with nature and ecology, and through people embracing the singular truth, the light, that is behind all religions and spiritual traditions. Yoga, through its practices, aims to unite mankind with that ideal through the wisdom teachings of Vedanta. The impact yoga has had on the world is immeasurable and in the short time of just over a century, great yogis left the shores of India to share the wisdom of Vedanta (truth), spreading its message far and wide. Perhaps for these sages,[154] seeing America as the land

---

154 America's earliest Hindu-yogis were Swami's Vivekananda, Rama Tirtha and Yogananda, although other Indian teachers had already existed in America as noted by Robert Love in *The Great*

of opportunity also meant America was the ideal place where the ideals of Vedanta could be spread to many other countries.

The entirety of India, from north to south and east to west, has been dedicated to God, devotion, and worship of the Divine in its many forms. I speak of the original Bharata and not of the modern India that has been influenced by colonialism and the ignorance of the global collective consciousness that has pervaded the world for approximately the two last millenniums.

The message of India's spiritual ambassadors consistently points in one direction, Godward. God had to leave humanity the pathway to fulfillment of spiritual enlightenment, life's most urgent desire, somewhere, and he left it in India. One cannot imagine living in a world without the presence and influence of Indian culture. Its wisdom, rich history, and, most importantly, its earliest teachings known as the Vedas, have enriched our world communities either directly or indirectly in one way or another. As expressed by the great Vedantic philosopher Adi Shankara, we can concisely summarize the entirety of India's vast contributions to the dharmic awareness of humankind by naming three spiritual blessings.

The first is that we are born into a human body (manushyatwam). The body is a gift from God and is a container for the soul where the soul can enjoy the world and discover one's unique expression. The second blessing is that we have the desire to know God (mumukshutwam). If a person has this desire, they will avoid the pain and suffering that comes from living blindly, ignorant of one's true nature. This desire to know God is an awakening that can occur at any time in life, ranging from youth to old age. The fact that so many people have had this awakening now is a great blessing because many understand that the world does not exist as a permanent place, and that materialism can no longer satisfy us. So many seek to solve the mystery of their purpose and connection to the Divine.

The third blessing comes when one has attracted a Guru (mahapurusha-sam-shrayah), an individual who has reached the summit of Realization and holds the key to this domain. This should not be confused with worship of an individual or a form. The guru is the teachings, and whether the guru is in a body or not does not matter. The guru is enlivened or embodied when their teachings are followed and practiced according to the specific manner that they have presented, as they have modeled through their own spiritually evolved life.

The Foundation for a Spiritual World Culture

Author Phil Goldberg[155] would probably agree that the original sparks of Indian culture in America began as early as 1805, with William Emerson, the father of the famous author Ralph Waldo Emerson. William transliterated the first Sanskrit text published in America, *Sacuntala*. We can assume that this influenced his son. Ralph Waldo Emerson is recognized as a naturalist and transcendentalist. He wrote spiritually themed essays and poems with many appealing yoga inspired titles such as *Brahma*, *The Over Soul*, *Self-Reliance*, and *Nature*.

It was his essays that I studied in an English course while I was a student at the University of Florida. In particular, his essay *Nature*, promotes an approach to nature that is not traditionally valued by most Americans, and it sparked my consciousness (agni) in ways I had never experienced before. His essay made me realize how fond of nature I was, how it made me feel alive and connected to something beyond my body. His writing gave my mind a sense of freedom that I did not have until then. I attended more to how I always felt at peace spending time outdoors, especially in the school's rural setting, where I could experience the farms, rivers, lakes, and serene wooded areas that surround the campus. These natural places provided me with the space and time for contemplation.

Although the early ambassadors of India's spiritual heritage were enlightened masters and venerated teachers of their own lineages, the religious landscape with which they had to contend in America was saturated with skepticism. As a result of the blatant bigotry against anything that was non-Christian and the stereotyping of India as a land of snake-charmers and sword swallowing magicians, the Western world had grown skeptical of the ancient East. Many people viewed the Indian heritage as outdated and India itself as a down-trodden place to live. At the turn of the 20th century, America was seen as the new land, where everything was clean and pretty, and where there was plenty of opportunity for accumulating wealth.

---

155 Phil Goldberg is the author of *American Veda*, and he wrote the foreword to my book, *Sun, Moon and Earth, The Sacred Relationship of Yoga & Ayurveda*.

The stereotyping of India was most likely augmented by certain occultist figures such as Pierre Bernard, known as the Great OOM. Bernard has now been forgotten,[156] he passed away in the 1950s, but he was known for publicizing Hatha Yoga and other aspects of Indian culture in America. He developed yoga centers and a massive country club, he organized public demonstrations, and he even started a Sanskrit college. To many Americans, he was a very interesting figure, worthy of attention, and to others he was controversial. As one of America's early mystics he influenced many people, prompting them to begin practicing yoga, including members of America's most famous and wealthy families of the era, the Vanderbilts, who became some of his main benefactors.

Bernard, like many yoga enthusiasts of modern times, found themselves in more trouble than success from their methods. Bernard was not properly taught how to integrate the teachings into a lifestyle of simplicity and humbleness. A life that tampers with the energies Tantra without fully understanding the teachings, is a perilous journey. We still see this today with many yoga practitioners. This is because the mind is very powerful and can be used to harmonize one's life with nature; however, the mind can be very dangerous when it is not properly channeled. Very few have had the opportunities that Bernard did to meet such great yogis as Yogananda and Rama Tirtha; yet his life was spoiled with problems, and he evidently lost the evolutionary direction that is the core purpose of yoga. The reason I use the example of Bernard as one of the earliest pioneers of yoga in America, is to point out how a full understanding of yoga is vital to success. Bernard, even though he made such a commendable effort to promote such an esoteric and valuable system, his misunderstandings scattered his energies into so many unhealthy directions that brought on promiscuity, legal issues, and the trappings of monetary affluence.

Yoga, when combined with ayurveda, provides a grounding effect, a connection between the mind and body, and a slowing of the mind which encourages us to return to simple living. One thing is evident: whether in India, Asia, or America, human beings are seeking for a new way, perhaps a universal way, to attain success. Material abundance, as displayed in America, is not real success because it often lacks spiritual values. We all live in a world bound

---

156 *The Great OOM, The Improbable Birth of Yoga in America* by Robert Love, Penguin Group 2010.

by the forces of duality: sun-moon; heaven-hell; devata and asura; or material efficiency and spiritual wisdom. We now can see that the foundation for living in non-duality is here.

Integrating the material efficiency of the West along with the spiritual wisdom of the East has finally begun. The knowledge is available to us, the teachings left for us by these great lineages is now in our hands. Now it is the responsibility of all of us to begin to repair the karmic damage humankind has inflicted upon itself and nature. Aspirants around the world need to rise to the global challenges and become examples for the dormant masses to learn from. Let us follow the higher path of evolutionary intelligence that is available to all. While most in the world rely on media and science for their solutions and directions in life, our global spiritual community (sangha) must learn to apply Vedic teachings and demonstrate to the world a new non-dualistic relationship that respects life, embraces compassion, and is reflected in a harmonious life.

The Value of Celibacy in Evolutionary Living

The practice of celibacy in Indian spiritual culture is derived from ethical and moral practices that were codified as derived from the Golden Age of Vedic culture and presented as part of the Royal Path of yoga. Brahmacharya consists of two words, *Brahma* meaning God or creator and acharya, meaning mastery or control. Thus, the two terms imply that one can recognize this energy as a formidable force and can manage it in a proper way. Firstly, as the inherent force of all human beings, God created humans with this downward and outward force (apana vayu) to manifest and perpetuate human life. Secondly, sexual intimacy is an intimate expression shared between husband and wife for creating a family. It is also shared between those who have made the commitment of being loyal to one another. Of utmost importance is that this intimate exchange is cultivated and shared in order for one to grow in consciousness and use this force as a movement toward self-realization.

Sexual activity is not required to Realize Brahma or an enlightened state as is incorrectly presented in distortions of Tantra Yoga by many modern enthusiasts. Quite the opposite, sexual activity, as a device of the lower chakras and most specifically svadhisthana (second chakra), can increase mental disturbances such as anxiety, insecurity, and attachment, and can demonstrate gross impurities of the ego mind. The success of any individual depends on their capacity to manage their sexual energy. The same energy that creates new life is the same energy that has spawned the greatest ideas and movements of human history, like those presented by Sir Isaac Newton, Herbert Spencer, Sweden Burg, Gandhi, Thoreau, and Walt Whitman. All these people were brahmacharies, observing a life of celibacy. On areas related to bisexuality, homosexuality, masturbation, birth control, and polygamy, yogic-Hindu teachings remain unprejudiced and quiet. Sexuality is considered a central aspect of life as part of the four ideals (purushartas). Kama neither endorses nor denounces it, although it does condemn adultery and abortion, the former as an act of disloyalty, and the latter is an act that defies ahimsa. It is important to remember that what someone has done in the past matters less than whether they have learned from those experiences and whether their life now is headed in an evolutionary direction.

The world population is high, and consciousness is low; however, when world population is low, consciousness is high, as it was during the Golden Age (Satya Yuga). Sexual energy has two forms, one is lower[157] and correlated to the instinctual nature that influences all human beings to behave like animals, as they often do, maintaining this attitude throughout their entire life. This form of sexual energy is a result of deceptive interpretations by ego which clouds the mind with impressions of being accepted, higher sense of self-worth, and an illusory sense of love. The ego develops superficial confidence as one becomes identified with the idea that sexual intimacy provides the power to overcome the challenges of life and create abundance. Although it may feel that one is attaining this all-conquering energy because of sexual interaction, this is a device of the ego to perpetuate the drama (lila). Sexual engagement at this level of comprehension has no end, it is never really satisfying, and has its fleeting moments producing emotional highs and lows that entangle the mind further into the world process.

Alternatively, the higher nature of the mind as purified intellect, buddhi, recognizes sexual energy as the capacity for insight, intuition, and the power of attention. Sexual energy is an expression of the soul's vibration when it is drawn towards the heart. It transmutes one's actions into gestures of compassion, charity, and enjoyment in transparent communication, not for the sake of opportunity, but as a reciprocal exchange that can lead to an increase in understanding. When sexual energy is transmuted into the heart it does not claim possession of any one person, nor does it associate or become identified with any particular gender

---

157 Lower realms of the mind are referred to as bhu (physical), bhuvaha (mental) and svaha (intellectual and unconscious) lokas.

label or group. Heart-centered intimacy leads one to thrive from participation in all types of relationships, sharing sentient attributes, and cultivating creativity. These are depictions of Real strength and courage as depicted by Hanuman, the monkey God, disciple of Rama.

Again, it is important to clarify that yoga is not calling for suppression of sexual energy, but rather the transmutation of it. Transmutation and suppression have two very different outcomes. For this reason, Hanuman is considered a God. He is worshipped and adored by millions of yogis and Hindus throughout the world because he symbolizes a direct path to Rama, God. Rama relied on Hanuman to attain victory over the demon Ravana, who is the ego, stealing us away from the source of all Divine virtues. Hanuman as the ideal brahmachari has gained a titanic power of awareness. A short paraphrase of one of the famous stories of the Ramayana expresses Hanuman's devotion toward Rama and depicts the use of the body's vital energy for seeking God.

> After victory over Ravana, Rama and Sita returned to the throne in Ayodhya to enjoy a wonderful celebration. When Sita was presented the gift of a remarkable necklace of precious gems she decided it was best to offer it to Hanuman, thanking him for all he had done for them. As members of the king and queen's court, their family, and citizens of their kingdom looked on, they were all surprised when Hanuman began biting and smashing the necklace, trying to break open the gems. The spectators were shocked and questioned Hanuman's behavior, they were confused as to why he would destroy such valuable gemstones, especially those given to him by Sita.
>
> Hanuman said, "I was simply searching to see if Rama was inside any of these jewels."
>
> Instantly, a furious onlooker shouted, "Well, if that is the case, then why don't you crack open your own body and see if Rama is there?"

With great confidence and dignity, Hanuman began to rip open his chest and replied, "Rama is inside of me." Inside of his heart, Rama and Sita were seated together, symbolic of shakti and bhakti.

Hanuman opening his chest, Rama & Sita Seated in His Heart.

This colorful fable demonstrates that real love is within us, and as we follow the path of devotion to Rama (God), we are given the strength of Hanuman, the power of devotion, awareness, and loyalty. Love is not found in gems or outside of our being. The journey of seeking God changes the heart, the seat of feeling. It opens a window of spiritual expansion that causes negativity to fall away and fears to disappear; and thus, the dimension of your personality expands beyond the body-mind, and moves towards the Sun. This is the metaphor discussed in chapter three as the ascending or northern course (uttarayana) that becomes an aspirant's entire goal of life, until one realizes that, "I am the Sun." Brahmacharya is a practice of directing the energy of life towards its goal and is the most valuable medicine for developing bhakti (devotion) that leads to liberation. As one of the versus from the Hanuman Chaleesa[158] asserts, "You (Hanuman) possess the potent remedy-the Divine Name of Rama, You are forever the Servant of Rama." Hanuman portrays the ideals of work (Karma Yoga), devotion (Bhakti Yoga) and knowledge (Jnana Yoga) that lead to the royal path (Raja Yoga).

Brahmacharya is a core principle within the framework of living an evolutionary life because one can rise above the lower domains of human consciousness. When one dwells in the lower domains, one is often consumed by dramas, preoccupied with emotional turmoil, and this often leads to the destruction of nature, chronic diseases, and over population. Swami Rama Tirtha once addressed this topic in India,[159] "Dear friends if you will not be vigilant and make efforts to lessen the population, Nature will have to use her cruel process of pruning and weeding, according to Maharshi Vasishta, through epidemics (pandemics), famine, earthquakes, war etc. Do not waste your vital energy, or else you will suffer and ruin your country. Sublimate this energy into Divine bliss and spiritual power."

Without a clear sense of who we are, it is likely the ego that will make choices to follow along with the rest of the pack. If your yoga sadhana is not dispelling fear and emotional turmoil in general, and affording you with greater discipline, then how can you live a life of dharma? Start with little things that challenge your courage and mental focus, then move onto larger things. If you maintain the idea that you, alone, are trying to accomplish something, then you create a very limited mental attitude. However, if you fill your mind with devotion for the Divine and realize you are part of a freedom-seeking cultural movement, then you begin to strengthen your capacity to surrender. Gain control of your body and sensory mind and practice Brahmacharya. See how many great things you can achieve as this tremendous power begins to move through you, supporting you with every need in life.

---

158 *Raama rasaayana tumhare paasaa, Sadaa raho raghupati daasaa*, Verse 32, *Hanuman Chaleesa*, translation and commentary by Swami Jyotirmayananda. This famous composition was written by Saint Tulsi Das in forty verses. It has been recited by devotees who are expressing devotion to Rama (God) when focusing on overcoming adversities and gaining courage and strength.
159 Swami Rama Tirtha likely intuited the direction India's population was headed in 1905. When he spoke on this topic in Uttara Pradesh, India's population was 238 million compared to today's 1.36 billion. During this time, colonialism was being challenged by the Bhakti Bengali yogis and an extensive list of Freedom Fighters like Gandhi, Jawaharlal Nehru, Sardar V. Patel, Subhash Chandra Bose, and many others were just beginning to lay the groundwork for what eventually led to India's independence in 1947.

Ayurveda and Sexuality

The ayurvedic perspective on sexual matters is much more liberal because sexuality is considered with respect to Mother Nature's cycles. Hormones are directly linked to fertility, and this presents the importance of balanced sexual function as the foundation for supporting the health and strength (dhatu-sara) of the tissues. Restoration (rasayana) is a cornerstone of ayurveda and so sexual intimacy, in moderation, is vital to the preservation of the immune system. Ayurveda's system of anatomy and physiology are based on seven vital tissues (dhatus), and, of those, the last is the reproductive fluid. The reproductive fluid is linked to endocrinology, so the balance of hormones reflects how sexuality may be affecting the body.

While ayurveda links sexual function to immunity, yoga views it as the energy for aspiring to know God. Herein lies the importance of ojas, the subtlest form of energy and that which supports the heart to continue its function during sleep. The heart is the organ of life, love and spiritual transformation. Immune deficiencies appear in various ways both in body and mind. Men showing low levels of testosterone and women show low levels of estrogen and progesterone imbalances. Sexual intercourse is not the only factor influencing ojas. When consistent sexual activity is combined with a modern lifestyle and its many detrimental aspects (stress, poor diet, medications, alcohol, and a lack of exercise) it takes a toll on the body, mind.

Spiritual evolution requires energy, time, and a sound vehicle to sustain the light of the life force. Ayurveda's torchbearer, Charaka, states that, "When the ojas is diminished, a person is fearful, weak, always worried, will have disorders in the sense organs, deranged luster (sense of reality) and mental ability and will appear rough and emaciated." Charaka also states that excessive loss of reproductive fluid (shukra) will lead to the loss of ojas.[160] It is not coincidental that the Sanskrit term for reproductive fluid is **Shukra**, which is also the name of the planet, Venus, known as the planet of sexuality, relationships, and sensual living. To promote healthy procreation, classical ayurveda emphasizes specific oil massage therapies, light steam or fomentation, use of purgation (virechan), a wholesome diet cooked with ghee, a pure mental attitude with aligned behaviors, and finally, timing. Basically, Charaka is suggesting that couples should unite in sexual intercourse only when both individuals are healthy, free of disease, and prepared for the responsibility.

---

160 *Charaka Samhita*, Chapter XVII, verses 73, 76-77.

A special ritual is presented in ayurveda for influencing the gender of the fetus. Three full days after menstruation no intercourse should occur, the woman should sleep on the earth, eat meals with her hands, and not cleanse her body in any form. On the fourth day, she should be anointed all over and bathed from the head down and then both are to wear white and place a garland on one other. Couples should enter sexual intercourse on even days to birth a boy and on odd days if they wish to produce a girl. The ideal position to receive the semen is supine because the doshas maintain their normal position this way. In other positions, the genital track is inflicted by vata (vayu) for example when the woman is on her knees, bending over, or on her side. If the woman receives penetration while laying on her right side, kapha is likely to enter and block the uterus, and while lying on the left side, pitta, as the sperm and ovum can become taxed with excess heat or burning. The wisdom that ayurveda provides for fertility, pregnancy, and birthing, is extensive and comprehensive as it regards the entire process as very sacred. Women interested in learning these practices should consult an ayurvedic practitioner who has been properly trained in Garbha Samskar (fetal impressions) so that these new souls entering the world will be given the optimum opportunity for health of body and support of mother and family.

Embracing an Eternal Tradition

In my view, the emergence of an eternal tradition that supports the current evolution revolution has finally arrived. The Indian spiritual traditions of the last 7,000 years emerged at the end of a long ice age. The traditions originated with the Rig Veda. Other earlier civilizations, such as Lemuria, perhaps provided for the earliest migration to the earth and India, either from other planets or a land mass in the Indian Ocean that has sunken into the sea. Madame H.P. Blavatsky[161] also spoke of the theory of Lemuria, and many have forgotten to credit her with spawning the earliest movement of Hindu mysticism and esoteric cosmology that influenced the Western world. The most extensive account of Lemuria was presented by Satguru Sivaya Subramuniyaswami in his scrolls that he attained directly from the Akashic library. His account begins with humans migrating from other planets to the earth during the Golden Age (Satya Yuga). Indigenous tribes in different parts

---

161 (1831-1891) Madame Blavatsky was the founder of the Theosophical Society and author of *The Secret Doctrine, The Synthesis of Science, Religion and Philosophy.*

of the world were emerging between three to five thousand years ago, and there were several cultures, such as the Eygptian and Mayan, demonstrating somewhat advanced practices of worship, prayer, architecture, and artistry.

However, no civilization has even rivaled the Vedas in their comprehensive knowledge encompassing all aspects of life, especially the four systems of Vedic knowledge addressed in this manuscript: Vedanta, Yoga, Ayurveda and Jyotish (Vedic astrology). India's people referred to the original Vedic teachings as Sanatana Dharma before the term Hinduism was used. The term Hindu was derived from the word Sindhu and associated with the people inhabiting the region of Sindhu River which flows through the northwestern part of India. This Punjab region was called Sapta Sindhu in the Vedas and translates as the land of the seven rivers. Some believe the term Hindu was used by the Greeks to describe lands and people in the Indus Valley region. Hinduism is a misnomer in that it does not accurately represent the Vedic culture and teachings that the Indus Valley civilization had always been linked to.

The ideology of living in accordance with an eternal tradition is broadened in scope by the planetary influences and astronomical laws like that of the longer yuga cycles (cycles of human-earth consciousness) that recognize that the sun has a binary relationship with another planet which transpires into the principle that everything in this world involves a relationship as indicated by the most influential planet-force. These cosmic factors show that human life is intrinsically connected to specific grander forces. It is not coincidental that humans in the last century have begun to tinker with planets outside of earth like the moon, and most recently mars, trying to discover something. They could awaken to the idea that every human being is a microcosm of the vast planetary system that surrounds us. The planets enliven us and animate human life through their respective cycles as arranged by the forces of cosmic intelligence.

In my view, the wisdom of India provides three primary values for the world to follow. The first is the value of one singular truth, a pure source of consciousness and intelligence that all religious systems promote as the experience of the Divine. The path or form of worship one chooses to follow is determined by one's affinity with the Divine. The second value is the importance and the recognition of the feminine aspect of the Divine for promotion of compassion and increasing mental sensitivities that enhance the intuitive faculties of the mind. Awareness of the Goddess will also promote shifting humanity's relationship with the elements, health, and nature. From the earliest time of human history, as documented in Indic history, worship of the Divine feminine, known as **Saktism** has always existed, and worship practices are found in the Rig Veda, Puranas, and Tantras. As discussed in chapter three, the original soli-lunar calendar can potentially reemerge again to support our current evolutionary movement and to further develop humanity's relationship with the natural world. Rather than viewing the world as separate, humans can, through the feminine Divine, see a more equal and integrated existence between spirit and nature. The third value is the comprehensive approaches to spiritual evolution, health, and wellness through yoga and ayurveda. Before there was a religion there was tradition, a way that the people of the earth related to one another, the planet, and a way of finding their own unique relationship with the Divine.

As the world's largest democracy and the land of devotion to God, India can lead the way to global harmony. It is evident that India was granted stewardship of a Divine intelligence and masterful teachers; within any span of time during any of the revolutionary periods India was consistently producing enlightened beings as rishis, yogis, or saints. When Christopher Columbus was landing in the Americas to prove to a dubious Europe that the earth was round, a great woman saint named Mirabai was born in Rajasthan, India. Mirabai was a great bhakta (devotional singer) who sang many original hymns that continue to influence countless aspirants throughout India today.

Similarly, during the same era when the Romans were conducting their brutal conquests, literal blood baths, destroying life, there was a great doctor in India named (Vaidya) Susruta who was developing one of the great ayurvedic scriptures that included remarkable procedures in general surgery and cosmetic surgery that are still being used today. These methods, in addition to pulse diagnosis, use of antiseptics, toxicology, and midwifery techniques, are still taught in small schools and universities, and are still in practice throughout the world. The tremendous contrast that exists in the world, in the realm of time and space is exemplified by the simultaneous occurrence of these two paradoxical phenomena. In Europe, the Roman conquest of territory and quest for power led to massive loss of life, diminished authentic spirituality, and a low level of consciousness was being applied to the definition of success. However, in India, because of India's internal struggles, there was large scale suffering accompanied by a compassion for suffering and regard for life. Susruta was focused on preserving life.

The Vedic wisdom of the higher ages has been preserved through the Rishi tradition. These unbroken lineages have carried the Cosmic light of intelligence forward through the dark ages. For example, Sri Adi Shankara, in the short span of his thirty-two years of life, revived Advaita Vedanta (non-dualistic philosophy) and established the Sanyasi order and its tenfold divisions. His guru recognized that, at the age of twelve, he was already prepared to begin writing commentaries on great scriptures, even writing his own scriptures, and he encouraged him to do so. Adi Shankara's work anchored India's spiritual heritage and heralded the evolution revolution that was later ushered in by Ramakrishna and many other gurus who followed him. Through the creation of the four maths (sacred temple sites), Shankara created a type of Vaastu approach to containing the energy of the higher realms within India so it can further its work in the world of guiding souls towards the goal of spiritual liberation.

India has been home to the world, and now the world is bringing India into their homes through yoga, meditation, chanting, vegetarian cuisine and many more traditions of Vedic knowledge. In so many ways, the wisdom of One Truth has found its expression into every aspect of our lives, from philosophy to yoga to even the beautiful red dot (bindi) that is placed on the third eye. All these practices point to the same domain: Brahman (God).

> *"Adorations to Sadguru who is the Bliss of Brahman,*
>
> *the Giver of Supreme Joy, the Embodiment of Pure Consciousness,*
>
> *beyond the pairs of opposites, Vast like the ether,*
>
> *Infinite, Eternal, beyond the three gunas and their modifications.*
>
> *To that Divine Guru, I offer my adorations!"* [162]

---

162 This is a chant often recited by Swamiji before his satsangas. English translation of the hymn, Adorations to Guru, Vedic Prayers and Mantras by Sri Swami Jyotirmayananda, Yoga Research Foundation, Miami.

A

Abhyasa – Repetition, consistency of sadhana.

Abhinivesha – One of the five kle-shas, cling, attached.

Adi Shankara – South Indian sage, promoter of Advaita Vedanta, non-dualistic philosophy.

Adityanath – Yogi Adityanath is an Indian Hindu monk, Peethadhishwar (Head Seer) of the Gorakhnath Math and politician serving as the 22nd and current Chief Minister of Uttar Pradesh.

Ahara – Food or general term for pulling inward.

Ananda – Bliss.

Ananda Tandava – Dance of Shiva or Nataraja.

Anasakti – Detachment

Apana vayu – Downward movement of prana which influences bowel movements, menstruation and the feeling of being grounded that correlates to tamas guna.

Aparigraha – Not claiming possession of anything.

Artha – Vocation, job.

Asakti – Attachment

Asmita – egoism, second of the kleshas.

Atman – Individualized soul, portion of Brahman

Agni – Sacred fire, general term for metabolism, fire of the mind or consciousness, Vedic God.

Ahimsa – Non-violence in thought, word and deed, primary principle for living an evolutionary life.

Avatara – God incarnated, specially sent by the Divine intelligence when human consciousness is troubled and lost in the illusion of maya.

Aurobindo – **Sri Ghosh** – **Yogi**, Vedic guru, originated the modern use of the term "integral" yoga. Small town or city named Auroville was built in Pondicherry, India implementing the principles of Aurobindo.

Ayanas – Solstices

Ayurveda – Vedic system of medicine.

B

Bastrika – Pranayama from the Hatha yoga system, referred to as bellows breathing in English.

Bhagavad Gita – Famous scripture of India, composed by Veda Vyasa.

Bhakti – devotion, love, path of yoga.

Bhavana – A combination of feeling and positive mental attitude, mood, sentiment.

Brahman – Hindu God, creator, pure consciousness, symbolic of the fire element.

Buddhi – Purified intellect, higher mind, intuition.

C

Chai – Spiced tea originated in India.

Chatrapati Shivaji – Maharastrian warrior who fought Islamic Rule and occupation in India.

Chitta – General term for the mind, consciousness, five states: Mudha (dull), Kshipta (distracted), Vikshipta (partial concentration), Ekagrata (one-pointed) and Niruddha (controlled), heart, the overall essence of ones being.

D

Daya – Compassion.

Dakshinayana – Suns southern course, first day of summer.

Dharana – Pure concentration, term used in Patanjali's Yoga Sutras, 6th limb of the Ashtanga system.

Dharma – Purpose, duty, principle, law.

Dosha – Mistake, dark or spoiled, term used in Ayurvedic medicine to measure the impact of the elements (air, fire and water) on the digestive system.

Dwesha – Aversion.

E

Equinox – The time or date (twice each year) at which the sun crosses the celestial equator, when day and night are of approximately equal length.

Evolution – Godward living, moving towards self realization, consciousness that is predominantly governed by sattva, intuitive mind.

G

Gandharva Veda – One of the upavedas, system of music.

Gandhi – Mahatma or great one, initiated into Kriya Yoga by Yogananda in 1935, major freedom fighter for India's independence based on ahimsa (non-violence) and satya (truth).

Goraksanatha – One of the main teachers of the Nath cult of Hatha yogis, disciple of Matsyendranath.

Gregorian – Calendar named after and influenced by Pope Gregory XIII in 1582.

Grihastha – Householder stage of life, typically begins at twenty five.

Guna – Quality, measure of the mind, explained in much detail in the Bhagavad Gita.

Guru – Spiritual guide, teacher, messenger or representative of God, term literally means to remove from darkness.

Guru Purnima – Day assigned to honoring the guru, the tradition began with Veda Vyasa's birthday.

H

Hatha – Sun and moon system of yoga for purification of the body and promoting mind-body synergy, sub-branch of Tantra.

Hiranyagarbha – The golden embryo, cosmic mind.

I

Ida – The primary channel that governs the energy of the moon, coolness and influences vata and kapha doshas.

Ishta mantra – Also referred to as the ishta devata or personal image of the Divine, mantra aligns with the aspirants preferred image or God.

Ishwara Pranidhana – Surrender to God, devotion to Ishwara, lord.

J

Japa – Recitation of Sanskrit mantras according to one's affinity with the Divine using a mala, Hindu necklace containing 108 beads.

Jatharagni – Metabolism, fire of digestion important in Ayurvedic wellness.

Jesus Christ – Founder of Christianity, student of India's wisdom traditions.

Jivamukta – Liberation while in the physical form.

Jivatman - Embodied soul.

Jnana - The yoga of knowledge, pure intelligence, realization through knowing.

Julian – (Calendar) – Named after Julius Cesar.

Jyotish – Vedic astrology, the science of light.

K

Kailash – Mountain attributed to Shiva in Tibet.

Kama – Sensual feeling, social life, friendship.

Kanda – Three divisions of Vedic teaching, Karma (rituals, practices, austerities), Upasana (meditate, worship) sit near to God, Jnana (wisdom or knowledge of scriptures. Kandas influenced to formation of the concept of Integral or Sampurna Yoga.

Kapalabhati – Pranayama for kapha, from the Hatha yoga system.

Karma – Actions, the law of cause and effect, yoga of action, behavior, activity, right intention.

Karunamayi Rasa - Grace of God.

Kumbha Mela – Oldest and largest spiritual festival in India, takes place at four river-bank pilgrimage sites, celebrated approximately every twelve years according to astrological alignments.

Kleshas – Mental afflictions, problems produced by five aspects of the mind.

Kriyamani karma – Present of fresh karmas that will influence one's future.

Kriya Yoga - Ancient art of pranayama, revived by Mahavatar Babaji in 19th century. Paramahansa Yogananda was commissioned to disseminate the teachings to the Western world.

L

Lahiri Mahasaya – Guru of Yogananda's parents and Swami Sri Yukteswar, also known as Sri Shyama Charan Lahiri Mahasay.

Love – The essence of living existence, what everyone can experience if they can simply remove the mental obstacles or conditions.

M

Mahadeva – Shiva.

Mahavakyas – The four utterances of the Upanishads

Mahapralaya – the great dissolution.

Mahat - Cosmic or pure intelligence, presented in the Samkhya philosophy.

Makara Sankranti - Festival celebrating the first day of winter when the sun enters the sign of Capricorn, usually incorrectly celebrated in January when the actual first day of winter takes place in December. The festival celebrates the sun as it begins its northern course.

Mala – Necklace used for japa mantra, maladies of the mind, waste of the body excreted from the body and its seven tissues (dhatus).

Manu – Original or archetypal man.

Manovaha – Channel (srota) of the mind.

Mansarovar – Lake in Tibet representing the feminine energy of the Divine or Shiva.

Maharastra – State in India, major cities, Pune and Mumbai, home state of Shivaji.

Matsya – Incarnation of Lord Vishnu, Fish Avatara.

Maya – Vedantic concept of illusion, the world is not real.

Moha - Delusion, confusion.

Moksha – Liberation, enlightenment.

Moksha Dharma – One of the four aims or purushartas of Vedic astrology, namely artha, kama, dharma and moksha.

Mumukshuttwa – Desire to know God, spiritual aspirations.

N

Nadi shodhana – Technique of alternate nostril breathing, also known as anulom vilom, considered an important prerequisite to meditation.

Namarupa – Names and forms

Nirodha – Neutralization of the mind, a type of mastery or control.

O

Ojas – Immunity, prime energy, vitality, fertility, energy that sustains one to attain Samadhi (enlightenment).

Om – Shortened version of AUM, cosmic sound of the universe. AUM is more aptly spelled with the three letters as the sound itself resonates with three levels of existence.

P

Parampara – Lineage, succession of wisdom passed on through enlightened being.

Parashara – Sage known for scripture on jyotish or vedic astrology.

Paratman – Supreme self.

Paramahansa Yogananda – Founder of SRF-YSS, father of Yoga in the West.

Patanjali – Sage and author of Yoga Sutras, also credited with influencing Ayurveda and Sanskrit, a commentary called Mahābhāṣya.

Pingala – the primary channel that governs heat, energy of the sun and influences pitta dosha.

Pope Gregory – See Gregorian.

Praktipaksha bhavana – Opposite thinking, replacing what is negative with positive, shift of the mind.

Prakriti – Constitution, mind-body type, determined at conception, term is also used to define creative capacity of existence, consciousness.

Prarabdha - Chronic karma, of many lives, difficult to change.

Prana – Life force, energy of life. Referred to as chi in Chinese medicine.

Pranava – Eternal joy, vibration of spirit, without end.

Preya – Delightful, attractive.

Purusha – Pure consciousness, unmanifest realm of existence.

Purusharta – known as the four dharmas or ideal aims of life. Kama, artha, dharma and moksha.

R

Ravana – Demon of the Ramayana.

Raga – Attraction,

Raja – Royal path of yoga, meditation, integral, ashtanga yoga.

Rajas – Outward energy, mental energy promotes activity and physical movement.

Rama – Lord, Main figure of the Ramayana.

Ramayana – Epic scripture of India, composed by Sage Valmiki.

Revolution – A period on earth that categorizes a broad shift in human evolution from the scientific or linear perspective. Cognitive, agricultural, industrial and scientific. The last century marks entry into the Evolutionary period.

S

Sadhana - Spiritual disciplines, practices.

Sadhaka – Spiritual aspirant.

Sakshi – Witness, observing capacity of the mind.

Samadhi – Spiritual liberation.

Samhita – Book, compilation.

Samana vayu – one of the five major forms of prana, governs balanced digestion.

Sampurna – Integral, full, complete.

Sanchitta Karma – past actions

Sanatana Dharma – The eternal tradition, original term for Hinduism.

Sanmatti – To become an instrument in Divine hands.

Sarada Devi – Wife of Ramakrishna, highly advanced yogi.

Saraswati River – Famous river in northern India correlated with the Indus Valley civilization, most mentioned river of the Rig Veda. Dried up and discovered in recent times through satellite images.

Satmya – Adaptation, habituation, body's capacity to adjust.

Satsanga – Spiritual gathering, discourse centered on truth, from the root *anga*, limb or connection.

Sattva – Purity, clarity and measure of the mind that reflects the souls prime virtues, upward energy.

Shakti – Power, Goddess, common term used in Tantra, consort of Shiva.

Shankara – Adi Shankara, young sage who revived Advaita Vedanta in India, author of very important texts and also commentaries.

Shilajit – Mineral pitch oozing from rocks, originates in the Himalayas, powerful rejuvenating medicine used by yogis and in Ayurveda.

Shishya – Disciple.

Shiva – Hindu God of destruction, symbolic of the air element.

Shreya – What is meaningful, Divine, intended for spiritual matters.

Shravana – Spiritual listening, subtle, identifying the wisdom or deeper meaning from life.

Shukra – Reproductive fluid, seventh tissue (dhatu), planet venus.

Seva – Selfless service

Siddha – Perfected being, has attained the eight powers, Babaji, SRF-YSS line of gurus.

Sivaya Subramuniyaswami – Founder of Himalayan Academy and Hinduism Today.

Soli-lunar – A calendar used originally in India and during ancient times whose date indicates both the Moon phase and the time of the solar year.

Solstice - The time or date (twice each year) at which the sun reaches its maximum or minimum declination.

Svadharma – Individual purpose, Divine birthright.

Swami Chidananda – Monk and direct disciple of Sri Swami Satchidananda of the Integral Yoga Institute.

Swami Jyotirmayananda – Direct disciple of Sri Swami Sivananda Maharaj, great modern exponent of Vedanta, founder of Yoga Research Foundation in Miami, Florida.

Swami Sivananda Radha – Direct disciple of Sri Swami Sivananda Maharaj and founder of Yasodhara Ashram in British Columbia, author of several books including "Radha, Diary of a Women's Search."

Swami Rama Tirtha – (1873-1906) Highly evolved mystic that also came to America. His lectures were recorded in a book series titled In Woods of God-Realization.

Swami Sivananda – Guru of Swami Jyotirmayananda, founder of Divine Life Society.

Swami Vivekananda – Disciple of Ramakrishna Paramahamsa, traveled to America in 1893 and taught Vedanta.

Swarajya - meaning "self-rule of Hindu/Indian people, a term used to define the return of the dharmic ideals of India's spiritual heritage.

Sukham – Happiness

Svasthavritta – Branch of Ayurvedic medicine that deals with lifestyle and selfcare.

Svadhya – Self study, study of scriptures, austerity for the mind.

Svarupa – Essence of ones being, Self.

T

Tagore, Rabindranath – Bengali poet, educator and freedom fighter.

Tamas – Downward energy, mental heaviness, hesitancy.

Tantra – Book, teaching, system or branch of yoga that worships Shiva and Shakti as the primary forces behind the sun and moon energies.

Tapasya – Self discipline, mainly of the body, austerities.

Tejas – Inner light, positive light, radiance, clarity and perception.

Totapuri – Guru, guide that initiated Ramakrishna into sanyas and received instruction of the identity of Brahman-Atman or non-dual consciousness.

Tridosha – The system of the three dosha used in Ayurvedic medicine.

U

Udana vayu – The upward flow of prana, influences the upper respiratory region of the body.

Upanishads – Culmination of Vedic knowledge, contains the essence of Vedanta.

Upasthambas – Three pillars for longevity in Ayurveda, food, exercise (sex) and sleep.

Uttarayana - Suns northern course, first day of winter.

V

Vaastu - Vedic branch of architecture and also works closely with Jyotish.

Vairagya – Dispassion, detachment, unaffected by the fluctuations of the world.

Vasana – Subtle impressions that eventually leads to desires.

Vedas – Ancient wisdom teachings of India from the golden age.

Vedanta – Meaning end of the Vedas. Most famous of the six Indian philosophies, truth, oneness.

Vichara – Self enquiry, exploration into the nature of ones true existence.

Vikriti – Term used to describe the doshas out of balance, can change depending on many factors.

Vishnu – Hindu God of preservation, sustainer, symbolic of the water element.

Viveka - Discrimation, minds capacity to discern between what is Real and unreal.

Viruddha Ahara – Incompatible foods, foods that lead to imbalance of the doshas.

Vishwaguru – Universal teacher, influencing broad movements.

Vrittis – Thought waves

Vyasa – Known as Veda Vyasa, author of the Mahabharata, influential rishi of Vedantic and Yoga teachings.

Y

Yoga – Union of mind-body-soul.

Yogananda – Paramahansa Yogananda, founder of Self Realization Fellowship and Yogoda Satsanga Society, author of the Autobiography Of A Yogi.

Yuga – Cycles of human consciousness, four periods, namely Kali, Dwapara, Treta and Satya, in total the measure 24,000 earth years. It explains the rise and fall of human consciousness as cyclical.

BIBLIOGRAPHY

Aggarwal, Bharat B. *Healing Spices*. New York: Sterling, 2011.

Chetanananda, Swami. *They Lived with God*. St. Louis: Vedanta Press, 1999.

Frawley, David. *Gods, Sages, and Kings*. Salt Lake City: Passage Press, 1991.

Frawley, David. *Vedic Yoga*. Twin Lakes: Lotus Press, 2014.

Jyotirmayananda, Swami. *Applied Yoga*. Miami: Yoga Research Foundation, 1971.

Jyotirmayananda, Swami. *International Yoga Guide*. Miami: Yoga Research Foundation, 2020.

Jyotirmayananda, Swami. *The Art of Positive Feeling*. Miami: Yoga Research Foundation, 1997.

Jyotirmayananda, Swami. *The Bhagavad Gita*. Miami: Yoga Research Foundation, 2007.

Mark, Joshua J., "Ancient Egyptian Religion." *World History Encyclopedia*, January 20, 2016. https://www.worldhistory.org/Egyptian_Religion/.

Sabnis, Mukund. *Viruddha Ahara*: A critical view. AYU: Journal of Research in Ayurveda, 2012; 33:332-6.

Subramuniyaswami, Satguru Sivaya. *Dancing with Siva*: Hinduism's Contemporary Catechism. Kauai: Himalayan Academy Publications, 1997.

"The 1752 Calendar Change," *Connecticut State Library Archives* (website), accessed November 2020, https://libguides.ctstatelibrary.org/hg/colonialresearch/calendar.

Tirtha, Swami Rama. *In Woods of God Realization, Vol. IV*. Lucknow: Rama Tirtha Pratishthan,1973.

Vasant, Lad. *Textbook of Ayurveda: Fundamental Principles, Vol. 1*. Albuquerque: Ayurvedic Press, 2002.

Vidyadhishananda, Swami. "New Moon Welcomes New Year and Navaratri Periods in 2020."

Hansavedas Self Enquiry Life Fellowship, accessed October 2020, https://hansavedas.org/navaratri-2020/.

Yogananda, Paramahansa. *The Science of Religion*. Los Angeles: Self-Realization Fellowship, 1953.

Yogananda, Paramahansa. "Training the Conscious and Subconscious Minds for Success, Part 2." *Self-Realization Fellowship Magazine Summer 2015*, Los Angeles: Self-Realization Fellowship.

ABOUT THE AUTHOR

Mas Vidal (Maheshananda) is considered a global ambassador for yoga, Ayurveda, Vedanta, and the wisdom of the Indian culture. Through his many programs, lectures and private counseling, Mas has become one of the most influential voices for evolutionary living based on the principles of yoga and Ayurveda. He is the founder and director of the Dancing Shiva School and he developed MoreLifeMarket.com, an online Ayurvedic Superfoods company. As an Ayurvedic Practitioner, he maintains an active international counseling practice that also integrates medical astrology. As a spiritual ecologist he continues to enjoy the abundant healing powers of the organic world.

About the Dancing Shiva School of Yoga & Ayurveda

The original Dancing Shiva School opened in Los Angeles, California in 2001 and now operates mainly through affiliate centers and locations in the USA and internationally. Dancing Shiva has become recognized internationally through Mas Vidal's teachings and offers health and wellness Vedic counseling services as well as a variety of learning platforms, from online programs to retreat trainings, internships, and India pilgrimages. *www.dancingshiva.com*

200 Hour Online Yoga & Ayurveda Certification Program

As the original and most comprehensive online Yoga and Ayurveda Studies program offered in the field today, Mas Vidal's Dancing Shiva complete online and correspondence format allows students the opportunity to study individually, at their own pace, and from their own computer. The course includes 108 hours of beautiful high definition (HD) video dynamic lectures, Hatha Yoga classes, meditation, online testing, homework assignments, and over 600 pages of reading-study material. Certification is for 200 hours as a Yoga and Ayurveda Counselor. *This course provides certification for 200 hours of study and is the primary course recommended for individuals who are new to the teachings.*

250 Hour Yoga & Ayurveda Teacher Training Program

This is the original Yoga and Ayurveda Teacher Training program that unites both sciences into an authentic teaching approach and lifestyle-training course. It is mainly focused on the application of proper asana and pranayama practice and the integration of an Ayurvedic lifestyle. This certification course is offered yearly in California and at affiliate locations internationally. The program provides a valuable foundation for becoming a yoga asana teacher and will serve those who are interested in deeper Ayurvedic studies. The school and its programs align with the lineages of Paramahansa Yogananda, Swami Sivananda, and Swami Jyotirmayananda. *This course provides certification for 250 hours of study.*

300 Hour Advanced Yoga & Ayurveda Programs

The advanced program modules provide a more comprehensive understanding of yoga and Ayurveda. Each advanced training offers certification via 100-hour modules and provides three levels of study with Mas Vidal and the Dancing Shiva faculty. This program is the most comprehensive approach to applying yoga as a therapeutic system for healing the mind-body relationship. *This course provides certification for 300 hours of study.*

600 Hour Ayurveda Counselor Program

This integral yoga certification program represents the essence of Vedic counseling. It is focused on the prevention of health-related issues and the promotion of longevity through Ayurveda, yoga therapy, medical astrology, and Vedanta. The program covers all aspects of dietetics, herbology, psychology, detoxification, and women's health. The course is based on Mas Vidal's years of experience and includes faculty members from both the USA and India. The program also includes study in India at both a private eco-village and at the esteemed D.Y. Patil University. *This course provides certification for 600 hours of study.*

India Programs and Detoxification

The Dancing Shiva school offers yearly Ayurveda programs led by Mas Vidal in association with the esteemed faculty from the International Academy of Ayurveda and D.Y. Patil University. International clients of Mas Vidal are also invited to attend for healing and detoxification (pancha karma) at a private eco-village. Clients experience custom healing and detoxification treatment plans created by Mas and his colleagues and the program includes yoga therapy, diet, herbs, and private cottages.

Traditional Study (Gurukul)

Each year, five individuals are accepted for a private study-internship with Mas Vidal in the manner of the Vedic tradition. Students are accepted based on specific circumstances and a structure is created that will best benefit the student's ability to learn the material and experience personal healing. The criteria for acceptance into gurukul range from previous yogic experience, schedule and timing, and karmic factors as reflected in the astrological birth chart. The one-year training period is divided into four modules and is a combination of private tutorials (live or online), reading, yoga and Ayurveda exercises, attendance at special programs, conferences or retreats, and includes assisting Mas with certain projects as opportunities to learn. The schedule and structure is adjusted according to each person, and the student can usually complete the certification within a one-year period or less.

Counseling Services

Mas Vidal offers practical Vedic counseling services based on Ayurveda, yoga, Vedanta, and Jyotish (Vedic astrology). His capacity for promoting health and spiritual wellness has been built over twenty years of private practice and clinical experience. Mas is recognized internationally for his insightful integral yoga wisdom combining integral yoga. Sessions focus on creating balance of the physical, mental, and emotional bodies and include review of the astrology birth chart, a determination of the dosha constitution and imbalances, lifestyle recommendations, specific prescriptions of diet, herbs, and yoga asanas. The initial session provides the client with a comprehensive overview of health factors visible in the body and also unseen factors, as reflected in the birth chart. Mas gives recommendations for beginning his unique methods of detoxification according to the wisdom of Ayurveda and modern scientific research. All sessions include a take-home booklet and a copy of the birth chart.

MoreLife Market
Products that Promote Evolutionary Living

This ecommerce Ayurvedic Yogi super-store offers premium Ayurvedic products that support evolutionary living. All products are focused on enhancing yoga practice (sadhana), increased immunity, promote longevity and beauty. The company integrates the importance of 100% organically sourced herbs and foods that embrace non-violence (ahimsa). MoreLife Market supports charities that align with the highest aim of ayurveda and yoga, spiritual freedom. Live Ayurveda, Practice Yoga, and let the Divine take care of the rest.
www.morelifemarket.com

Sun, Moon and Earth
The Sacred Relationship of Yoga and Ayurveda

Mas Vidal

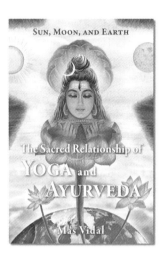

An interesting work that explains how the mystical powers of Yoga and the lifestyle disciplines of Ayurveda can restore the bodily energies for wellbeing and spiritual evolution. Sun, Moon and Earth is a bold proclamation for lifestyle reformation through the balanced practice of these traditions. I encourage all students to read it!

Prof. Subhash Ranade,
Chairman, International Academy of Ayurveda.
Pune, India.

ISBN: 978-0-9406-7640-4
$22.95 pb, 392 pages, Item# 990692

Sun, Moon and Earth tells the story of the "twin sciences" of yoga and Ayurveda. Weaving in the author's long professional and personal experience as a yoga teacher and Ayurveda practitioner, it explores how these traditions can be integrated into our lives as a practical means for balanced living and spiritual evolution. It is written for the growing audience of hatha yogis interested both in asana or postural yoga and a more conscious, Ayurvedic lifestyle.